KILLERS OF EDEN

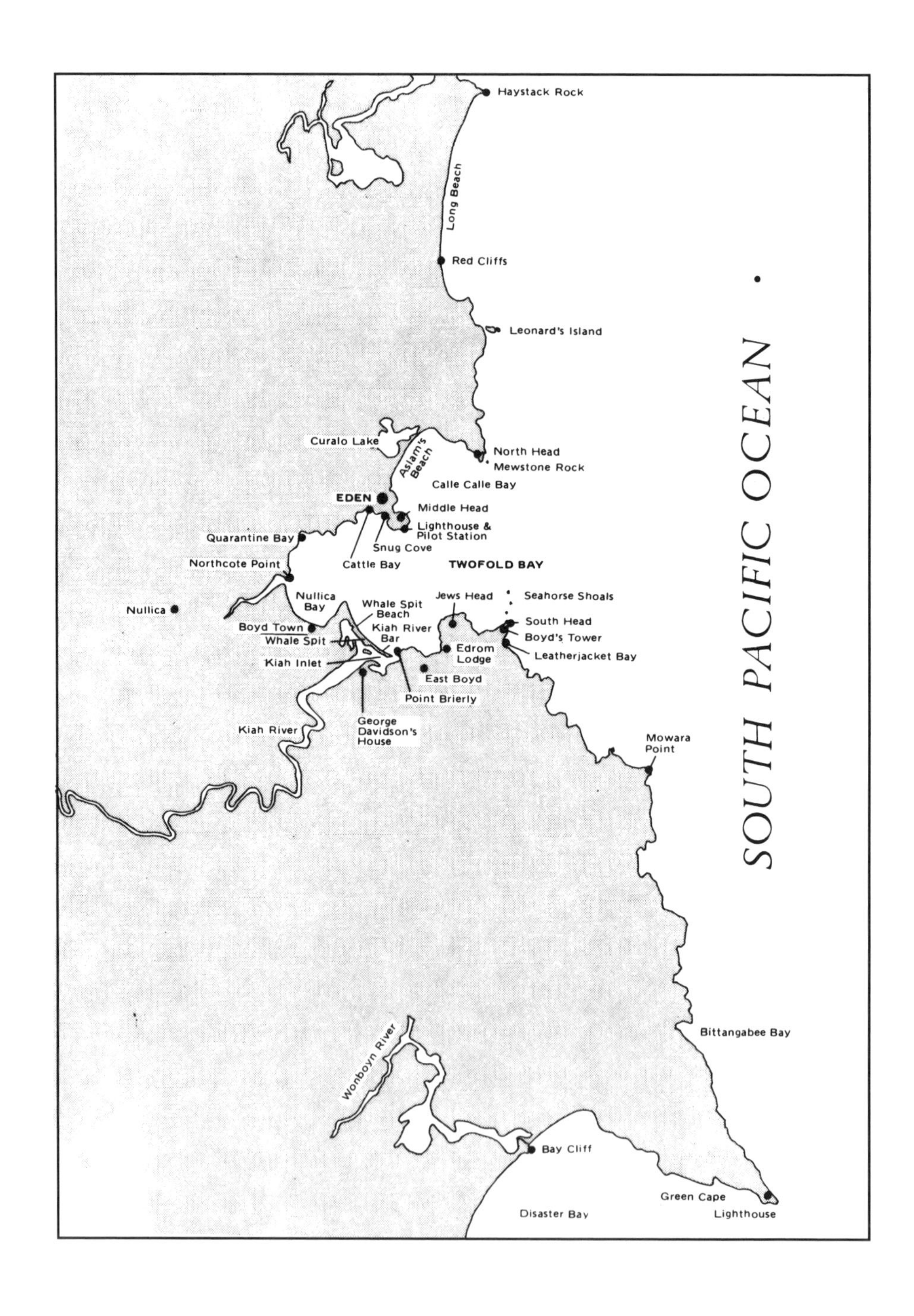
Haystack Rock
Long Beach
Red Cliffs
Leonard's Island
SOUTH PACIFIC OCEAN
Curalo Lake
Aslam's Beach
North Head
Mewstone Rock
Calle Calle Bay
EDEN
Middle Head
Lighthouse & Pilot Station
Snug Cove
Quarantine Bay
Cattle Bay
TWOFOLD BAY
Northcote Point
Nullica Bay
Whale Spit Beach
Jews Head
Seahorse Shoals
Nullica
South Head
Boyd's Tower
Boyd Town
Kiah River Bar
Whale Spit
Edrom Lodge
Leatherjacket Bay
Kiah Inlet
East Boyd
Point Brierly
George Davidson's House
Kiah River
Mowara Point
Bittangabee Bay
Wonboyn River
Bay Cliff
Green Cape
Lighthouse
Disaster Bay

Killers of Eden

The Killer Whales of Twofold Bay

Tom Mead

Sydney · Australia

Killers of Eden
The Killer Whales of Twofold Bay
by Tom Mead

First published by Angus & Robertson 1961-1991
Hardcover and 9 paperback editions:
Angus & Robertson Pacific Books 1967
Arkon paperback 1973
Arkon reprint 1975
New Angus & Robertson paperback 1977
A&R Classic Series 1980 and 1983
Hardcover by Vantage Press New York 1986
Hard and soft cover editions for libraries
by Large Print Australia 1991
Talking books version for libraries 1994
New enlarged soft cover edition by Dolphin Books 1992
Re-printed 1994 and twice in 1996
This edition first published 2002
Reprinted 2008
More than 75,000 copies sold

Publisher: Dolphin Books
18 Herbert Street Oatley NSW 2223 Australia
Phone: 61 2 9570 1972 Fax: 61 2 9570 7270
Enquiries should be addressed to the publisher.

ISBN 978 0 9585325 3 2

Printed and bound by

McPherson's Printing Group, Maryborough, Australia

Cover design and artwork by

Mainspring Productions Pty Ltd Sydney, Australia

Cover plate: Oswald Brierly's painting *The Death Flurry* dramatically depicts the final moments of a whale chase off Twofold Bay. In the foreground, several killer whales can be seen swimming near the closest boat.

Reproduced by permission of the National Library of Australia

To my wife, Vaila

George Davidson, the last and most famous of the master whalers of Twofold Bay, aged in his eighties, photographed with his wife Sarah shortly before she passed away in 1951. George outlived her by just eighteen months.

George and Sarah Davidson, their daughter Sarah and daughter-in-law Anne were my main source of information on the bay whaling and the killer whales at Eden. I am very grateful for the time they so selflessly gave, that enabled me to write a truly accurate account of this story.

Tom Mead

Preface

This is a true story, providing yet another example of truth being stranger than fiction. It is a story involving the exploits of men who hunted whales for a living, yet it does not intend to glorify or justify the killing of whales – quite the contrary. Whaling at Twofold Bay - a magnificent but very neglected harbour on the far South Coast of New South Wales - was for many years a fairly large industry. John Raine began the first whaling from the Australian mainland at Twofold Bay in 1828, although the first whalers of any real note were the Imlay brothers, who established their industry a few years later at Eden, the township on the bay.

Benjamin Boyd, a colourful personality who tried to build a great city on the western shores of Twofold Bay at Boydtown, considered whaling from the bay to be a good enough proposition to engage in it extensively and at one time had nine deep-sea whaling ships in addition to several shore-based whaling boats.

But Boyd is another story. This book tells of the Davidsons and the killer whales of Twofold Bay. Alexander Davidson came to Australia to work for Boyd in the middle of the last century as a carpenter and cabinetmaker. He achieved much more fame as a whaler and established an industry which he, his sons, and their sons carried on for more than eighty years. George Davidson, the last of the master whalers of Eden, was alive when I began to write this book, but he did not live to see it completed. He died at Bega in June, 1952, about eighteen months after the death in Eden of his wife, Sarah, who figures prominently throughout this story.

When George Davidson put away his harpoons and lances one day in 1932 he closed down what was quite a unique industry. Certainly, under twentieth-century conditions, bay whaling had become unprofitable. But Davidson didn't retire for economic reasons, he went out of business because he had lost his main asset - the team of killer whales that were as invaluable to him as a pack of trained dogs to a drover.

The killers are a fantastic tale in themselves. Animals have often been credited with human intelligence, but rarely has it been claimed for marine creatures - cetaceans, to give the killers their correct classification. That the killers possessed this peculiar intelligence is in itself strange enough. That it seemed to be confined to one particular pack of killer whales, which made Twofold Bay their base each whaling season for almost a hundred years, is beyond explanation.

Yet it actually did happen, and at Twofold Bay, the only place in the world to see it, men used a pack of killers to hunt whales. The most famous of the killer whale pack was Tom, whose skeleton is on display in the Killer Whale Museum at Eden.

I have been very careful to ensure that the killers' part in this narrative is authentic. Most of the facts came from Mr and Mrs George Davidson, their daughter Sarah, and daughter-in-law Anne. Other incidents came from the files of old Eden newspapers. The Davidsons readily told me what was true and what was exaggerated, and every old newspaper report I could find confirmed their statements. The pictures speak for themselves. Most of them were supplied, very kindly, by Eden resident Mrs Mary Mitchell, whose father, Mr C. E. Wellings, spent months in the boats with the Davidsons taking photographs of the whales, the killers, and the things that happened in those whaling days. More pictures came from the Killer Whale Museum at Eden, thanks to the secretary, Mrs Jenny Drenkhahn, Mr Jack Dickinson and Mr Rene Davidson, a grandson of George Davidson. The pictures by W. T. Hall are used with the kind permission of his daughter, Mrs Gandon.

Nowadays there is little need to hunt whales for their oil, bone or meat, as many economical substitutes are available. Yet some nations still justify killing whales in large numbers by claiming it is for scientific research. Whales are hunted using big, powerful ships, ice-breakers that can chase whales almost literally to the ends of the earth, kill them using explosive harpoons fired from steam-powered cannons and then immediately process the carcasses. Coincidentally, in many of the countries that participate in this kind of whaling, whale meat is considered a delicacy and brings a high price at restaurant tables. Many conservationists believe that the world whale population is dwindling. They fear that today's 'floating abattoirs' are so brutally efficient that many of the whale species that have managed to survive the onslaught of the last couple of centuries could soon (for scientific purposes or otherwise) be hunted to extinction.

This story however, happened back in the days when the need for conservation and preservation of whales was never dreamed of and whales were considered infinitely plentiful. Back then whale products were considered essential commodities, and the men who hunted them in frail wooden boats must have been exceptionally brave. Today, only some eskimos, and those who catch whales for subsistence still hunt whales in oared wooden boats, fastening to whales with hand-thrown harpoons and killing them with lances like the men of Twofold Bay. Yet nowhere in the world, then or now, except at this one place and time, have men hunted whales in partnership with a pack of killer whales.

This is an extraordinary story, as unique as it is true.

Tom Mead

Chapter 1

Tom was dead. The morning tide that slid lazily between the piers of the Eden wharf had shoved his floating body gently into Twofold Bay during the night and left it drifting around Snug Cove just out from the little beach. That was where the fishermen found Tom when they went down to the wharf.

"It's him all right," said one.

"Yeah," the other agreed. "I'd reckon I'd know Tom anywhere. Looks like he's been dead a couple of days."

The two men stood looking at the floating corpse, but neither moved to touch it. One suggested bringing the body ashore. His companion shrugged his shoulders and said they should leave it alone. There was no callousness in his tone. He looked thoughtful for a moment, then walked across the wharf, picked up a dew-sodden rope and tugged at it to bring the bow of a motor-launch within boarding distance.

"George Davidson will know what to do," he murmured as he jumped aboard.

The first chatter of the launch engine disturbed a few sea gulls that had been scavenging near the water's edge and sent them screeching and circling over the top of the wharf sheds. They quietened with the engine as it took up the load in gear and assumed a steady throb, pushing the launch out into the bay, still glassy in its early-morning serenity. Around the wharf the rolling wake of the moving craft rocked other moored boats, lapped across the bloated, derelict carcass, and finally spent itself on the sand of the little beach and adjacent rocky shores. Soon the sea gulls had landed again and, when the chug of the launch faded out behind the cliffs, only the lazy murmur of the soft ground swell broke the morning stillness.

It was just as quiet on the heights up the steep hill from Snug Cove, where the sleepy little town of Eden straddled the high land dividing the two folds of Twofold Bay. A straying horse had sole possession of Imlay Street—the town's main street—which started in the hollow near the post office where the Prince's Highway swept south to Melbourne and north to Sydney. Imlay Street climbed straight from its branch from the highway here, levelled itself out on the heights between some shops and business premises, then dropped sharply round the cliffs to just above water level on a narrow isthmus near the wharf. The land rose abruptly again from the isthmus and fanned out into what looked like a plump island. This was Middle Head. On the right-hand side going up from Snug Cove was a stone building with a pillared doorway which in years gone by had been the Customs House. On top of the sheer cliffs facing the Pacific Ocean the white signal mast and beacon of the lighthouse peeped above a horizon of tea-tree bushes.

Far away to the north the sea glistened in the morning sun around the tip of North Head before it rolled into the northern bay and shattered gently on the surf beach. The southern bay, which was Eden's harbour, reflected a pleasant blue, laced at intervals with golden beaches. Inland from the southern bay, towering above the other mountains, rose the sloping figure of Mount Imlay, like a giant reclining at ease.

The fishermen were miles away down the coast before the town began to stir and somebody else saw the body. Within an hour more than fifty people stood along the wharf. But none made a move to interfere. Some spoke in awed tones. They said it was strange that Tom should have died in the bay, or, if he had died at sea, that the sea should have brought him in. Tom was very old. Nobody knew just how old because nobody had been around Eden as long as Tom. George Davidson, the master whaler, who lived on the southern side of the bay at the mouth of the Kiah River, thought Tom was about ninety years old. Most people could believe that, because George Davidson and his folk before him had whaled from Twofold Bay since Ben Boyd's day and Tom had apparently been about since then. He was the last of a pack of killer whales that had made the bay and adjacent ocean their winter hunting ground for almost a century.

Now that Tom would hunt the whales no more, those who stared sadly at the porpoiselike carcass felt they had seen the passing of an old friend. But if anyone had lost a good friend, it was George Davidson, who had used the killers like a pack of trained hounds. To the folk who lived their lives in Eden, there was nothing extraordinary in Davidson's unique method of catching whales. It was something they had accepted as part of their environment, and they saw no reason why it should amaze the visitors who saw the killers at work. Yet they lived in the only place in the world where killer whales had ever worked with humans. When George's father whaled from the bay, there had been about a hundred in the pack. But gradually the number had diminished, until the last couple of years saw Tom mooching about on his own.

In the days when he had Humpy, Hooky, Stranger, Jackson, and Old Ben as lieutenants, Tom commanded a most extraordinary army. The killers, using Leatherjacket Bay outside South Head as a forward base, prowled the sea for whales that migrated up and down the coast during the winter months. If the whalemen were there when a whale came within reasonable distance of the coast, the killers would work with the boats, harrying the whale and trying to force it into the bay. If the whalemen were not handy, the main section of the killer force would round up the whale while another detachment dashed into the bay and flopped about the water near the whaling station until the whalemen came out in their boats. Then, even at night, they would lead the men in the boats out to where the other killers had the whale.

Equally remarkable was the fact that these particular killers had a homing instinct that brought them back to Twofold Bay every year for the whaling season. At the beginning of summer they disappeared to the Antarctic seas, but with each winter they returned, led, as far back as anyone could remember, by old Tom. Now Tom was back for the last time. His body lay peacefully on the waters of the bay he loved.

George Davidson came across from the Kiah immediately after he heard the news. He took his launch alongside the dead killer and stood for several minutes looking at the pathetic remains of what to him had been a better friend than many a human being.

''What are we going to do with him, George?'' a tall fellow in sea-boots asked when he came ashore.

''Don't know,'' George replied. He looked sadly across the water for a while. ''I've been trying to think of something. We can't leave him in the bay to rot or be torn to pieces by sharks, and he'll certainly attract all the sharks in the Pacific before long. Seems to me the most sensible thing to do is to tow him out to sea and give him the decent burial he deserves.''

A few more gathered round. Most of them towered over George. He was one of those little men whose deceptive appearance cloaked amazing strength and activity for all his nearly seventy years and slightly stooped shoulders. When he walked he moved briskly with a springy kind of amble, his arms swinging freely by his side. A nose with a prominent arch and clear blue eyes that usually sparkled keenly were the most noticeable of his features. Those eyes looked so trusting, and yet they could sum up a man in as many minutes as it took George to make his acquaintance. He tilted back the grey felt hat he was wearing, showing his snowy hair.

''Well, I suppose he had to go some time,'' he remarked. ''Although, Alex and Bill Greig told me they saw him the other week while they were fishing near Leonard's Island and they reckoned he was as active as ever, playing with a grampus he'd caught.''

George turned to go. He had business at the bank that he might as well do now that he was in town and it would give him time to think. Slowly he walked along the wharf and started up the hill. A couple of times he stopped and looked back. Then he quickened his pace and kept going. Near the bank in Imlay Street he met John Logan, who owned the big house across the bay at East Boyd, and Logan, like the others, asked him about Tom. George said he thought he might tow the carcass to sea and sink it.

"Why I asked you," Logan said, "was because I heard a fellow in the pub talking about cutting off Tom's head and getting the teeth out."

"Will he?" George said fiercely, his eyes flashing. "I'd like to see him try. Like hell he will! He'll make a few lousy bob that way over my dead body."

"Why not tow him over to your tryworks and we'll clean down his bones and wire them together?" Logan suggested. "We could keep the skeleton in Eden always as a memorial to Tom and the other killers."

And so it was agreed. Logan went on down to the wharf and George entered the bank. But his mind was far from money matters as he picked up a pen and scratched at a withdrawal form. The date? The wall calendar made it 17 September 1930. That must be right. He lost count of time so much nowadays. The pen scribbled the date under semiconscious directions and moved to the next line, but in George's mind the leaves of the calendar were flying backwards—twenty, forty, sixty years. . . .

Chapter 2

Lunch hour at the Eden school must have been nearly over when the shouts from the direction of Imlay Street penetrated the din of the schoolyard. George Davidson, a sturdy little figure in short pants, sprang to his feet and listened for confirmation of what his keen ears had picked up.

"What's the matter with you?" asked another chubby little chap, who was reclining on the grass nearby.

"I think there's a whale," George told him.

"Don't be silly. It's too early for whales yet."

"My father says he's killed them before in May. Look at the people running up near the lighthouse, Charlie. There's something doing."

Charlie Scott stood up and looked towards Middle Head. They could see men running and could hear shouts in the distance. "Rusho, rusho," someone was calling.

In Eden that word meant one thing—a whale chase. But it was sufficient to cause enough mass hysteria to completely disrupt normal business activities and upset domestic routine. Men would dash from hotels, leaving their beer on the counter, or would spring up from half-eaten meals to join the mad rush for vantage points round the cliffs. To the men who comprised the boat crews, the call was even more urgent. The difference of a few seconds in getting their boat away might put them just a few yards behind a rival boat when it harpooned the whale, and unless the whale managed to break loose again, the latecomers were out of the race, for it was an unwritten law that the whale belonged to whoever got fast and remained fast to kill it.

To young George Davidson, the shouts in the distance were like something magnetic. He ran across the yard and wriggled through the school fence.

"I'm coming too," Charlie announced, scrambling through after him, and away they raced.

Imlay Street was deserted except for a few carts and buggies, their horses tethered to kerbside posts. It was as if a plague had suddenly descended on the town and the inhabitants had fled in panic. Onwards sped the two boys as fast as their legs could carry them, down the hill past the Commercial Hotel to Snug Cove, where the boats were kept, past the boatsheds, and up the track to the lighthouse. George thought his father must have set off with a good break over his opposition, because at this early stage of the season, John Davidson would have more chance than his rivals of mustering an experienced boat crew at a moment's notice. The widow Barclay, who owned the opposition fishery, would have more or less a scratch crew, apart from her head man, Bob Love. From the heights of the headland, the boys could see the two boats racing out to sea, one about three hundred yards ahead of the other.

"It's him all right," George squealed, jumping about in his excitement. "Barclay's boat hasn't a hope of catching them either."

"Bet ten to one Barclay," a big fellow with a mop of curly black hair was calling. "I've got ten pounds to one if anyone fancies a bet on the Barclay boat."

"What price Davidson?" a voice called from the crowd.

"Don't want it. Tens Barclay."

"There he is," George shouted, pointing to a spot about two hundred yards ahead of his father's boat where the sea had broken into foam and a column of vaporized water was shooting upwards. George had seen the same sight many times. It was the whale coming up to breathe. He could see his father standing at the steer oar, urging his men for that little extra pace which sometimes made all the difference between success and failure. Behind them Bob Love was trying desperately to make up leeway. There was a small easterly ground swell and a light north-east breeze—just enough to make it choppy. The watchers on the cliffs could see the spray flying as the boats raced for the prize, five oars apiece swinging forward and dipping as fast as five pairs of hands could manipulate them. As they watched, the whale lashed the water with its huge tail and dived quickly.

"The killers are worrying him," George murmured. "Did you see Tom nearly jump out of the water?"

"Jackson's there too," said Charlie. "I saw him a minute ago."

For a while there was no sign of the whale or the killers, who had dived with the whale. Then the killers reappeared. At frequent intervals one or two of them would flop about like porpoises, spouting whale-fashion, to indicate the course the whale was taking in its frantic efforts to get away. Below, the other killers turned the whale back towards the bay whenever it tried to break for the open sea. George knew the odds were against its escape, for if it eluded its harriers it would still have to contend with another patrol of killers about a mile farther out.

Ever since he was old enough to know what it was all about, George had been intrigued by the way the killers kept the hunters informed of the whale's movements under water while they hindered its escape. By some uncanny means these strangely intelligent creatures seemed to be

This is Tom, the famous leader of the killer whales who helped the Eden whalemen catch whales for more than a century. These pictures of Tom and the other killers show how the Eden people knew the killers by the shape of their fins. The photographs were taken from whale boats by the late Mr C. E. Wellings, an Eden resident, who lived with the Davidson family for weeks at a time and went out in their boats with them. This, taken just south of Twofold Bay, shows Boyd's tower in the distance.

Hooky, another of the better-known Twofold Bay killer whale leaders, showing again how they were known by the shape of their fins.

—Photo by C. E. Wellings

Killer whale Jackson in Twofold Bay. Jackson came to a sad end, as the story tells.
—Photo by C. E. Wellings

Killer whale Cooper during a whale chase at sea off Twofold Bay.
—Photo by C. E. Wellings

able to communicate with each other, even when miles apart, and it was still more uncanny how they sometimes tried to communicate with the men in the boats and give them directions.

"I can't see Humpy," George said suddenly.

"Well, I'm blowed!" A big fellow who had been standing nearby moved closer and was looking down at the two boys. "How do you kids tell these damned killers from one another from so far away?"

"Oh, we know them, mister," George told him. "If you knew them as well as Charlie and me, you could pick out most of them from here, but close up you couldn't miss any. For one thing their fins are all different. Tom's fin is sharp on the point and has a round knob on it; Stranger has a long straight fin with a diamond-shaped top; Ben's is long and straight and sharp-pointed; and Hooky's hangs down over his side nearly into the water sometimes when he comes to the top. You're one of the sailors from the ship at the wharf, aren't you?"

"Yes."

"Haven't you ever seen killers before?"

"Killers? Yes, sonny, I've seen killers in many seas, but none that were kept like pet dogs or trained seals to help men catch whales, and as for knowing them personally by name—"

"Look, he's up again," somebody yelled as the whale rose almost under the bows of Davidson's boat. It looked like that from so far away, although probably at least sixty yards separated the whale and the boat.

"They've got him!" George shouted, jumping up and down with one hand on Charlie's shoulder.

"Not yet, Georgie," cautioned an old fellow in front of the crowd. It was Jack Graham, who had whaled with George's father for many years until rheumatism and approaching age forced his retirement from such a strenuous occupation. "I've seen 'em get away sometimes right under our noses."

"He'll get this one," George insisted. "Sam's up with the harpoon now."

Davidson's boat had steadied down and the bow oarsman, hurriedly peaking his oar by placing the end in a socket on the side of the boat opposite the tholepins, had grabbed a harpoon and was bracing himself for the throw. George had recognized the figure as that of Sam Haddigaddi, one of several aborigines and half-castes who worked with his father. These "darkies," as they called them, were good whalers. For reasonable distances they could row like fury; they had eyes like hawks and to most of them, who could spear even small fish underwater, hurling a harpoon into the huge bulk of a whale was child's play.

Sam held the harpoon over his right shoulder for a brief moment.

Then, as his figure relaxed, the other four oarsmen backed for their lives away from the spot, almost obliterated in a shower of spray. Stung by the harpoon, the whale had given one terrific lunge with its tail and dived. Suddenly the boat was careering along like something berserk, foam curling from its bows in a long train. George could see his father standing in the stern clinging to the big sweep—a very important post because that whale could turn sharply, wheel on its course or even come up beneath them, and one false move with the steer oar could easily mean disaster. All five oars were peaked now. While a whale was towing them it would be fatal for an oar to flop into the water and slew the boat round. At the right time Sam would take the sweep and John Davidson would go for'ard to kill the whale by lancing it in the vulnerable spot—about three feet back from the side fin at the water's edge.

Many had wondered why it was necessary for the headsman, as the skipper was called, to change over with the man who threw the harpoon instead of leaving him to do both jobs, but it had been the practice since time immemorial and that was all about it. The boat-steerer, who was actually the bow oarsman, threw the harpoon, and the headsman steered the boat until he went for'ard to kill the whale with the lance.

The crowd on the cliffs had quietened now. All the yelling in the world would not help the men in the boat to kill the whale any quicker. George and Charlie stood tense, waiting. Far behind Davidson's speeding boat Bob Love and his crew plodded on. At any moment the whale could get loose and come towards them, and they must be ready. Rival boats did not give up the chase merely because another crew had harpooned the whale. The whale broke surface frequently, harried by the killers, who never relaxed for a second, dashing about, leaping out of the water and heading off their victim like a hunting pack. They would even throw themselves on top of the whale when it surfaced.

"Why do they keep jumping on him, George?" Charlie asked. "They can't hurt him."

"Well, Dad reckons they throw themselves over his blowhole because they seem to think they can stop him breathing properly," George explained. "Other ones swim under his head to keep him on the surface and stop him from going down."

"Good God!" remarked the sailor who had spoken to them before. "Don't tell me these killers are that good. I suppose they can read and write too."

Had George thought the man was trying to make fun of him or the killers, he might have retorted sharply, but it was apparent the remark contained only good humour. "Oh, they're pretty good, mister," he answered and left it at that.

In any case he was too interested in what was happening to start an argument. The whale had turned south-east and George could see his father's boat careering away in the direction of South Head. Soon it was just a speck bobbing about a couple of miles off the headland. Then it seemed to stop and a splurge of spray and foam appeared nearby. The two boys were not the only cliff watchers who held their breath. Last year they had seen a similar sight from much closer range and on that occasion the huge flailing flukes of a whale in its death-throes had smashed a boat to pieces. The few seconds they were kept in suspense seemed like minutes before the flurry subsided and they saw the boat moving again, this time as if following the arc of a circle.

"They've lanced him," George said with obvious relief. "He's milling."

"He's what?" the sailor asked.

"Milling. Going round in a circle. They usually go for about half a mile before they die."

Now the crowd was roaring encouragement again, the fellow who had tried to lay the Barclay boat at ten to one bellowing as loudly as anyone.

"What's up with you?" old Jack Graham chided him. "Anyone'd think you were holding a few hundred quid on the result. There wasn't anyone silly enough to back the widow with you, was there?"

"Didn't hold a penny, Jack. I'm glad, though, to see Davidson start the season well."

"Even though you didn't win on it?"

"Even though I didn't win. I don't know, I can't do any good at all lately. Just as well someone can."

"He hasn't got it yet," remarked a tall, thin man who was standing nearby holding a horse. "I've seen 'em do in a boat after they've been lanced."

"Oh, shut up." The betting man turned his head sharply. "If he loses it, I'll blame you, so look out."

A fresh outbreak of excitement interrupted the argument. The boat in the distance had stopped again and the tiny figures in it were moving about.

"They've got him now," George yelled triumphantly. "He's dead."

In a few minutes the Barclay boat and another boat which had gone out in case of accidents had joined the victors. It was some time before the three boats headed for home. The whale, apparently, had been anchored and buoyed, for had the boats been towing the dead whale, they would have been moving at a snail's pace instead of the four or five knots they were doing. George knew the killers would not let the men work now, even if they wanted to bring in the whale. The killers would be claiming their reward for services rendered. They would seize the whale's carcass and take it to the bottom, where they would eat out the tongue and feast on the lips and other tender delicacies. In a couple of days, sufficient gases would form inside the whale to float the carcass and it could then be towed to the tryworks for treatment.

The two boys were waiting on the beach near the wharf when the boats eventually arrived. They grabbed the edge of the gunwale and helped the many eager hands pulling Davidson's boat ashore as the crew shipped their oars and jumped out. John Davidson had stepped onto the beach and was picking up some of his gear from the stern when he noticed them.

"What are you doing here, George?" he asked sternly. "Why aren't you at school?"

"Oh, have a heart, John," old Jack Graham pleaded, looking at the lads, who seemed too scared to reply. "You'd have done the same thing yourself when you was his age. Besides, you ought to be overjoyed, getting a whale so early in the season."

"Yes, give him a chance. He'll soon be old enough to go with you, and a damned good whaler he'll make too." The crowd laughed with the speaker, John Hopkins, a cheery big-faced man who ran the horseback mail from Bega to Bombala twice a week, as well as having a butcher shop.

"All right," said John Davidson, breaking into a smile. "But get along home now and see if you can do anything for your mother."

George knew better than to dally longer. Reluctantly he and Charlie Scott started to walk from the beach—not very quickly though, because they wanted to hear as much as they could.

"Have any trouble with the whale, John?" they heard someone ask.

"No, he wasn't much bother. Nearly cracked us when I lanced him over near South Head."

"Looked like a pretty big bloke from the cliffs."

"About forty feet I'd say—a black whale. Hey, Sam—you other fellows—get that gear out of the boat. You'll get to the pub soon enough."

To George and Charlie, walking up the hillside to Imlay Street had dawned another startling realization. In the excitement they had forgotten about running away from school.

"I suppose we'll be in for it tomorrow morning," Charlie remarked ruefully. "Old Bateson will be onto us first thing."

"I suppose so," George agreed.

"I don't care, anyhow."

"Neither do I." George looked back wistfully at the beach, where the men still stood or squatted near the whaleboats. "I wish I was big enough to go whaling with the old man," he said sullenly. "Bateson could go to the devil then."

But both knew that any bravado they were building up would break down when they entered the schoolhouse next morning. They might as well be going to the devil himself. At least he would be no more terrifying than schoolmaster Bateson, whose temper was as red as the huge mass of whiskers that adorned his face in a most conspicuous beard.

Stranger, another killer whale identity, chasing a whale in Calle Calle Bay, Eden.
–Photo by C. E. Wellings

Chapter 3

With the advent of the whaling season each year, George Davidson grew more and more restless at school. Mr Bateson, if he had ever seriously entertained the thought of grooming George for a white-collar job, had other ideas by the time the lad was fourteen, and it was not hard to agree with John Davidson when he suggested one day that he might take George away from school.

"I'm thinking of going back over the bay to East Boyd," Davidson told the schoolmaster over a pot of ale in the Commercial Hotel. "This boarding house we've got here in town is too much for the missus. So help me, if we stay here much longer she'll be worn out. I think George and Margaret are old enough to be taken away from school. That's what I meant to talk to you about, Bateson. I might be right about taking George away, or then again I might be wrong. What do you think?"

"Well, I don't know." Bateson paused, stroking his red beard. "It's hard to say, John, but I think you're probably right. The boy has always wanted to go whaling with you and there doesn't seem much sense keeping him on at school. He'd be handy to you now, too. He's as strong as a horse."

"That's just another reason." John Davidson put down his pot and wiped the froth from his beard—jet-black and not quite as prolific as Bateson's. "I'm going to be short of good boat-steerers this season, and with Powers and Whelan starting in opposition, George would be handy. I'll have three boats, you know, and that means about fifteen men at least. Alex Greig is a good man. So are most of the others. But particularly with opposition you must have those you can trust. Whelan's been trying to buy over some of my darkies. I know, because I've been told."

"There's Whelan now," Bateson said softly.

John Davidson didn't need to look up. In the mirror behind the bar shelves he could see a tall man approaching the counter from the side door.

"Good-day, Bob," the newcomer greeted the barman. "Give us a pot and have another ready. One won't touch the sides."

It didn't. Roger Whelan was depositing the empty container on the counter when he too looked in the mirror.

"Hullo, John," he said, turning side on and leaning with one elbow on the counter. "Reckoning up how many whales you hope to get this season?"

"No, Roger," Davidson replied casually. "Although that'd be easier than reckoning up how many you won't get."

Whelan turned temporarily to get the second pot of ale, shoved it round the counter in a wide circle to clear the bottom of the slops in which the barman had deposited it, drained half the contents quickly, and put the glass down on a clear area of the counter.

"You and that old Solomon think whaling is your monopoly," he said tauntingly. "We might do better than you think, and wouldn't that hurt. It'd hurt old Solomon in the pocket, and you couldn't hurt him in a better place. Anyhow, drink that up and have one with me. You too, Bateson."

"No, thanks," said Davidson. "I was just leaving."

"Thank you." Bateson smiled politely. "I must be going too."

"Be seeing you on the high seas then."

"No doubt," John Davidson agreed. "But there's one thing I'd like to tell you, Roger. Leave my men alone."

Whelan looked surprised. "What do you mean?" he asked.

"I think you know," Davidson said with emphasis. "You wouldn't be trying to buy a couple of my best darkies, would you?"

"Who told you that?" Whelan snapped. "It's a damn lie."

"Never mind who told me. Just leave them alone."

"He doesn't seem to like Sol Solomon," Bateson remarked as they walked along Imlay Street together. "You know, John, I've often wondered about your partnership with Solomon."

"Have you?" said Davidson. "So have I."

Bateson looked at him curiously. He was about to pursue the subject, but thought better of it.

"About young George," he said instead, "I'd suggest you leave him at school until the end of this term if you can. When are you likely to be going over to East Boyd?"

"In about a month or so. I'll be starting to get the place ready this week. It'll take some cleaning after being empty for a few years. The tryworks has to be put in order and there's quarters for the men to be fixed up."

"Must be a costly business, this whaling," Bateson remarked. "How many whales do you reckon you'd need to get each season to make it pay?"

"Well, that all depends. The main thing is the price of oil and whalebone, and that varies from year to year, but on the average I'd say at least ten to fifteen whales a season. For a start it costs about three hundred quid for two boat crews, and reckoning on oil being worth twenty-five quid a tun now and bone about two hundred and fifty quid a ton, it'd pay if you finished the season with a ton of bone and about ten tun of oil, but there wouldn't be much profit in it, and a man has to live."

"But I've seen some seasons when you got only one or two."

"That's like everything else. You've got to take the bad with the good."

"There must be a lot of waste in a whale," Bateson said thoughtfully when they stopped outside Davidson's house. "I mean what you don't use. You just take the oil and the bone and throw the rest away. Some day what you discard might have many valuable uses."

"Perhaps," Davidson agreed. "I can't see it, though."

"Young George might." Bateson stroked his beard for a moment. "Yes, it's quite possible," he remarked. "Well, good evening, John."

Davidson closed the gate behind him and stood for a few seconds watching the figure of the schoolmaster ambling away down the road. The setting sun was casting its last feeble rays round the top of Mount Imlay, emphasizing against a dull-yellow background the mountain's dark bulk. Many times Davidson had seen it like that, poking over the horizon, when he was far out at sea and no other land was visible, and it always gave him a comforting feeling as it pointed a clear path home. From the stern of his boat he had watched the lovely effects of the sunsets round the mountain's upper regions, wondering upon the marvels that produced them; but John Davidson, essentially a simple man, was quite satisfied to take it all for granted and just enjoy what he saw.

He turned and began to walk slowly up the pathway towards the house, dimly conscious of the sound of the sea breaking on the rocks at the foot of the cliffs, for the sea was another thing John Davidson took for granted. The swish of the waves came at slow intervals. There was no sea running—just a small, lazy ground swell. Across the bay he could see the mouth of the Kiah River behind an occasional patch of white water where the rollers were breaking gently on the end of the long beach known as the Whale Spit. It all seemed too peaceful to be true and too quiet to promise continuance. Not that John Davidson expected lasting good behaviour from the weather, which he always regarded with the alert suspicion of a man who uses the sea to earn a living. The weather was one thing he did not take for granted. Another was the safety of his boats. The boats were always stowed well above high-water mark, even on a lovely evening like this.

The boats flashed into Davidson's mind instinctively as he entered the hall and glanced, also instinctively, at the barometer.

"Looks like a blow tonight," he remarked thoughtfully, giving the glass a few smart taps to make sure that the hand had settled. It had dropped nearly half an inch since early morning, from 30 inches to just on 29.5. John Davidson hung up his hat and went through to the kitchen to greet a tall woman who was sitting at a table shelling peas.

"Do you know where George is?" she asked curtly.

The question was accompanied by a frown, which was always there when Effie Davidson was irritated or impatient or both. She was inclined to worry over many little things that would not have troubled her husband. Not that he blamed her for getting impatient with George occasionally, although the lad's adventures caused him much silent merriment as well as irritation.

"No," he replied slowly. "Why? Isn't he home yet?"

"Obviously not," she retorted. "I wouldn't be asking you if he were."

"No, I haven't seen him."

"Well, he's going to get something when he does come home," she said firmly. "Every evening now it's the same. He gets away with that Charlie Scott and doesn't come in to do the messages or anything. Yesterday they were down at Cattle Bay and someone told me George was trying to ride a bullock while the sailors were swimming it out to a ship. He'll be getting drowned, next thing."

"He can swim, can't he?"

"That's not the point. Anyhow I've had enough of it."

John Davidson knew it was useless to argue further. If Effie said she had had enough, that was that, and George could look forward to a good whacking when he came home. But down in Cattle Bay, no thought of parental anger had yet penetrated to spoil George's enjoyment of a new game he and Charlie Scott had devised.

In a borrowed dinghy, they were "whaling" the bullocks being swum out for loading into the coastal ship *Devonport*. Charlie Scott was rowing the dinghy and George, standing up in front, was prodding the bellowing bullocks with a stick "harpoon" tied to the kellick rope. The fun of the situation, naturally, did not appeal as much to the harassed animals or the sailors as it did to the two boys in the dinghy, and as time passed and some bullocks became increasingly difficult to load into the ship, the patience of the men wore thinner. The storm burst when one bullock with a poor sense of humour went nearly mad and kicked so much as it went aboard in the sling that it almost stove in one of the ship's boats. The *Devonport*'s skipper roared louder than the bullock and when he began to shout certain instructions to his crew, pointing to the dinghy, George and Charlie decided it was time to head for home hurriedly.

George's father was sitting on the veranda talking to one of their boarders when George appeared at the gate and entered rather sheepishly.

"Where have you been, son?" his father asked quietly. "Your mother's been looking for you."

"Down at Cattle Bay with Charlie Scott," the boy answered. "We were watching the men load bullocks on the ship."

"Your mother's going to give you Cattle Bay. You're getting too fond of going down there. Come here. What's that you're holding behind your back?"

George's hand came forward clutching a wet undershirt. "It fell in the water," he explained.

John Davidson's tone lost its gentleness as he demanded, "What were you doing with your undershirt off? Have you been trying to ride those bullocks in the water?"

George was startled. "How do you know?" he queried.

"Never mind how I know. I thought you had more sense than that, son. Apart from the foolishness of trying to get on a bullock's back while it's swimming, there are too many sharks about to take risks. And, besides, those fellows from the ships are no company for young boys. Keep away from Cattle Bay. Now go in and see your mother."

The sounds coming from inside shortly afterwards were a clear indication that it was now young George's turn to be prodded with a stick.

"He doesn't know it yet, but he's going to get some real work to do in the boats sooner than he thinks," John Davidson told the other man on the veranda. Davidson then proceeded to give his attention to filling his pipe. The other man nodded dreamily from his chair. He was mainly intent on absorbing the beauty of Eden, where he had chosen to holiday from his business interests in Sydney. A quiet holiday was what he wanted and so he had gone to Mrs Davidson's boarding house, hoping to avoid the possible boisterousness of a hotel.

In the Eden of John Davidson's time, the hotels were frequently boisterous, especially when the crews of deep-sea whaling ships came ashore, but Davidson and others who lived there, sadly agreed that the town was slipping back. When the Kiandra goldrush was on twenty years before, Eden was booming, but when the gold went so did Eden's boom. John Davidson shared with most Eden people the view that their town could become a prosperous city and their harbour a busy port, being the natural inlet and outlet for a vast area of New South Wales and Victoria.

But they knew, too, that Sydney interests wanted to keep Sydney in control of the State's commerce, and development of a place like Eden with a good harbour had to be prevented.

Twofold Bay, Eden, probably taken circa 1920, looking across Snug Cove to Mount Imlay in the background.

–Photo by C. E. Wellings

Chapter 4

Six weeks passed before John Davidson had his family installed in the old Kiah home, his whaling crews quartered in the bunkhouse and the tryworks cleaned out and ready for use again. On two occasions bad weather and nasty seas round the Kiah River bar held up operations, and then the woman who was taking over the boarding house in Eden arrived several weeks late. Davidson fumed at the delay because he wanted to have everything ready for the whaling season. He could not afford the delay with Whelan so keen to catch whales.

George left Eden with a touch of sadness penetrating his excitement at the prospect of becoming a whaler at last. He would miss Charlie Scott and the good times they had together. Parting was not easy when they had been firm mates for so long, starting school on the same day and, not merely by coincidence, leaving on the same day.

"If you leave, I'm leaving too," Charlie had told him. "I've had enough of that school and old Bateson."

Charlie had tried hard to go with his companion, but six different attempts to persuade John Davidson to take him on as a junior whaler met with the same answer. Charlie was too young to leave home and live with rough whaling men, so John Davidson said, and no matter what the two boys thought about it, that had to be taken as final. They still had hopes, though, right to the day when George's father said they would move to East Boyd next morning—"without Charlie Scott."

George could see Charlie standing on the wharf waving long after they pulled out, but he couldn't wave back. He was rowing tub oar behind Sam Haddigaddi, and with his father standing at the steer oar in the stern and looking straight ahead, he wanted to make an impression pulling with these seasoned whalers. Space in a five-oared whaleboat being by no means plentiful, George had been told it would save room if he occupied a rowing seat and got some practice in case he was needed in one of the boats during the season. His elder sister, Margaret, was sitting in the stern beside the tall upright figure of her mother, and Archer and Boyd—the two boys younger than George—were huddled in a small space behind the bow oarsman.

George did not find the Kiah home strange. Until he was about eight years old, they had lived just over the hill in the old cottage built way back in Ben Boyd's day for Boyd's manager, Oswald Brierly, later Sir Oswald Brierly. He remembered the lovely old mulberry trees near the back door, particularly the big tree with the thick foliage where he and Margaret would perch for hours eating mulberries when they knew mother was looking for them. He had vivid memories, too, of the aborigines who used to camp nearby, about a hundred of them spending most of the year in a community not far from the house.

Many of these darkies worked for John Davidson in the boats and the tryworks during the whaling season, and, brought up among them from infancy, the children never knew the average child's strange, instinctive fear of the "blackfellow." George and Margaret, when they lived at Brierly's cottage before, had often stared in wonder at the dances and corroborees of the natives. What fascinated them most was the way the dancers decorated themselves in their traditional war paint. Sometimes the fascination took a practical form and the two little tots would plaster themselves with their own war paint, made from mulberry juice and dance around the mulberry trees with sticks for spears, trying to imitate the natives' weird cries and songs. They thought it was great fun, but the enthusiasm was not shared by their mother, who would spank them soundly and make them scrub off the juice. John Davidson derived a lot of quiet amusement from the juvenile corroborees. "Leave them alone, Effie," he would say to his wife. "They're only kids."

One old darkie named Brierly—they called him after Oswald Brierly—had become a complete exasperation to Mrs Davidson. He and George became firm friends when the little chap was about six years old. Brierly would often take George into the bush all day looking for bees, and when they returned in the evening Mrs Davidson would be waiting for them with a stick. George had learnt a good deal about the bush and the things in it, although Brierly could never teach him to keep out of trouble with those bees. Boyish curiosity proved his undoing and he yielded repeatedly to the temptation to poke his nose into things—a practice that is usually fatal when bees are concerned.

Now, after an absence of nearly six years, they were going back to live at East Boyd—not at Brierly's cottage, but in the old family home near the mouth of the Kiah River. It had been built many years ago by George's grandfather, Alexander Davidson, with timber from the wreck of the *Lawrence Frost*, an American ship that came to grief on Whale Spit beach. Unofficially there was not much mystery behind the disaster that befell the *Lawrence Frost*. It was at the time of the Kiandra gold rush, when the crew of a ship in Twofold Bay might have been excused for becoming restless in an atmosphere infectious with gold fever, their restlessness increased, no doubt, by the precautions taken to stop them deserting. But men inspired with a get-rich-quick madness will try anything, and there were a few men of initiative on the *Lawrence Frost*. One evening when a moderate nor'easter was blowing in through the heads, they slipped the anchor cable, and before anything could be done to save her, the *Lawrence Frost* was aground on Whale Spit. The crew ran away to the diggings, and there the ship lay until Alexander Davidson made a deal and bought her.

Some of the timber could still be seen poking out of the sand, but most of it had gone into the building of the two solid cottages perched on the hillside up from the tryworks. One served as sleeping and living quarters. The other contained the kitchen and a dining room long enough to seat the crews of several whaleboats in addition to the Davidson family. Most of the whalers were quartered in a large bunkhouse at the rear, or could, as some chose to do, camp on the property. Buying the *Lawrence Frost* had saved Alexander Davidson the trouble of hewing his own timber from the forests, or having it transported across from Eden.

George could not help feeling excited as he tugged at the big oar in rhythm with the other men and the whaleboat glided over the light swell that was rolling down the bay towards Boydtown. At last he was to become a whaler. Instead of being a spectator on the cliffs, he would actually be in the boats with his father and these rough men who had been his heroes all those boyhood years. With his grandfather and his father preceding him, George Davidson was now the third generation of the family to work in an industry they had established back in Ben Boyd's day.

They crossed the river bar and in a few minutes the boat was alongside the long primitive ramp of tree trunks where chunks of blubber were hauled up to the tryworks on the edge of the bank after dissection from the whales. George stayed with his father and the men after Margaret and his mother had gone up to the house. Ostensibly he had stayed to help Sam Haddigaddi and two other darkies clean out the boat after they had pulled it up on the ramp, but his real anxiety was to hear what his father said to Alex Greig. Beyond the fact that he was going to work with them, George had been told very little.

"Might as well take the three boats," John Davidson was saying. "Whelan's pretty keen, but he's not going to get one catch if we can help it. He's too damned cocky altogether for my liking."

"I put the men on the lookout this morning," he heard Greig say. "They tell me two killers were in Leatherjacket Bay yesterday—probably part of the pack old Jim saw the other day down at Mowara. We've got these two boats ready and I'll get Sam to stow the gear in that one when they're through washing it out. By the way, who's going to take number three?''

George looked quickly over his shoulder. Greig was leaning against a post of the boat shelter adjoining the tryworks. It was an open shelter—just a roof on beams across the tops of posts—and inside he could see John Davidson walking slowly up and down between the two whaleboats.

''Fred Wilson, I suppose,'' came the somewhat thoughtful reply. ''I don't like it, Alex, because . . . well, you know what I think about Whelan. Anyhow, you and I'll keep our crews and put the others in with Wilson.''

George could contain his curiosity no longer when he saw his father walking away up the track to the house. ''Do you think we'll get a whale soon, Sam?'' he asked the old boat-steerer, feeling with youthful cunning for the right opening.

''Dunno, young George,'' the darkie replied. ''This boat won't, anyways, if you don't coil that line properly.''

George paid slightly more attention to the whale line he was coiling in the stern of the boat, but one eye was still searching Sam's face for the lead he wanted. He came out into the open. ''Am I going with you and dad or in Alex's boat?''

''I dunno.'' The old darkie looked at him curiously, but it was quite apparent he didn't know. ''Hasn't boss told you? All I know is he tell me you comin' to work along with us. Why don't you ask him?''

George did that evening, and found to his disappointment that he was not going in any boat.

''You're going to start up on the lookout with Uncle Jim,'' his father told him.''I've got enough men for the boats. You'll get your chance, though, and it might be sooner than you think.''

The lookout with Uncle Jim! That meant he would still be watching from the shore. He would spend all day at Boyd's Tower on South Head scanning the sea for whales travelling within sight of the coast. He realized, of course, that the lookout was important, especially with an opposition fishery in existence. Wise foresight had made John Davidson lease all the land from the Kiah River to South Head and this gave him a big advantage, because his spotters had an exclusive box seat on the heights of the headland. Their view of the sea for many miles north and south frequently meant a lead that rival boats could never catch. Chief of the lookout squad was John's brother-in-law, Jim McNee, known affectionately to everyone as Uncle Jim. George remembered many nights when the sound of horses' hooves in the distance had been sufficient for his father to scramble hurriedly out of bed and rouse the men, knowing that when Uncle Jim rode in like that at night there was a whale out at sea.

"Will I go over to the lookout with Uncle Jim in the morning?" George asked.

"No," his father informed him. "He's staying on South Head all the time. You can come round with me in the boat in the mornings and return with us in the evenings."

This at least was some consolation and, his disappointment alleviated somewhat, George departed for bed. It was not quite daylight when his father called him and gave him a steaming hot cup of tea.

"Come on," he said. "You've got to spring to it sharply now. No lying in bed."

George had barely rubbed the sleep from his eyes before he joined the men at the tryworks and helped them to launch the boats. He saw a few new faces among the crews, but most of the men there were no strangers. Sam Haddigaddi, Charlie Adgery, and Alf Gardiner he had known as far back as he could remember. There was, too, that big Swede they called Bullock, probably because he had the strength of a bullock and could use it behind an oar. Darky Whitty, another old hand, was mumbling something to a young half-caste aborigine who had signed on the day before, and leaning on an oar rather than holding it was Bert Penrith, a big white-faced fellow who always wore a wide-brimmed hat turned up in front. Bert, so they said, was more than a bit scared of whales and kept the hat turned up in front to give him a better view of things. His own version of the turned-up brim was that he had worn the hat in so many whale chases that the brim had just gone that way from the rush of the wind.

Another character was Bobbo, a giant young Solomon Islander, who had found his way to Eden in a ship some years ago and had decided to stay there and go whaling with John Davidson. Bobbo claimed he could throw a harpoon farther than anybody else, and he could, too, but his greatest asset was a quick wit, a cheery grin, and a likeable personality. Only one thing could upset Bobbo and that was drink. Sober, Bobbo would not harm a fly. Inflamed with rum he was a real menace.

Dawn was breaking through the eastern sky as the three boats left the tryworks and headed in procession for the river bar and the open waters of the bay. Along the edge of the beach a school of mullet flip-flopped about as if resentful of this early-morning intrusion into the tranquillity of their surroundings, previously shattered only by the burst of a roller occasionally on the rocks at the point. Out in the bay the water was glasslike in its appearance, untroubled as yet by the after-breakfast nor'easter. George, perched up in the front of his father's boat, looked about him eagerly, glancing at the other boats and listening to the chatter of the crews, but giving most of his attention seawards in the hope of sighting a whale. He had a strange, excited feeling. Many times he had ridden in a whaleboat and it had been more or less a novelty to him. Now, for the first time, he was there on serious business.

John Davidson's boats were always painted green, a fact George probably did not consider of any significance until later years. To him, in his youthful enthusiasm, they would have been just as beautiful had they been painted in all the colours of the rainbow. Light but strong, these sleek boats were clinker built of cedar, about thirty feet long, nicely flared and pointed at each end. It was important that they should be double-ended because speed in backing away from a harpooned whale was only a common-sense advantage, a double-ended boat being much more manoeuvrable in reverse than one with a blunt stern. Four or five feet of the stern was decked in and through this decking protruded a short post called the loggerhead, used for checking the whale line. Right on the point of the stern a leather strap held in place the huge sweep—sometimes as long as the boat itself—with which a practised boat-steerer could swing his craft round almost in its own length.

John Davidson used five-oared boats. Most whalers favoured boats designed for an odd number of oars—usually five or seven—because when the harpooner left his oar and stood up for the throw it left an even number of oars on both sides. Technically, the positions from bow to stern were: bow harpooner, bow oarsman, midship oarsman, tub oarsman, after oarsman, and headsman. The bow harpooner was more commonly called the boat-steerer. After harpooning the whale, he went aft and took the steering oar while the headsman went for'ard ready to kill the whale with the lance. To anyone but a whaler this seemed a peculiar practice. It seemed much more logical that the harpooner should remain in the bows and lance the whale, while the headsman continued to steer. But that was how it was done.

When the boat was fast to a whale and was being towed, the oars were "peaked" by placing the ends in sockets on the sides opposite the tholepins but lower down, enabling them to rest at a sloping angle so that the blades would not catch a wave. Beneath the middle and aft thwarts were two tubs, each containing about two hundred fathoms of line which passed aft around the loggerhead and then went for'ard through a niche in the bows and under a small iron bar. This ensured that the boat would always be pulled forward and, if a whale began to play up, he could not drag the line from anywhere else but the bows.

The sun was still struggling to make an impression on the eastern sky when the three boats drew in under the lee of South Head alongside a big red rock like a natural wharf. In calm weather when there was no sea running they always moored there. Back from the edge in the cliff-face was a fairly large cave where they could keep supplies and find shelter in wet weather. John Davidson allowed opposition crews to land there too if they wished, and they usually did, because the arrangement suited both parties. The opposition wanted a base of operations; John Davidson preferred to have them there under observation without having to worry about the possibility of them stealing a march on a whale.

Uncle Jim, who had apparently seen the boats coming, was there to meet them.

"What's up, Jim?" Alex Greig greeted him. "Couldn't you sleep?"

"Sleep be damned," Jim retorted. "No respectable man sleeps at this hour of the morning. Anyhow, I'm hungry. Did you bring the tucker?"

"Yes," John Davidson assured him. "You, Pigeon, get that tucker out and take it up to the tower. Give him a hand, Joe."

Two half-caste lads sprang into Greig's boat and unloaded four bags that had been stacked in the bows.

"You'd better get us all something to eat," John Davidson suggested. "You can't row on an empty guts and I want everything clear before Powers and Whelan get here. No sign of anything, Jim?"

"No." Jim dug his hands in his waistcoat pockets and leant against the rock cliff-face. "The killers are about Leatherjacket Bay, but no sign of a whale. I don't know, they seem to be pretty slow working up the coast this year."

"Powers and Whelan haven't been about, have they?"

"No."

"They will be now we've started. Anyhow, they'll need to be damned smart—much smarter than Whelan thinks he is."

Jim grinned. "They tell me he's been doing a bit of talking round town," he said. "Telling everyone you won't get a whale this season."

"So he says." John Davidson snorted, walking slowly towards the path up the cliffs and beckoning Jim to follow him. "I'll go up and have a look round the tower with you, Jim. Hey, Pigeon, hurry up and get that fire going. These blokes will be so damned weak they won't be able to catch a jellyfish if they wait for you and Joe to feed them."

"Yes, boss. Hurrying, boss," Pigeon mumbled.

"What did boss say?" Joe asked him.

"He meant other fellow crews hungry," Pigeon snapped. "Anyhow never mind what he said. Get more wood."

"I don't like that bloke Pigeon," John Davidson was saying as he walked slowly with Uncle Jim. "I saw him hanging about town last week with Whelan and I told you Whelan was trying to buy one or two of my

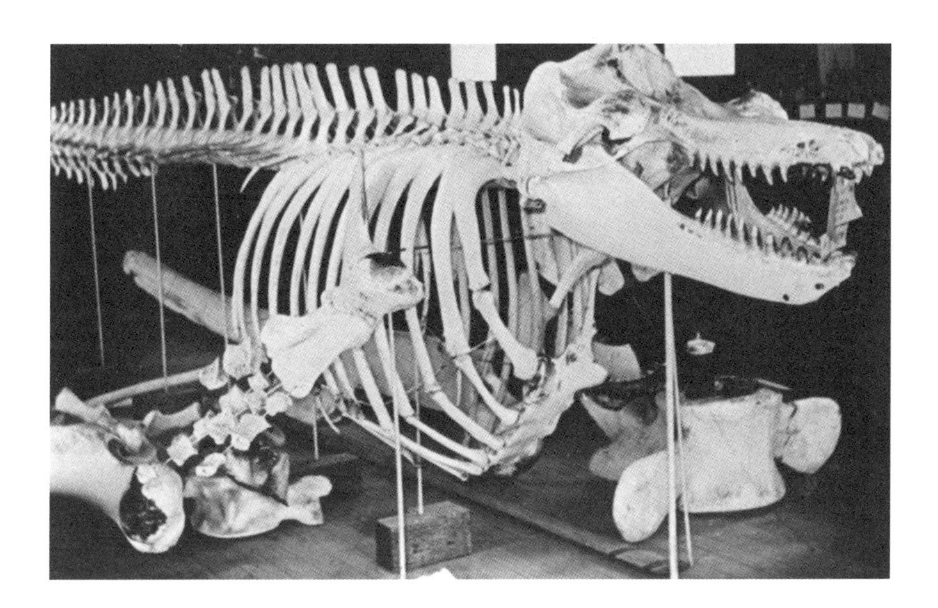

The skeleton of Tom, which is preserved in the Eden Killer Whale Museum with other relics of the whaling days.

Fast to a whale in Twofold Bay, the oars are peaked and the rowers are taken for a ride. George Davidson is steering with the big steering oar at the stern, but at the right time he will go for'ard and lance the whale to kill it. The line attached to the harpoon can be seen faintly near the bow of the boat. The killer Tom is swimming alongside, close to a whale calf, which has surfaced.
—Photo by C. E. Wellings

The old Davidson home at East Boyd near the mouth of the Kiah River, built by George Davidson's grandfather, Alexander Davidson, with timber from the wreck of the American ship Lawrence Frost, *which broke up on the Whale Spit beach in Twofold Bay during the gold-rush days. This was where the family went to live when George began his whaling career while still a boy.*

The house that George built for himself closer to the mouth of the Kiah River. The carcass of a whale can be seen in front of the tryworks, where the oil was extracted from the blubber.

darkies. Pigeon's the type who'd sell his soul for a bottle of rum, but I'm so damned short of good boat-steerers I've got to keep him for the time being. That Wilson fellow, too, might need watching."

"What about young George?"

"I'm leaving him up here with you for a while. George is a good lad, very keen—too keen, perhaps. Wish he were a bit older, Jim. You can't put an old head on young shoulders, although he seems to have plenty of sense for a kid, and he's as game as anyone else I've got. Anyhow, if things go wrong, I'll put him in my boat and let Charlie Adgery take number three."

"I don't think you'll go wrong," Jim assured him. "Listen, John, that young bloke is the makings of as good a man as yourself."

"Maybe better," John Davidson agreed, "but it won't do any harm to let him watch from up here a bit longer. You can talk to him and teach him a lot. He'll talk to you all day about whales and boats."

"All right." Old Jim laughed. "I'd be very surprised, though, if there's much he doesn't know."

Chapter 5

In the weeks that followed—weeks of waiting for whales which seemed to have forsaken the Eden coastline—Uncle Jim found his assessment of George's knowledge justified. He found that the lad had obviously made an intense study of the killers and their habits and knew more about whales than some of the men who had been years in the boats. For instance, it had never occurred to Jim until George told him during one of their watches that whales were coloured dark on top and light underneath for a very good purpose. He realized then that fish were dark on top and light underneath for the same purpose—protection. It made them harder to see from above and camouflaged them similarly against attack from below. George knew, too, that a whale had nostrils on top of its head to enable it to breathe while exposing only a small portion of itself over the surface of the water.

They spent most days watching from the ramparts of Boyd's Tower, the high stone tower Ben Boyd had built as a lighthouse, though its actual use for that purpose had hardly justified its cost. The tower was strongly built of sandstone quarried at Pyrmont, in Sydney, shipped to Twofold Bay, and carted to South Head by bullock wagon. Of square design, the tower had four windows at each level and the name "Boyd" chiselled into the ramparts on every side. On Boyd's instructions, Oswald Brierly had placed a light in the tower on one or two occasions, but it never became a regular lighthouse because the Government of the day would not assume responsibility for it and the Crown did not sanction private lighthouses. The tower had remained unused for more than forty years, until John Davidson acquired it with the lease of the surrounding area and decided it was a good whaling lookout.

From the top of the tower they could see as far down south as Green Cape—the direction they usually looked in May and June when the whales were coming up from the Antarctic—or north to a point somewhere near Merimbula, where they looked in the latter part of the season when the whales were coming back from the warm northern waters to return to the Antarctic. George was well aware that most of the whales travelled wide of the coast, too far out to be seen, but many travelled fairly close in from Gabo Island to Montague Island. This season, though, they had apparently deserted the coast, unless they had passed by at night fairly wide out. During the first week in June, George and Uncle Jim sighted two spouting about five miles out, but the killers must have taken a holiday and the boats came back without getting anywhere near their prey.

It was almost the end of the month before their vigilance was rewarded again. The south-easterly breeze had freshened towards midday and Uncle Jim had settled himself behind the southern rampart of the tower where, sheltered from the wind, he was dozing comfortably in the sun. George stood leaning on the stone edge of the tower's east side, gazing abstractedly out across the miles of blue sea speckled at short intervals by the prancing white horses of the waves. With the sea so choppy it was slightly more difficult to see what he was looking for—the telltale waterspout of a whale coming to the surface to breathe. The air taken in at the previous breathing, hot and humid with water vapour, condensed itself into a column of steam or spray when forced out again into the cooler atmosphere, and if the whale actually began to blow before its nostrils were clear of the surface a large quantity of water sometimes went up with the blast. It was just such a picture that penetrated George's daydream.

"Uncle Jim," he panted excitedly, shaking the old fellow by the shoulder, "I can see one blowing."

Jim sprang to his feet and peered over the edge of the tower. "Where?" he demanded.

"About a mile off Leatherjacket," said George. "He's gone down now, but you wait a minute."

The waiting period before the whale breached again seemed like ages to the pair of watchers scanning intently the area of sea where the whale should reappear. Suddenly it broke the surface in a flurry of foam, blowing furiously, performed a kind of half roll and then dived, its huge flukes thrashing the water as it went down.

"Looks like a black whale," George remarked. "The killers have got him, too."

"I'd reckon they had by the way he kicked about," said Uncle Jim.

"I think I saw a couple of killers near him."

"Well, never mind." Uncle Jim was literally dancing about now. "Get down and yell out to your father. Hurry up."

A shout from Jim broke up the draughts game. Squabbles were forgotten as the players and their backers leapt to their feet and rushed for the boats. Scrambling down the ladder inside the tower, George almost lost his hold in his excitement, but he touched ground safely and ran swiftly to the cliffs on the lee of South Head where the boats were waiting.

"Whale," he shouted. "Rusho."

Figures reclining about the rocks sprang to life and began to tumble into the boats. One young darkie miscalculated the jump as Alex Greig's boat swung away from the rock ledge in the surge, but grabbed the gunwale as he went down and hauled himself aboard before the rest of the crew had their oars out. Davidson's third boat, in charge of Fred Wilson, was past the point well clear of the others, but Roger Whelan was after him. George ran along the rocks, yelling and pointing in a southeasterly direction. He knew that, once around the headland, they would soon see the whale for themselves.

They passed the point as close as they dared, twenty-five oars slashing frantically at the water to propel the five boats seawards in a race for the prize. George could hear Roger Whelan screaming curses at his oarsmen. John Davidson's exhortations to his crew, about fifty yards behind in third place, would not exactly have met with approval in mixed drawing-room company.

"Get stuck into it, Sam, you lazy swine. Pull, Bobbo . . . go on . . . I'll sack the bloody lot of you if you let Whelan beat us."

Wilson's boat was still well ahead about half a mile out, but Whelan was not far behind him now. George could see the spray flying as the boats bashed through the choppy crests of the rollers. Driving at a tangent across wind as they were, it was inevitable that the men should get wet, though that was a small detail. Their only thought was to get within harpoon range of the whale as quickly as possible.

"Go on, John," shouted Uncle Jim, who had scrambled down from the tower and was now standing on the cliff's edge beside George. "What's wrong? They're losing you." It made no difference to the old fellow that John Davidson couldn't hear him out there.

They saw the whale breach again, still harried by the killers, trying to make out to sea in a north-easterly direction. The men guiding the boats saw it too, and changed course accordingly.

"I think the killers have headed him in," said George. "He might come up next time almost under Wilson's boat. Pigeon's getting up now."

Pigeon had shipped his oar and was standing up in Wilson's boat with the harpoon ready. Not far behind—the gap had closed considerably—was Whelan's boat, and Jack Bedford, Whelan's boat-steerer, was getting ready too. Suddenly there was a patch of foam and the whale broke surface just ahead of Wilson's boat.

"Give it to him, Pigeon," George and Uncle Jim shouted together.

Pigeon tossed the harpoon, but nothing happened. He had missed. Before he could recover the harpoon—it all happened in a matter of seconds—Whelan's boat was alongside and the harpoon hurled by Bedford caught the whale as its back was sliding beneath the surface. Its flukes lifted out of the water and came down viciously as the oarsmen backed away frantically. Then they peaked their oars and within a few more seconds the boat was in tow.

George was not only disappointed. He was furious. "Pigeon shouldn't have missed that," he moaned. "He couldn't have missed. The whale was almost underneath him."

"I've seen 'em missed before," remarked Uncle Jim. "That one was pretty close though, George."

"My sister, Margaret, could have harpooned that bloke," George insisted. "I'll bet father's cranky."

Father *was* cranky. He would have been even had he been perfectly satisfied Pigeon's miss was just one of those things that happen, but John Davidson's anger was intensified by a very strong suspicion that it had not been accidental—Pigeon was one of the men with whom Whelan had allegedly been conducting negotiations. Then there was the coincidence of Whelan's boat being close to seize the missed opportunity. In other words, it appeared Pigeon had been bought.

"Keep after them," John Davidson scowled. "Bend to it. Put your back into it, Charlie. They haven't got him yet."

Standing in the stern clinging to the steer oar, Davidson muttered curses at Pigeon through his beard. He was still cursing to himself half an hour later when they stood by off North Head and watched Roger Whelan give the dying whale a final lance. A small black whale, it would probably yield about two and a half tuns, and with oil at twenty-five pounds a tun and bone bringing a fair price, Davidson estimated that catch should be worth about a hundred and fifty pounds.

"Bad luck, John," Roger Whelan called to him as they pulled away. "Never mind, you might do better next time."

"We'll harpoon you next time," Bullock shouted back. "You—" He broke off abruptly at a warning glance from Davidson.

"Oh, shut up, Bullock," he said. "Don't say things like that. Accidents happen sometimes and a jest might afterwards be taken as a threat. I'd like to harpoon that Pigeon though—fair in his fat backside."

John Davidson ordered his boats back to the Kiah. They were halfway across the bay when he remembered George and veered over to South Head to pick up the lad. The other two boat crews were waiting near the tryworks when Davidson stepped ashore and walked straight up to the cringing Pigeon.

"That was a bad miss, Pigeon," Davidson said sternly.

"So sorry, boss," the darkie pleaded. "So help me, boss, I don't know how I miss. I thought I had him."

"Roger Whelan wouldn't have had anything to do with it, would he?" Davidson insinuated.

"Roger Whelan, boss? What, boss?"

"Oh, nothing." John Davidson glanced helplessly at Alex Greig. After all, suspicions, no matter how strong, were not proof. "You're finished anyhow, Pigeon," he said. "Get your things and get out as soon as you like."

"But, boss—" the darkie began to plead.

"No, it's no good. I'm not satisfied with you. I don't want you in one of my boats again."

"How can I get over to Eden then?" Pigeon asked with a trace of truculence, realizing that John Davidson was determined and further pleading would be useless. "The sooner I get out of this hole, the better pleased I'll be too."

"You can damned well swim," Davidson roared. "I'm not sending a boat to take you over this evening. These other fellows have worked hard enough today and I wouldn't ask any of them to pull their guts out getting back with that sou'easter coming up. Get your friend Roger Whelan to come and pick you up."

Pigeon shrugged his shoulders, grinned uncomfortably, and walked away towards the path up the hill. "Thanks," he sneered. "I'll walk round through Boydtown."

"Bit tough making him walk, aren't you, John?" remarked Greig, who, like the others, had watched the proceedings in silence. "Looks like nasty weather coming up and he'll be battling to get over the other side by dark."

John Davidson had already realized the same thing, and with the subsidence of his anger came a twinge of conscience. By no means an unreasonable man, he knew he had let a burst of temper get the better of him. "Harry," he called to one of the darkies. "Go up and tell Pigeon he doesn't have to go tonight. Tell him he can stay until tomorrow if he wants to. Now come on the rest of you. Get those boats up."

"What do we do now?" Greig asked. "We're a boat-steerer short."

"I know," Davidson said. "It makes things awkward, but we must have men who can be trusted. I'll have to take young George with me, I suppose. Where is he? Hey, George."

"He's up on the point, boss," Sam Haddigaddi advised.

"Up on the point? What the hell is he doing there? Hey, George."

George scrambled round the edge of the riverbank near the tryworks and stopped apprehensively.

"You've got to give the others a hand now, you know," his father told him. "What were you doing up there?"

"I was watching them towing the whale in," George replied. "The two boats are dragging it past the lighthouse now."

"Towing it in?" John Davidson looked inquisitively at Alex Greig. "I thought they were going to anchor it."

"They could've brought it in," Greig remarked. "There weren't many killers about today, so Whelan's probably got it away from them. I suppose he's scared he'll lose it if this weather comes up tonight and reckons it's worth trying to get it home now."

"He should've let the killers have their feed anyhow—although I suppose he knows what he's doing. Now listen to me, George. You stay with the men while there's work to be done, and even if I'm not here do what Alex or Sam tells you. From now on you're going in my boat. For a start you can give them a hand to clean it out and get it in the shed."

George's face was expressive enough. He broke into a broad grin and the excitement in his eyes was obvious. "Gee, Dad," he said, poking his hands into his pockets and puffing out his chest, "that's great."

"All right." John Davidson couldn't help smiling. "Now go on. I want to talk to Alex."

By sunset the south-easterly was blowing harder than ever and the sea was coming up. Swift-moving rollers glided down the bay towards Boydtown, churning themselves into vicious foam as they broke on the Kiah bar and Whale Spit beach. On the rocks below the lighthouse and around Middle Head they crashed like distant thunder, hurling spray high into the air, and the little rock island off North Head, which looked like a whale resting on the surface, was completely obliterated behind a white screen. Just before dark a small coastal schooner came scuttling round South Head and anchored in the shelter of East Boyd Bay, the skipper no doubt breathing a prayer of thankfulness that he had been able to make port before nightfall instead of having to ride through a night at sea like this promised to be.

By next morning a howling gale was pelting the coast and the rain it brought scudded in sheets across the bay. Knowing this would continue for a few days, and it might be a week before the seas went down, Uncle Jim came in from the lookout and turned out his horse in the paddock on the hill. John Davidson cursed the weather. Two months of the season had gone already without one catch, and now, when it appeared a few whales were coming along, they had to contend with an easterly gale.

"Things will need to brighten up a bit to pay expenses," John told Alex Greig when they were having lunch. "Old Solomon was dead against having a third boat. He moaned like blazes about the cost, and with the extra wages and overhead, he'll probably take a stroke if we don't show a profit on the season.

''Oh, we've started off like this before and come out all right,'' said Greig, looking through the window at the rain. ''What's Solomon got to moan about anyhow? He's better off than either you or me, and he takes more than a fair share of the profit from what I can see of it.''

''Well, we're never light on for food and provisions.''

''Shouldn't think we would be, although that's a possibility if this weather keeps up for a week. This team we've got here will eat the damn place out before we can get any more over from town.''

In the bunkhouse out back, Uncle Jim was arguing with Bullock and Bobbo that present-day whalers were not made of the ''good old stuff.''

''Why I remember one day we went out after a whale and it was blowing nearly as hard as this,'' he said. ''It was blowing so hard you could scarcely swing the oars for'ard to dip 'em. Things is different now, though. Why even the whales seem tame as kittens compared with what they used to be.''

''That one we hooked at the end of last season was no kitten,'' said Bobbo. ''He damned near smashed us up.''

''Smashed you up?'' Old Jim snorted. ''You've never been smashed up. But you'll know it though if one of them ever does take to you.''

''You've had to swim a few times, haven't you, Jim?'' one of the young fellows asked.

''More than once,'' Jim told them. ''The worst fright I ever got was about twenty years ago. We harpooned a big black whale about two miles down the coast. It dived when we harpooned it and then came up right under the boat. A very nasty sensation, I can tell you, to feel the whole boat being lifted out of the water on the whale's back and then watch it slip helplessly down into the water again. Oars are no use then—not that anyone was worrying about them with a mad whale trying to show us who was boss. The boat had hardly touched the water again when he swung his flukes—bigger than this building they were—and chopped the boat in two like a knife going through butter.''

''Did you dive, Jim?'' Bobbo teased him.

''What would you do?'' Jim growled. ''Anyhow, we all had the sense to dive, and it was mighty unpleasant I can tell you, struggling in the water in a thick coat and heavy sea-boots until the other boat picked us up.''

And so they spent three more days while big seas lashed the coast and rain swirled from the grey skies. Charlie Adgery, Sam Haddigaddi, Alf Gardiner, and Fred Wilson won and lost their wages several times over playing poker. Uncle Jim, when he was not arguing with someone, dozed in his bunk or spent the time reading. Pigeon sulked in a corner, waiting for the weather to clear so that he could take to the track. The rain went and the wind dropped, but left behind a big ground swell that lasted another couple of days. By Friday evening the sea had gone off considerably and John Davidson ordered action stations for the following morning.

A humpback whale and calf in Twofold Bay. A close-up view of the sight that would send George Davidson's men racing for the boats and Eden folk jostling for a vantage point on the clifftops.
–Photo by A. G. Tooth

Chapter 6

Action was to come before morning. It came unexpectedly just after dinner when John Davidson was sitting with his family and Alex Greig by the fire in the living room, where Mrs Davidson was getting Archer and Boyd ready for bed, despite their protests that it was too early. Margaret sat quietly in one corner of the room, sewing, and George squatted on the floor in front of the fireplace, staring into the fire and listening to the conversation of the two men.

"There's nothing like a good fire on a night like this," John Davidson was saying. "Makes a man feel sort of contented, you know—just sitting doing nothing in particular. Strange thing that, Alex. If the fire wasn't there, you'd be restless."

"Damned cold, too," Alex remarked. "I wouldn't like to have to swim tonight."

"No colder than any other July night," said John Davidson, reaching for a match to light his pipe. He struck the match, then paused with it halfway to the pipe. "What's that?" he said, sitting straight up in the chair and listening. "Did you hear anything, Alex?"

They listened for a few moments, George with his ears cocked too, but the night was still except for the sound of the sea.

"Funny," said John Davidson, dropping the burnt-out match and picking a fresh one from the box. "I thought I heard a noise like a humpback being hounded by the killers. By God, I did. There it is again."

This time there was no mistaking the sound. On clear nights the distinctive *whoo-oo-oo* of the humpback whale as he rose to the surface harried by killers could be heard miles away. It was quite different to the cry of the black whale, which was not so loud and resembled the muffled roar of a bull. Then, through the night from much closer range, came a series of sharp, explosive noises.

"Come on," John Davidson yelled, leaping from the chair and springing for the door. He grabbed his hat and coat from a peg as he wrenched the door open and dashed out into the darkness towards the bunkhouse. "Rusho," he shouted. "Sam, Charlie, get them out quick. Come on."

Scuffling footsteps were followed by a light in the door of the bunkhouse, and George and Alex saw the dim figures of men tumbling out into the night, hastily donning coats as they ran. Bert Penrith wore his hat with the brim turned up in front, but hobbled over the grass clutching a pair of boots, trying to get them on his feet between strides. There would be no time to put them on once they shoved off in the boat, and since getting the boats away was the first consideration, Bert's only chance was to get into his boots as he ran. Had it been later in the night their dressing problem would have been even more difficult. When a whale came in at night there was no time for attention to such things as correct attire. All a man could grab in a hurry was a pair of trousers and a coat.

"Get a move on," John Davidson was shouting. "Jim, bring that light down with you. Alex, where are you? We'll only take my boat and yours. Get them out quick."

George ran down the track to the water's edge, his heart beating much faster than the exertion of his movements was causing. He could hear the whale bellowing inside South Head. Between the bar and the mouth of the river the other noises continued. He knew what made those sounds. Killers were throwing themselves out of the water and hitting it like a man in a flat dive. They always did that when they had a whale bailed up at night. While the bulk of the pack kept it at bay, two or three others would dash in to the river entrance and flop about to attract the attention of the whalemen. They had only to follow the killers, easily distinguishable, even on dark nights, by the phosphorescent trails they cleaved through the water, and these strange creatures would lead the way to where their companions had the whale cornered. Sometimes the whalemen would be chasing a whale miles out at sea before the killers were on the scent. They had merely to splash hard with the oars and the killers would come and find them.

Within a matter of minutes from the time of the alarm, the two boats were sliding into the river from the tryworks skids. Uncle Jim stood on the bank holding the hurricane lamp until they were clear and speeding towards the open bay. Then he turned and walked up the path again. He would sit on the point overlooking the bay to await their return, but would not show the lamp until he heard the boats, because it was possible the opposition had been caught napping and a light showing on the point near the Kiah might attract their attention.

The two boats cleared the river mouth and headed north-east in the trail of the killers. George, sitting in the bows of his father's boat, watched fascinated. There were three killers, though it was too dark to see which ones they were. All he could see were three phosphorescent trails moving ahead of the boats, sometimes circling round and coming up almost under the bows as if trying to urge the hunters to make more haste. Now and again one of them would give way to its impatience and jump right out of the water, coming down with a loud flop and sending out a shower of luminous beads that flared silver for a brief instant before they were extinguished in the common blackness of the sea and the night. George was virtually a passenger, for the time being at least. The five rowing seats were occupied by the usual team and his father was standing in the stern rises at the steer oar.

Margaret and Mrs Davidson stood in front of the house until the sound of the oars died into the distance. Then they turned and went inside.

"Your father worries me sometimes," Mrs Davidson said with a hardly disguised sigh of resignation. "He shouldn't have taken George with him for the first time on a dark night like this."

"Don't worry about George, Mother," said Margaret. "He's as good as any other man in the boats, and he's growing up now, you know."

"I don't care how good they are," Mrs Davidson insisted. "It's bad enough chasing whales in broad daylight, but anything can happen on these dark nights. No whale is worth it. Anyhow I'm so used to it now after all these years that I wonder at myself for even getting upset. You'd better go to bed, Margaret. They'll probably be away until all hours of the night."

"Oh, it's not late, mother, and I'm not tired either. I'll wait up with you."

"Please yourself." Mrs Davidson shrugged her shoulders and settled down to some sewing. As she had remarked, after all these years she should have been used to her husband rushing away to sea at night after whales. Perhaps it was different now when he had one of their children with him.

It might have eased her anxiety had she known that George was not the least bit worried, that he was thoroughly enjoying this new and exciting experience. No night is so black as to totally obliterate everything, once the eyes become accustomed to the darkness; and in addition to the figures of those with him he could make out the blurred outline of Alex Greig's boat slightly ahead of them on the port bow, just in front of the phosphorescent circles left behind by the oars. Once he looked over the bows of their own boat to marvel at the beauty of the silvery V-shaped waves it cut through the black velvet of the bay and the brilliant flashes of blue and purple that darted among the silver. The sea, fortunately, was fairly calm. There was no wind, just a slight swell.

John Davidson had told the men to "cut their gabble" and row as quietly as they could without sacrificing speed. So far there was no sign of boats putting out from Snug Cove on the Eden side of the bay, although it was a wonder somebody in town hadn't heard that humper bellowing, especially as the killers seemed to be taking it across Middle Head. But Davidson was taking no chances. Voices carry a long way over water on a calm night. Guided by the three killers, they rowed quietly and swiftly around Middle Head, keeping well out to avoid the nasty rocks off the point. At intervals of every two minutes or so, they heard the whale blowing and bellowing as it came to the surface, tormented by the killer pack, and the sound was louder each time now. Its source could not be far away.

"I'd reckon they're herding it into the north bay, boss," Sam Haddigaddi remarked softly. "Sounds like a pretty big humper."

"Oh, you can't always tell," said John Davidson. "I've heard little ones sing out louder than some twice their size when old Tom and his boys start playing chasings with them."

"See it yet, boss?" Alf Gardiner asked.

"No, not yet," Davidson replied. "Come down here, George, and take this sweep. I'm going for'ard."

Picking his way carefully, but with complete assurance, through the rowers, George sprang down aft and took over the steer oar while his father went to the bows and stood leaning against the thigh-board, peering into the night. They passed round the headland, Greig's boat leading by a small margin.

"Keep her out a bit, George," his father mumbled from the darkness up front. "Come on, you blokes. Bullock, Alf, put your backs into it."

Suddenly there was a dull splash about two hundred yards ahead and away dashed the three killers who had been acting as guides. "That sounds like him," remarked Alf Gardiner. "We're near the money now."

Back came two of the killers. They wheeled sharply and sprinted ahead again. Now the excitement which had kept George so tense since leaving home began to mount and he realized that he was more than a trifle scared. He had watched this procedure often from the shore and wished to be in it, but now, actually in the boat for the first time and with the climax approaching, he wondered whether he would not be happier with firm soil under his feet instead of the heaving stern rises of a flimsy whaleboat. Besides, for a boy of fourteen it was a big responsibility to be placed on that steer oar. It came home to him only too clearly that he had the lives of his father and the other men in his two hands clutching the big sweep.

He could see the whale now, or rather the huge area of phosphorus it was creating under the water just ahead of Greig's boat, and darting about it were the trails of the killers. George could almost hear his heart thumping above the creak of the oars, the heavy breathing of the rowers and the lapping of the water against the planks of the boat as it ploughed through the swell. His father was giving him instructions from time to time. He could see the dim figure standing up for'ard, but he wished fervently it was daylight and he could see what that whale was doing. A terrible thought struck him. What if the whale suddenly doubled back and came up beneath them?

Then they lost sight of its trail. Evidently the killers had forced it down deeper to keep it under longer and prevent it coming up to breathe. George gripped the sweep harder, waiting in youthful terror for hell itself to burst from the Stygian blackness that was the sea.

"Come up here again, George." His father's voice interrupted the awful stillness. "Get that harpoon ready and keep your eyes open," George was instructed when they had changed positions. "Take it easy, boys. He should come up somewhere hereabouts."

For George the tension was greater than ever as he stood holding the harpoon in his right hand, peering down into the surrounding darkness. Greig's boat was not far away on the port side. They could hear Alex's voice, "Get ready, Fred. We're just about on him. Keep her going steady."

Suddenly George saw the phosphorus again. It seemed to be rushing up towards them at a terrifying pace. "Back, Dad," he yelled in his excitement. "Back, quick."

The oarsmen needed no second instruction. They backed away as fast as they could dip oars. Then the black sullen water burst asunder in a huge sparkling fountain.

"Lay off," John Davidson shouted. "Steady, steady. Give it to him, George."

For a fraction of a second George stared almost petrified at the dim bulk of the whale on the surface only about fifteen feet away, the air roaring through its nostrils as it blew hastily, knowing that its breathing spell would be very short. The killers were snapping at it everywhere like a pack of hounds trying to drag down a deer. The whale, so huge and terrifying, could easily swing that monstrous tail and smash the boat to pieces. George grabbed the harpoon with both hands, extended his arms above his head, braced himself against the thigh-board and hurled the harpoon away with all his strength.

The reaction was instantaneous. The whale's flukes reared skywards and fell back to the water with a thunderous smash as John Davidson shouted to his crew to back for their lives. The boat rocked and pitched madly on the waves the whale created as it dived almost alongside them;

then the line attached to the harpoon was racing out, roaring as it sped through the niche in the bows. George crouched on the floorboards, knowing that his father would check the line round the loggerhead at the right time.

Listening to the water thumping against the bows as the boat sped through the darkness, George breathed a prayer of thankfulness that there was not a heavy sea running. Even in the slight swell, they were at times almost flying over the tops of the rollers. He stared ahead at the fiery trail left by the line. It was one of the most fascinating sights he had ever seen—so beautiful and yet so terrifying.

For more than half an hour they rode it out, sometimes dashing seawards when the whale gained a brief break from the killers, then turning back into the bay as the submarine pack wheeled their victim and hunted it towards shallow water or cliff-faces where it would literally have its back to the wall. At one stage the whale swerved sharply and the men in the boat were drenched with spray. George shivered as the water showered him and saturated his shirt. In his hurry to get into the boat he had left home without a coat, wearing merely a shirt and trousers. For a while his excitement and concentration on what was happening had given him no time to think of the cold, but now, in a wet shirt, he realized that he was half-frozen.

Curses from the crew followed their involuntary shower bath. "That bloody old Tom again," roared Alf Gardiner, wiping salt water from his eyes. "I'll bet he did that. He'll finish up jumping right into the damn boat one of these days."

"Oh, shut up grizzling," said John Davidson. "A little drop of good clean salt water won't hurt you. Anyhow we've pretty near got him now. Come aft and take over, George."

Again they changed positions, and George was clutching the sweep while his father got the lance ready for'ard. It was obvious that the whale was beginning to tire, and any minute now might give John Davidson the opportunity to make the kill with the lance.

"Oars ready," he ordered suddenly. "Pull now. Go up alongside, George. That's it. Steady, steady. Stand by. Now back. Quick."

A violent upheaval in the sea nearly swamped the boat. The killers attacked in full force now, leaping out of the water and hurling themselves at the whale, kicking feebly in its dying struggles.

"Go alongside again," John Davidson ordered. "Not too close, George. He might still have a good kick left in him."

Shivering with cold, but aware that it would be colder still if he put the boat within reach of those enormous flukes, George brought the boat up broadside-on about fifteen feet away and then swung her nose in.

"That's right," his father mumbled. "Hold her." The lance flew through the dimness and thudded into the whale's side. Although George had complete confidence in his father, he was terribly scared, knowing that unless the lance was aimed accurately it would merely irritate the whale and cause no end of trouble. They backed away smartly, but there was no movement except the mad splashing of the killers. George breathed a sigh of relief. Both shots had found their mark and the whale was dead.

The excitement over, George relaxed his grip on the sweep and stood in the stern gaping at the dim outline of their catch. It was a big humpback—about fifty-two feet. Average length of humpers was about forty-five feet. This one was nearly twice the length of the boat and many times as heavy.

"Get that hurricane lamp, George," his father requested. "Take it from him and light it, Alf."

John Davidson would never light a lamp in the boats at night until after the chase. A lamp was too easy to upset and there were hazards enough without the possibility of blazing oil being spilt while they were fast to a whale. Alf Gardiner lit the lamp and passed it to John Davidson, who held it aloft.

"Swing her round and come up alongside," he directed.

"Well, he was worth chasing anyhow," Bert Penrith remarked, blinking in the lamplight at the big carcass rising and falling beside the boat in the swell.

Over on the other side they could hear the killers darting about. George knew well enough what was going on now. Some of the killers would try to force the whale's jaws open for others to tear out its tongue, or they would get a hold on the fins and flukes with their teeth and by a combined effort drag the carcass to the seabed to feast at their leisure. Usually John Davidson didn't mind. The tongue was the only part the killers would eat and it was their reward for the help they gave.

"He's a plenty big fellow, boss," said Bobbo.

"Take some towing," Penrith commented, calculating to himself that they were about five miles from home. Charlie Adgery was thinking the same thing.

"Not going to drag it in tonight, are we boss?" he asked.

"No," John Davidson replied. "The killers wouldn't let us work now, even if we wanted to on a damn cold night like this. Get a couple of anchors and some line out."

Guided by the light, Greig's boat joined them, and for nearly three-quarters of an hour they worked on the carcass, attaching the lines with anchors and marker buoys. George was not the only happy soul when eventually John Davidson said, "He'll be right until morning," and they shoved off and headed for home.

Long before they passed the lighthouse, George's hands and feet were aching with cold. But he wouldn't complain. He sat quietly, watching for the light Uncle Jim would show on the point when he heard the boats coming. It seemed to be hours later when the light appeared in the darkness about a quarter of a mile off the port bow, and by that time he didn't care much. Nor did his father or any of the others realize the condition he was in until the boat grazed alongside the skids and George didn't spring out.

"Come on, George," his father snapped at him impatiently. "Get out. Don't go to sleep there."

George tried to move, but it was no use. His limbs were numb and useless. "I can't, Dad," he mumbled miserably.

John Davidson knew now that something was wrong. He sat down in the front of the boat and bent over the hunched figure. "What's wrong, son?" he asked. "Are you sick?"

"No," George squeezed out between chattering teeth, "I'm cold, Dad. I think I must have cramp, because I'm all numb and can't get up."

"Give us a hand here, Bobbo," his father said. "Bring that light over, somebody."

Between them they lifted George out of the boat on to the ramp, where Bobbo and Charlie Adgery started to massage his arms and Uncle Jim began to rub furiously up and down his legs, but after a few minutes of this vigorous treatment he was still unable to walk.

"It's no use rubbing him down," said Alex Greig. "The boy's clothes are wet. It's a wonder he's not frozen to death, being out there all that time without a coat on a night like this."

"I thought he would've taken a coat," said John Davidson. "To tell you the truth, Alex, I didn't even notice he was without one. Anyhow, I'd better take him up to bed. Jim, you bring that light with us. Get the boats in, Alex. Never mind straightening them out. We'll clean up the mess in the morning."

Uncle Jim grabbed his lantern and led the way up the path ahead of John Davidson, who was carrying George.

"By gee, he's a game kid that," said Bert Penrith as they turned to the task of hauling up the boats. "He must've been nearly dead with cold and wouldn't let on."

"He's a fly young devil," Bobbo agreed.

"Well," said Alf Gardiner, "I had the wind up plenty tonight when the boss sent him for'ard to harpoon that whale . . . and putting him on the sweep too. But he'll do me. He's even gamer than his old man, and that's saying a damn lot."

Had George been able to hear the comments his head might have swollen a size larger, but he could not hear them and his main worry was what his mother would say. She was standing in the doorway holding a lamp when they emerged from the little orchard and came into the light.

"Good God!" she cried, moving quickly down the steps to meet them. "What on earth has happened, John? What's the matter with George? You madman. You had no right to take him with you at night. I knew something would happen. He's hurt—"

"Take it easy," her husband consoled her. "Calm down, woman. He's all right. There's nothing wrong. He just went out without a coat and he's cramped with cold, that's all."

They carried George inside and sat him in a chair near the fire. Uncle Jim took off the boy's shirt while his mother brought a blanket to wrap round him. Then they stripped him and rubbed him down with towels, Mrs Davidson lecturing her husband fiercely and continuously until he walked into the back room and returned with a glass containing some red liquid.

"Drink that, George," he said. "It'll do you more good than anything."

"Rum!" Mrs Davidson screamed, her keen sense of smell discerning what the glass contained. "John, you're not going to give the boy that. Haven't you done enough for one night?"

"It won't hurt him, Effie," he said, ignoring her anger. "Get it down, George, and I'll put you to bed."

George took the glass and sipped the rum. He didn't like the smell or the taste, but he could feel it warming him, and in a few minutes he had sipped it all. A few more minutes and he was tucked between warm blankets, drowsy and ready for sleep.

"Did I do all right tonight Dad?" he murmured as his father turned to leave the room.

John Davidson paused in the doorway and looked back. "Well, you didn't miss him, George." He grinned, and there was more than a small trace of pride evident in his expression. "Pigeon could've stabbed his with a penknife—and in broad daylight. Good night, son."

George smiled too. The door closed.

Chapter 7

With one large-sized humpback being sliced up for the try-pots before the end of July, John Davidson was looking forward to the prospect of a good season, although previous experience had taught him never to be over optimistic with such unpredictable things as whales. Several times they had started the season with an early catch which turned out to be their sole catch. In many ways it was like a game of chance. If they didn't clear expenses one year, the following winter might bring them in about twenty whales to more than make good the loss.

Young George soon discovered that whaling involved plenty of hard work apart from the actual catching and killing. His first taste of it came the day after the capture of the humpback when they towed the carcass home against a stiff westerly breeze. George went against stern opposition from his mother, who contended that after the performance of the previous night he should be staying in bed. He had no illusions about convincing her otherwise, but this was his first whale—he had harpooned it himself—and he was going with them to bring it home. John Davidson knew even better the futility of argument at a time like this. He casually ignored the storm, even the parting shot about one madman being quite sufficient for one family.

Before they were halfway back with the whale in tow, George almost wished he had listened to his mother. Had the whale been floating on its back, towing would have been much easier. But it was almost on its side, its mouth partly open and one fin dragging under the surface, and if it chose to float that way there was nothing they could do about it, except grumble and keep on rowing. The westerly didn't help either, and the short choppy seas it kicked up added to the discomfort of the crews by showering them continually with spray. Now and again someone would curse the whale and another would make a joke about it, but mostly they just put their backs into the work and rowed with the wind blowing, the spray flying, and flocks of sea gulls circling and diving for the scraps of offal left in their wake.

Except in cases of emergency, the whales were always towed in at high tide so as to float them over the bar into the mouth of the Kiah. There a hawser was put round the tail and the crews manned a capstan to haul the carcass into shallow water alongside the tryworks under the limbs of a big gum tree providentially placed on the edge of the bank where something was needed for hanging a block and tackle.

Next morning at low tide, all hands went to work on the carcass with boat spades—razor-sharp implements with which they sliced off the blubber. George, spitting from time to time when the stench from the carcass became almost overpowering, worked with Alf Gardiner, who had instructions to put him through a thorough apprenticeship in the trade of deblubbering.

"It won't do you no good spitting, young George," Alf told him once. "Deblubbering is hard work and it's dry work, but you get used to the stink and you won't even notice it."

"Oh, it's not so bad, Alf," the lad replied. "I've smelt dead whales before, but this one seems to be easily the worst. Perhaps it's because I've never helped to cut one up yet. I'll get used to it, though."

"Better get used to it," Bobbo called from the other side of the carcass. "You be big feller boss one day. No smell, no whale, no money."

"That's right, Bobbo," came from John Davidson, who had emerged from the tryworks and was standing on the skids. "The last part about no money, anyhow. And it'll apply to you blokes if you don't hurry up and get that blubber into the pots."

"Yes, boss," Bobbo answered, swinging his spade more vigorously. "Working damn hard, boss."

George dug into it too. He knew it was important to work as fast as they could before the tide came in again. One by one big blanket pieces of blubber were rafted from the water and hauled up the skids into the tryworks. They cut along the water's edge, each side as low as possible, then across the centre and across the neck, and when these pieces had been taken off they chopped right through the centre of the whale and through the neck to sever the head. The carcass, divided into three sections and stripped of its blubber above the water, could be turned over one section at a time and the remaining blubber taken off. That was where the tree and the block and tackle were handy, and even then it needed many strong hands on the rope.

In the tryworks another team, supervised by Alex Greig, was cutting the blanket pieces of blubber into strips about fifteen inches long by five inches wide and five inches deep and throwing the strips into a long vat. Others then put the strips through a mincing process, with knives that worked at almost lightning speed, and tossed the small pieces into the try-pots for boiling. Uncle Jim was the chef. Standing beside the try-pots with a large perforated skimmer in his hands, he took his job very seriously and his eyes never left the pots for a minute. From the big try-pots, the oil automatically flowed over a lip into a smaller pot, where it cooled and was ladled off into tanks ready to be casked. From time to time Uncle Jim dipped his skimmer into the pot and examined the pieces of blubber fished out. If they were brownish and dry in appearance, they were thrown on a heap in the corner to be used for fuel under the big pot. It was quite good fuel, too—even better than wood or coal, because it left very little ash.

All this was no novelty to George, who had seen it dozens of times. He had been brought up with the stench of the tryworks in his nostrils. Whale oil had flowed from these pots ever since he could remember, just as it was flowing now. In the tryworks and round about, oil was everywhere, saturating the ropes, glistening on the rocks, spreading a film over the water near the bank, and making the floor of the works a hazard for those who did not watch where they stepped. But oil was their wealth. It was worth twenty-five pounds a tun and John Davidson reckoned this humpback had produced nearly four tuns. With the bone bringing good prices too, it needed only a few more whales to clear the season with a fair profit. That evening he went over to Eden to see Solomon and came back with a load of stores in the boat and a definite smell of rum about him.

''Old Sol's very pleased,'' he told his wife, who met him at the tryworks.

''Obviously,'' she commented. ''He must be when he shouts you rum.''

''He shouted for the boys, too, and so did I. They worked damned hard on that humper.''

''H'm,'' she snorted. ''Did he give you any money?''

''Well, no, Effie. No money. He gave us a load of stores.''

''I should think he would,'' she remarked, opening one of the bags and inspecting the contents. ''John, you trust people too much. We haven't seen anything like real money for ages, and there's dozens of things about this place that you can't get without money.''

''I might need a new boat for next season.''

She let the top of the bag flop on the ground and stared hard at him. ''New boat?'' she exploded. ''You've got three now.''

''I'm not saying definitely, Effie. We don't know what next season will bring. I just said I might need a new boat. Solomon told me this evening Fred Newland is building a thirty-eight–footer.''

''Well, get Solomon to build one and take him to sea with you.'' She grinned. ''He'll probably be so sick he'll never want to have any more to do with whaleboats.''

John Davidson laughed. "Hey, Charlie," he called, "take these stores up to the house for the missus."

Between the whaling seasons—from October to April—most of the whalers became timber-cutters, or earned an equally dull stop-gap living gathering wattle bark for shipment to Sydney tanneries. They never went with any real will to the timbermen's camps among the tall trees of the Kiah and Wyndham districts, nor did they exchange oars for broad-axes with any relish, but this year John Davidson, ignoring Effie's sarcasm, had his way and kept some of the crews to help build a new boat. He knew what was going on. Roger Whelan and John Powers would be doubtful starters in May after their poor showing in the previous season, but there were still people who thought easy money was to be made from whaling. Dick Hayes, the Clerk of the Petty Sessions in Eden, was the latest enthusiast, and it was Hayes who was providing most of the finance for the thirty-eight–footer Fred Newland was having built. That meant a seven-oared boat, so Davidson set to work and built one forty feet long. He was not going to be caught napping when the season started, trying to chase seven oars with five, although had he been able to foresee the outcome, he might have saved himself the trouble and expense of a new boat.

The weather was bad that year and whales were scarce, and by the time October came round John Davidson was inclined to regret having spent money on the boat. Solomon moaned. So did Mrs Davidson, who recalled her advice with a triumphant "I told you so" air. But if John Davidson was fed up, Hayes and Newland were even more so. Unlike Davidson, who could carry on year after year and average out his profits, they had sunk too much in the venture to risk losing everything in another bad season, and they didn't offer much resistance to Davidson's proposal to sell out and cut their losses.

"Why bother to buy their boat and gear?" George asked curiously. "They've had enough. They won't start again."

"No," his father agreed, "perhaps not. But while that boat and gear are lying about Eden, somebody else is always likely to get the idea and buy it."

Perhaps Hayes and Newland really meant to finish with whaling when they sold out to John Davidson, but the following season they were to dabble in it again in a way he had never even imagined. It might have been careless of him to leave try-pots and other processing equipment on their hands, but then who would have thought of them getting a whale to process without a boat and gear to catch it? John Davidson didn't, and the last thing that would have entered his head was the possibility he might catch the whale for them himself.

It was his second catch that season—a forty-foot humpback. He and Alex Greig killed the whale about four miles south of the bay and anchored and buoyed it for the night. With the sea making and the sky to the south-east promising anything but pleasant weather, they were not going to risk being caught halfway home with a dead whale in tow. They had barely rounded South Head before the first gusts hit the water, and as they hugged the southern shore along to the Kiah they could see the bay and the ocean behind them churning into angry waves that rushed headlong before the wind like thousands of maddened, stampeding cattle. When the gale blew itself out a few days later, there was no sign of the marker buoys or the carcass.

For most of one day the three boats searched the coast and far out to sea, but apart from an occasional shark, all they saw was a schooner beating up from Gabo, wide out, and a small boat under sail coming up as if from Mallacoota. It was this small boat that attracted Greig's attention some hours later.

"That boat's been making pretty slow headway with a fair breeze behind it," he remarked. "Have any of you blokes noticed it?"

"Did occur to me once or twice he wasn't making much pace," Bert Penrith agreed. "What do you reckon? Is he in trouble?"

"Don't know. He will be, though, if it's what I think it is."

"By cri'!" Bobbo exclaimed. "Him feller might have whale."

"He might," Greig said. "Bobbo, you're smarter than I thought you were. Signal to the boss. We're going to have a look."

They rowed slowly until John Davidson's boat caught up and Greig mentioned his suspicions.

"Looks like he's towing something," Davidson agreed. "We could be wrong, though. Pull across casually near Leatherjacket Bay and we'll give him a glance over."

"Isn't that Fred Newland standing in the stern?" George asked when they were close enough to distinguish the figures in the boat. "It is. Dick Hayes is with him too, and they're towing the whale."

John Davidson rubbed a hand across his black beard and stood looking at the boat a while longer before he replied. He thought he could see daylight now, but it was advisable to make sure.

"Go alongside, Alex," he instructed. "Come on, you team. Pull."

The two whaleboats sped across the water to meet the oncoming sailing boat. About a hundred yards off they eased pace and turned to drift slowly on a parallel course.

"Good day," John Davidson greeted the men in the stern. "I thought you two turned up whaling."

"Well, we did really," Hayes replied.

"Where did you get this one? Find it?"

"That's exactly what we did," Newland answered, "Why?"

"Well, it's the same one as Alex and I killed the other day. It broke loose in that gale and we've been looking for it. Where did you pick it up?"

"Down the other side of Mowara."

"That'd be it," Alex said. "Thanks for finding it. We'll tow the body in ourselves now."

"Why?" Newland challenged.

"Well, it's our whale," Alex exploded.

"No, it's not," Hayes said calmly. "We found this whale and it belongs to us. We're going to take it in and get the blubber. You can have it then if you like."

"What!" Davidson roared.

"Finding's keepings," Newland taunted.

"Keep quiet," Hayes told him. "Now listen, John. There's no proof that this is the same whale you killed. And, besides, you know the law as well as I do. Once a whale breaks loose it becomes common prey for anybody. Even if this is the one you killed—and you'd have a hard job proving that—it was loose. We found it and so we keep it."

John Davidson was fuming. "I've never heard of such a lousy trick," he bellowed across the water. "I still don't think you're serious. Now come on, because if it's a joke I don't appreciate it."

"It's no joke, John," Hayes assured him. "I've just told you we're keeping the whale and taking it back to our tryworks."

"It's no use arguing with them, Dad," George interrupted. "We'll just go and take it from them."

"You've got two minutes to cast it adrift before we come and get it," Greig shouted angrily. "Do you think we work our guts out to kill whales for loafing swine like you? We've rowed miles today looking for that carcass. Hand it over quick, or we'll tow you behind with it."

"Pretty quick fix him feller," muttered Bobbo, grabbing a harpoon.

"Put it down, Bobbo," yelled John Davidson, who had seen the move out of the corner of his eye. "We don't want any trouble. The law is on our side and we intend to keep it that way." Bobbo scowled, but put the harpoon back.

"I'm warning you, Hayes," John Davidson continued, "that if you deblubber this whale I'll sue you."

"That'd be funny, the Clerk of the Petty Sessions having to serve a writ on himself," Alf Gardiner remarked, but nobody was in the mood for jokes.

"I told you what I'm going to do," Hayes insisted.

"All right then," said Davidson. "You've been warned. You might think you know the law, Hayes, but I know what's right. Alex, you go on ahead and get Solomon down. I'll stay with these birds."

Solomon was dancing about on the beach in Snug Cove like the proverbial cat on hot bricks when John Davidson stepped ashore and they waited for Hayes and Newland.

"They can't do this, John," he screamed. "It's robbery; it's piracy. Why didn't you stop them?"

"Stop them?" Davidson snarled. "You complain about them breaking the law. Do you want us to break it too by assaulting them?"

"What do you mean by taking our whale?" Solomon yelled across the water to Hayes and Newland. "I'll have the law on you."

"Oh, go and jump in the bay," Newland called back.

Some of the crowd that had gathered laughed, but Solomon wasn't amused. He nearly boiled with rage. The general reaction in Eden was like that, too. A few thought it was funny, but most people were indignant. In the long period of Eden's whaling industry, nothing like this had ever happened, because those who engaged in the industry, although they might have cut each other's throats to catch a whale, regarded a dead whale as the property of whoever killed it. So while everybody speculated as to who was right and who was wrong—though there was little doubt as to the town's verdict—John Davidson took out a District Court writ against Hayes and Newland, claiming two hundred pounds' damages.

"I don't know why you want to bother bringing 'em to court," old Captain Russell, the pilot at Eden, told him. "When I was whaling, John, we'd have had our own ways of dealing with 'em."

"Perhaps," John Davidson agreed. "They used to throw a rope over a tree pretty smart for horse thieves. There may not be much difference between stealing a horse and stealing a whale, but the fact is that these men have broken the law and I don't intend to break it too with the possibility of facing a charge more serious than theft."

Cappy Russell was one of the old school of sailors. Rough and ready in his manner, he knew only one law, and that was rough and ready too. Many years of the hard life he had spent at sea had been aboard whaling ships—hell craft that spent up to two years and more at sea in an occupation which was certainly not one for weaklings. Nobody knew just how old Cappy really was, but those who watched his picturesque figure ambling about the town—frequently in the vicinity of the Pier Hotel—agreed he was pretty active. He was standing outside the Pier Hotel when John Davidson came down to the wharf.

"You going to have a drink, John?" he asked.

"No, thanks," Davidson replied, fearing a lengthy session if he entered the hotel with the old pilot. "I must get over the bay. The men are waiting for me alongside the wharf with the boat."

"I'll walk down with you," Cappy said, fumbling in his pockets for his old curved pipe and plug of tobacco. "You know, John, I still think you should've let the boys deal with Hayes and Newland."

"Why? What would you have done?"

"What would I have done?" Cappy snorted. "We threw a nigger overboard once for pinching tobacco, and I'll tell you what happened to a Swede who pinched a tenner from the mate on the old *Southern Queen*. He got a knife in his gizzard. That was in Hobart about forty year ago. You never sailed with a bigger bunch of thieves and cutthroats in your life than on those whaling ships, but it was Lord help anyone caught pinching."

John Davidson laughed. "Bobbo wanted to harpoon Newland," he said.

"Well, why didn't you let him?"

"No. Seriously, Cappy, there's only one thing to do and I've done it."

"You're determined, then, to take 'em to court?"

"Yes," Davidson answered, throwing some parcels down to his crew and preparing to descend into the whaleboat.

"Well," the old pilot told him, "good luck to you, and if there's anything I can do, just let me know."

"I might call you as a witness to state what you know of the law on whaling."

Cappy Russell lit the pipe he had been stuffing with tobacco and tossed the match into the water. "Never been in a court in my life," he said. "I'll go, though, if you want me to."

Chapter 8

Cappy Russell was as good as his word. On the day of the District Court sitting, he arrived at the courthouse dressed somewhat uncomfortably in his best suit, walked briskly through the gate, baulked at the door, and went instead to sit on a log near a group of Davidson's whalers.

"Careful, skipper," Alf Gardiner warned him as his suit tightened in the process, "you'll bust those buttons."

"I'll bust your head," Cappy retorted. "Anyhow, what are you all doing outside? Why don't you go in?"

"We can't," Alf explained. "We're witnesses and if we went in they'd only put us out again until they call us."

"You jibbed at the door yourself," Bert Penrith remarked. "What's up? Do you think it's like a church, with the roof ready to fall in on old sinners?"

"No," Russell replied triumphantly. "Don't you know I'm a witness too—an expert witness, so the solicitor bloke said. I'm to tell the judge about whaling law. Bill Ross is going to do the same."

"Expert witness!" Penrith roared, laughing. "You're an expert old reprobate."

Every seat in the courthouse was occupied when Judge McFarlane entered and bowed to the bar table. The little building would not accommodate many spectators, but those who could squeeze in had done so. George, excused from having to give evidence, had found a seat early and sat tense, waiting for proceedings to begin. Apart from his natural interest in the issue involved, it was the first time he had ever been inside a court or had seen a judge and lawyers in wigs and gowns. He leant forward on the seat as Mr Manby, the Bega solicitor engaged by Solomon and his father, began to outline their case.

"Your Honour," Mr Manby said, "this is an action for damages brought by my client, Mr John Simpson Davidson, against the defendants Hayes and Newland, in which we claim that the two defendants wilfully and without just cause took and unlawfully misappropriated a dead whale, the property of Mr Davidson. The defendants will claim that the whale was not the plaintiff's property, that they found it ashore dead, and were quite entitled to take it. In many ways, Your Honour, this case is quite unique. I don't think I could recall a precedent. It does, though, follow certain points of law which I propose to outline. Briefly, the facts are that the plaintiff and his whaling crew harpooned and killed a humpback whale south of Twofold Bay. They did not tow the carcass home immediately, but anchored it and attached lines with buoys to mark its position. That, I might explain to Your Honour, is the common practice because it is not always possible or convenient to tow in a whale immediately after killing it. We claim that if a crew kills a whale it is their property and cannot be interfered with, even though it breaks clear of moorings and comes ashore somewhere, unattended."

"We'll see about that," mumbled Mr White, a Sydney barrister, who was appearing for Hayes and Newland.

"You will hear about these things from the whalers themselves," Mr Manby continued, ignoring the interjection, "but I propose to quote, with Your Honour's permission, from a Tasmanian Act introduced in 1838. This says: 'Where the harpoon shall remain in the whale so struck and a line or boat shall be attached thereto and continue in the power of the striker or headsman, such whale shall be deemed fast, and although struck by any second or subsequent harpoon shall be the property of the first striker or headsman only. But where the harpoon so struck shall break or become disengaged from the whale, or the instrument shall remain fast in the whale but the line affixed thereto shall break or be wholly run out, or the whale from any other causes not be in the power or under the management of the striker, such whale shall be considered loose and become the property of the actual taker thereof.' "

"Your Honour," Mr White interposed, "what has Tasmanian law to do with this case? I object to my friend introducing law which is irrelevant."

"I admit, Your Honour," Mr Manby hastened to explain, "that neither of the parties in this case would be bound by a law passed by the State of Tasmania, but this is not irrelevant. I am using it mainly as an example of the general laws, written and unwritten, which apply to the whaling industry. I intend to show—"

"All right, Mr Manby," said Judge McFarlane. "You may proceed."

"Your Honour pleases," Mr Manby continued. "Now there is yet another section of this law which says: 'If after the striking any person shall maliciously cut or destroy the line attached to such harpoon while it remains in the whale or shall prevent the striker from killing or taking, or shall obstruct him in taking or in his endeavour to take . . . he shall be liable to a fine not less than £10 nor more than £100.' That is a pretty good example of the law which whalers the world over recognize, although in some countries they are only unwritten laws. I think the time is not far distant when there will have to be international laws governing whaling, but that is beside the point because no such international laws exist at present." Mr Manby looked quickly round the courtroom, glanced at Mr White, who was staring through the window across the bay, and then continued. "This is the first time any of these whalers have ever had to resort to legal action, simply because nobody except the two defendants has ever thought of stealing whales instead of catching them."

Mr White jumped to his feet. "I object to that, Your Honour," he protested. "My friend is assuming too much of—"

"Yes, Mr White," Judge McFarlane said, holding up his hand as if to restrain the protest. "I'm sorry, Mr Manby, but I must have that struck out."

"Very well, Your Honour," Mr Manby assented. "Well, I don't propose to take up the time of the court by elaborating any further. With your permission, I will call the witnesses and let them tell the story."

The judge nodded.

"Will you go into the box please, Mr Davidson," Mr Manby requested.

There was a murmur of voices from the back of the court as John Davidson rose and walked to the witness box, where Constable Thompson was ready with the open Bible in his hand. George, sitting in one of the back seats, leant slightly to one side to peer round the rim of a large hat which the spectator in front had perched on the back of the pew. He glanced back quickly to Uncle Jim beside him, but the old fellow was sitting stiffly erect with his arms folded on his chest, and was looking straight ahead.

Then came the voice of Constable Thompson. "The evidence you are about to give before this court shall be the truth, the whole truth, and nothing but the truth. Say, So 'elp me God."

"So help me God," John Davidson repeated after him and handed back the Bible.

"Your name is John Simpson Davidson and you are a master whaler residing at the Kiah River, East Boyd?" Mr Manby began.

"That is correct."

"And you know the defendants, Hayes and Newland?"

"Yes."

"You will recall a certain transaction some time last year with Mr Hayes and Mr. Newland?"

"Yes, it was after the last whaling season."

"Would you tell His Honour what that transaction was all about, Mr Davidson."

"Hayes and Newland had been whaling in opposition to me," John Davidson explained. "It was not a good season, and when I offered to buy them out they agreed to sell me their boat and gear. I made the purchase, thinking they would be finished with whaling and I would have the field to myself."

"In other words, Mr Davidson, er . . . " Judge McFarlane smiled. "In other words, you intended to create a monopoly."

"Yes," John Davidson replied bluntly. "Whaling is my livelihood. I had no compunction about buying out people who were in it as a sideline to their ordinary occupations. Besides, the boat and gear were more use to me than lying about Eden waiting to be put into commission by somebody else."

"Oh, quite."

"Mr Davidson," the solicitor resumed, "did the defendants engage in whaling subsequent to this transaction when you purchased their boat and gear?"

"No."

"But they retained such equipment as try-pots and other things which could be used for treating the carcasses of whales and extracting oil from the blubber?"

"Yes. I didn't bother to buy that because I had my own tryworks and I didn't think they would use it if they were not whaling themselves."

"Did they use this tryworks at any time between the sale of their boat and gear to you and the date of this action now before the court?"

"Yes, they used the works to try the whale they took from me."

Mr White was on his feet again. "I object to that, Your Honour," he said. "I must protest against my friend using leading questions. In any case, he is premature in having the plaintiff assert that the whale was definitely stolen."

"All right, all right," said Mr Manby, holding up his hands in mock rebuke. "Now, Mr Davidson, towards the end of the season did you and your crew chase and kill a whale off the south head of Twofold Bay? Would you describe that whale?"

John Davidson stopped stroking his beard, and brought his hand to rest on the edge of the witness box. "Yes," he said. "It was a humpback whale about forty feet long."

"You were the only whalers in the chase, you fastened to the whale, and ultimately killed it by lancing?"

"Yes, I lanced it myself."

"You didn't tow it home immediately though?"

"No. It looked like bad weather coming up, and since the killers were with the whale, we attached anchors and marker buoys to the carcass and left it, intending to go back and get it when the stomach gases brought it to the surface again."

"Did you subsequently go back for the whale?"

"Well, it blew like blazes for a few days and we couldn't get out. When we did, there was no sign of the carcass or the buoys."

"Will you tell us of your search for the whale and what happened during the search?"

John Davidson told how he and members of his crew had searched the sea for miles looking for the whale, how they had encountered Hayes and Newland with the carcass of a whale in tow, and of the conversation he and Alex Greig had with them.

George sat nervously, listening intently to every word. He knew that what his father said was right in every detail, but this legal procedure was strange and awesome to him, and his nervousness increased when Mr White rose and began to cross-examine.

"Did you see the defendants actually take possession of this whale, Mr Davidson?"

"No," Davidson replied. "But they told me they found it near Mowara."

"I see. Were there any irons or other implements in the whale?"

"No."

"Couldn't this whale have died from natural causes and drifted ashore where the defendants found it?"

"That could happen, but I'm sure it didn't happen in this case."

"Why are you sure, Mr Davidson?"

"Because I could see the wounds where I lanced it."

"It couldn't have been killed anywhere else or by anybody else?"

"Hardly, because the only whaling on this coast is done from here. Besides, the whale I killed was the only one killed in this vicinity for months."

"What did the defendants say when you claimed the carcass they had in tow was your whale?"

"They said it was not mine. Although," he added fiercely in a louder tone of voice, "I knew damn well it was."

"Silence," Constable Thompson's voice shouted above the laughter.

"I'm sorry, your Honour," John Davidson apologized when the laughter had subsided. "I was just a little carried away for the moment."

"Yes, of course, Mr Davidson." The judge suppressed a smile.

And so the case went on. Alex Greig gave his evidence, simply and with unshakable determination. He knew this lawyer was questioning him in an effort to trick him into providing a loophole, but he knew, too, that if he told the truth and nothing more, as he had sworn to do when taking the oath in the witness box, no lawyer could find a weak point to drive a wedge into the facts of Davidson's case. Mr White, no doubt, had been hoping to find something uncorroborative in Greig's evidence. He questioned and probed in vain.

Then Constable Thompson ushered in old Captain Russell. Followed by the gaze of the public gallery, which had met him at the door and travelled with him along the aisle between the seats, he ambled across to the witness box and paused until the constable caught up and gently steered him into the box. Having repeated "So help me God," Cappy smoothed the creases from the front of his best coat and stood, legs slightly apart and hands behind his back, as he might have done on the deck of a ship, to tell of the laws of whaling as he had always known them.

"You say you have had considerable whaling experience, captain," Mr Manby asked him. "Have you ever known of a case like this before?"

"No," Cappy replied. "I've sailed amongst some tough crews in my time, but tough and all as whalers are, they respect their laws when it comes to whaling."

"Do you claim that whalers the world over would not take a carcass after it had broken adrift?" Mr White challenged him.

"I'm sure of that," Captain Russell answered with a confident nod of his head.

"Your experience has been confined to the Australian coast, hasn't it?"

"Certainly not," the old captain almost roared. "I sailed from Hobart Town on an American whaler when I was just a young chap—before you were even born."

The gallery laughed. Even Judge McFarlane could not restrain a smile at the look of wounded pride on the face of the witness; but many years on the bench had taught him that such a witness would be very susceptible to baiting and subsequent answers might be even more explosive.

"Captain," he interposed judiciously, "just answer Mr White's questions. Don't engage in an argument."

"I'm sorry, sir. He was trying to make out that I'm not a gentleman of the truth, sir," Cappy insisted. "I said before that I'd sailed in many ships in many seas. Why, when I signed on the Yankee ship in Hobart, I was—"

"All right, captain. Just answer what Mr White asks you. I shall see that he is not unfair. That is why I am here. Proceed, Mr White."

"Thank you, Your Honour," Mr White continued. "Now, Captain Russell, there is only one other question I would like to ask. In your experience at sea—and in Eden too—have you ever seen dead whales floating, or have you seen them come ashore?"

"Yes, often. Whales can die like anything else."

"Isn't it feasible that the carcass found by the defendants died at sea and drifted ashore?"

"Could be, but I don't think so in this case. In fact I'm damn sure. It was Johnny Davidson's whale and they took it."

"Captain," the judge interrupted, this time more sternly, "you have been told merely to answer the questions. You must not express opinions like that."

"Yes, sir."

"That is all, Your Honour," said Mr White, resuming his seat. But his cross-examination had prompted the thoughts of Mr Manby.

"Excuse me, Your Honour," he said. "Captain Russell, you are the pilot at Eden, and as such you would be familiar with the currents and the coastline in the vicinity?"

"I would say so."

"You know where Mr Davidson said he killed the whale and anchored it. Would it be possible for the currents at this time of the year to carry that carcass to where it went aground, or where this carcass was found?"

"Currents are peculiar things," Cappy explained. "Very peculiar things. I know that week the current had a strong sou'westerly set, which would have taken the whale from where it was killed to where it was found."

"Thank you, captain."

Bill Ross, an old Tasmanian whaler, gave similar evidence of the rights and wrongs in whaling as understood by the men in the industry. Then Hayes and Newland told their story.

"I will be very brief, Your Honour," said Mr White when the evidence was concluded and he rose to make his address. "I am submitting that no case has been made out for the plaintiff—that in point of law there is no law. The whole case as made out by Mr Manby has been based on law which does not exist in statutes applicable to this part of the world and is, as he admits, more or less a gentleman's agreement. Even allowing that the whale my clients found was identical with the one killed a few days before by Mr Davidson, which we do not admit, doesn't the question of ethics enter into the case? Your Honour has seen gentlemen's agreements argued in many jurisdictions and knows even better than I the difficulty of proving them in law.

"Now, as to the whale in question. Mr Davidson did not follow the course taken by the whale he killed after it broke from its moorings and started to drift. He did not even see it break adrift and for all we know it might still be at the bottom of the ocean. He did not see it come ashore at Mowara. In fact he had not the slightest idea where the whale was, as shown by his own evidence when he told of the long search for it. He has not proved that the whale was identical with the one he killed, nor has it been established that, if such were the case, my clients committed robbery by taking the carcass after it broke adrift.''

''He's argued it pretty well,'' George remarked nervously to Uncle Jim as Mr White sat down and Mr Manby rose.

''Pretty well,'' Jim admitted, ''but see what Manby says.''

''In this case, Your Honour,'' Mr Manby was saying, ''it has been shown to your satisfaction, I am sure, that the whale brought into Eden by the defendants Hayes and Newland was the whale killed by my client, Mr Davidson. There is Mr Davidson's evidence to show that it was the only whale killed in this vicinity for some time prior to the incident, that he was the only person actively engaged in whaling in the vicinity, that he anchored and buoyed the carcass, which broke adrift in bad weather, and, when he inspected the carcass picked up by Hayes and Newland, could see the wounds where it had been lanced. That last point in itself disposes of the argument that the whale could have died from natural causes. It is true, as my learned friend pointed out, that nobody saw the whale come ashore, and only the two defendants Hayes and Newland

Men of Eden who manned the boats in the whaling days. From left: Rasmus, Peter Peterson, Bob Warren, and "Doc" Cameron.

Where some of them lived. "Doc" Cameron outside his hut in Snug Cove, Eden. The round object is a lobster pot, used by professional fishermen to catch lobsters.

Twofold Bay, Eden, showing Mount Imlay in background. This was taken from Snug Cove in the early part of the century. Looking from there today, the scene is much the same. The beautiful foreshores on the far side of the bay are virtually in their natural state.

know how and in what circumstances it was found. They have admitted finding it. They made no claims to having killed the whale themselves. Each said quite openly that they found the carcass ashore at this place called Mowara, where, as evidence has shown, it could quite easily have drifted after breaking from its moorings.'' Mr Manby paused and indicated Hayes and Newland with a sweep of his hand. ''I submit, Your Honour,'' he continued, ''that these men knew it was Davidson's whale. They still had a tryworks and boiling-down equipment and apparently thought this was a chance to make easy money by taking the whale back to Eden, deblubbering it and extracting the oil and bone. I leave it to Your Honour.''

Mr Manby sat down. The silence of the courtroom was broken by a murmur of voices for a few seconds while Judge McFarlane glanced through some papers. Then he sat forward, and the voices died down as Constable Thompson called for silence.

''This has been a most extraordinary case in many ways,'' the judge said. ''I am inclined to agree with you, Mr Manby, that it is quite unique. At least I certainly do not know of a precedent. However, be that as it may, the facts are not very complicated. The plaintiff, John Davidson, claimed that he and his crew killed a whale, which they moored in the vicinity of what is known as South Head, and during a gale it broke loose and drifted away. They searched for the dead whale, but could find no trace of it until they encountered the two defendants towing a whale, which they claimed was identical with the one they killed. The defendants, Hayes and Newland, made no claim to killing the whale they were towing. They said quite openly that they found it ashore at the place referred to as Mowara. Evidence has been given by the pilot, Captain Russell, that it would have been quite possible for the currents to have taken a dead whale from the place where one was moored by Mr Davidson to Mowara, where the defendants found it, and I am inclined to believe that this is actually what did happen.

''Mr Manby, you quoted Tasmanian law relating to whale fishing, and you mentioned, too, the unwritten laws which the whalers regard among themselves as a strict code. It is unfortunate in a way that there is no statute law covering such possibilities as the case I have been called upon to deal with here, and I agree with you, too, that there should be international laws governing whaling, but since no such laws apply here I must consider this case on the basis of common law, which all devolves upon one point—the taking of property which rightfully belongs to another. I am quite satisfied, taking the evidence and all the facts into consideration, that Mr Davidson had a just claim to the whale after killing it and mooring it with his own lines. If Mr Davidson had moored one of his whaleboats and it broke loose, a person finding the boat ashore somewhere down the coast would not be entitled to claim it. The law does not define certain goods which may not be stolen and other goods which anyone may take with impunity. It states quite definitely that no person shall take the property of another. In this case, being satisfied on the evidence that the whale was the property of John Davidson, I find it inexcusable on the part of the two defendants that they took and converted to their own use this carcass. However, they have not been charged with stealing and I am concerned only with the question of damages. I find that the plaintiff, John Davidson, was seriously inconvenienced in his means of livelihood by the taking of this whale, representing as it did a considerable loss to him, and I intend to award a verdict for the full amount claimed. Two hundred pounds.''

There was an excited babble from the back of the court. George felt like cheering wildly. Perhaps only the thought that Uncle Jim might frown upon such behaviour in the august precincts of the court prevented him from doing so, although when he glanced at the old man he wondered who was the more excited. Alex Greig was leaning over his chair shaking John Davidson's hand. Alex was literally beaming, but George noticed that his father seemed fairly calm. He shot a quick glance at Hayes and Newland and was not surprised to see them looking far from pleased.

''Silence!'' the court attendant commanded. ''Stand up, please. This court stands adjourned *sine die*. God save the Queen.''

Outside the court, John Davidson was surrounded by his crew and others offering their congratulations. ''It's nothing to crow about,'' he told them. ''I didn't want to bring two neighbours into court, but I had to do it to claim my rights and, now it's over, I'd rather the whole thing was forgotten.''

''They won't take any more whales,'' Alf Gardiner remarked triumphantly. ''By the time they've finished paying for this they'll—''

''Excuse me, John.''

John Davidson turned to face Dick Hayes and a malevolent stare, but he knew that was intended for Alf Gardiner, who had transformed the remainder of his remark into a mumble. Fred Newland was standing a short distance away.

''What is it, Dick?'' he asked.

''Could we see you for a minute?''

''Certainly,'' Davidson agreed.

They walked across to where Newland, looking rather crestfallen, was waiting near the side of the courthouse building.

''By cri','' Bobbo muttered. ''If they touch boss—''

''Don't be silly, Bobbo.'' Alex Greig scowled.

"What do they want, Alex?" George queried.

"Oh, I don't know. I suppose they want to make some arrangement about paying. Your father ought to have more sense than to argue with them."

Alex was right. Payment was the main problem confronting Hayes and Newland. "About this money," Hayes began nervously and then paused.

"Well, what about it?" John Davidson asked.

"We can't pay you straight away," Newland said bluntly. "You see . . . well, things aren't too good. I haven't got my share and Dick isn't much better off. Two hundred quid is a lot of money, John."

"You should've thought of that in the first place," Davidson said, looking from one to the other.

"We should have thought of a lot of things," Hayes agreed ruefully. "Anyhow, the position is that we haven't got two hundred quid. It's going to take a long time to pay it off, if you take it in instalments."

John Davidson thought quickly for a moment. He had suspected something like this and now he realized that Hayes was quite right.

"I'll tell you what I'll do," he said thoughtfully. "You give me the oil and bone you took from the whale and pay all the expenses of this case, give me your tryworks and any other gear, and keep out of the whaling game and we'll call it quits."

Hayes and Newland looked at each other, but both knew they would be foolish to hesitate.

"Agreed," Hayes said promptly.

"All right with me," Newland said.

"Good," said Davidson, turning away. "I'll see you tomorrow."

He joined Alex and George and they walked towards the gate where the others were waiting.

"I'd have made them pay every penny," Alex declared firmly when he heard of the transaction.

"But they haven't got it," John Davidson said simply. "What do you think about it, George?"

"I think you're a damned fool," George burst out, parental respect cast to the winds. "I know what I'd do with them."

"What would you do with them?" his father asked, the trace of an amused smile accompanying the question.

"Leave them without a bed to sleep on," the lad said emphatically. "It was low the way they did that. They don't deserve sympathy."

John Davidson laughed. "No, son," he said, shaking his head slightly. "I have a bed to sleep on. So have you. What good would it do to deprive two other men of their beds?"

Chapter 9

With the passing of another whaling season, George found that he had graduated very quickly from the apprenticeship stage and was as handy as any of the older men in the boats. His father noticed not only this, but also the fact that he seemed to have an uncanny knowledge of the killers and their way of working, at times even sensing in advance what they were going to do. Then there was his obvious lack of fear—though it did not amount to recklessness—and his ability to make split-second decisions. John Davidson felt that George would be quite capable of taking charge of a boat next season when he would be eighteen, provided the other men would not resent his youthful command.

Alex Grieg settled the problem for him one evening as they sat talking outside the boatshed. ''We'll need a few more men, John,'' he said. ''Better try to get a couple in Sydney. Some of those types who hang round the waterfront; they couldn't be any worse than the two darkies I had with me last time. I don't want them again. They're too damn lazy to get out of their own road.''

''So were some of the blokes we've brought from Sydney,'' Davidson grunted. ''I'll take a good look at them before I sign on any more of your adventurers. Anyhow, you're coming to Sydney with me, aren't you?''

''I think so.''

''Well, we'll see. I've been thinking about young George, too. He seems responsible enough now to take one of the boats. The only thing is, how would the men take it?''

''How do you mean?''

''Would they trust him enough? Would they resent him?''

''I wouldn't worry,'' Alex assured him. ''George is capable. He gets on well with everybody and he's been a boat-steerer for a while now.''

''Perhaps you're right,'' Davidson agreed. ''I'll think it over.''

By the time they returned from Sydney he had made up his mind, and George learnt with unrestrained pride of his promotion. His father thought, however, that it might be wise to give the lad a few words of advice. ''Don't forget you're dealing with men older than yourself who've had more years than you in the boats," John Davidson told him. "You want those men to work well with you and give of their best. They'll do that only if they respect you and if you treat them fairly. Never take a mean advantage, don't make enemies, and don't let your head become so big that you get yourself disliked. Another thing. This doesn't mean you're excused from ordinary work about the place. You'll work with the men just the same."

Beyond babbling a few words of thanks, George had no other comment. But the advice sank in past his excitement, and many times in later years he was to remember his father's words.

John Davidson brought back from Sydney three new recruits—Peter Lia, a tall blond Norwegian who smiled at the slightest provocation and seemed in a perpetual state of happiness; Tom Earl, a quiet character who looked somewhat out of place in a whaling crew; and Dick Gatley, a stocky type common on the waterfront of any big city. Peter Lia was always singing, in the boats, in the tryworks, as he washed outside the bunkhouse in the early morning, and sometimes in the evenings when he would sit on the edge of the veranda with little Charlie, the youngest member of the Davidson family. Charlie, a fat little fellow full of constant chatter, would sit quietly and gaze in wonderment while Peter sang to him. There was one song he always demanded if Peter happened to forget it.

"What is that thing?" Mrs Davidson asked one evening as she came to collect Charlie for bed. "I hear you sing it often. Charlie asks for it."

"It's a Norwegian lullaby, Mrs Davidson," he told her. "Charlie is older than a baby now, but older children like it too. I liked it when I was a very big boy. My mother would sing it for me nearly every evening."

Mrs Davidson took Charlie by the hand. "It's a lovely song, Peter," she said. "You're very good."

Tom Earl frequently walked up to the headland in the evenings and sat there staring out to sea until it was dark. To most of the others, Earl was a strange character in an atmosphere to which, obviously, he did not belong. Apart from his good educational background, there were his manners and his clothes and the way he spoke. Some thought he was moody. Others agreed he was a bit quiet at times. John Davidson suspected that Tom Earl was not the man's real name, but was the name under which he had signed on. As long as a man was respectable and caused no trouble, Davidson did not ask questions. He had wondered in the first place why the fellow wanted to go whaling. Alex Greig had wondered too and, after speaking to Earl in Sydney, had expressed the opinion that it was just another case of a member of the idle rich looking for adventure. But Davidson's reply to this was, ''What odds? He'll have to work the same as anyone else.'' In any case, John Davidson had sufficient faith in his own judgment of men to engage Earl.

Before they left Sydney, Alex told him he had heard that Earl was the brother of a nobleman in England.

''What about it?'' Davidson asked.

''Well,'' Alex ventured, ''some of the boys might give him a rough time if they thought he was a duke or an earl or something like that.''

''I don't think he is,'' John Davidson said. ''Anyhow, we'll see.''

The subject arose again a few weeks after their return to Eden. Alex came back from town one day and drew Davidson aside while the men were pulling the boat up the slipway.

''I was right about that bloke Earl,'' he said.

''Right about what?'' Davidson asked curiously.

''About him being a gentleman. He gave me some letters to post in Eden and one of them was addressed to Lady Loftus at Government House in Sydney. She's the Governor's wife. If he writes to her, he must be somebody.''

''Not necessarily,'' Davidson remarked dryly. ''A beggar can write to the Queen if he wants to. Anyhow, Earl has been working well enough, and I'm not going to bother about his private affairs.''

As the weeks passed, there was more to be done than wonder about Tom Earl's ancestry. George lanced his first whale—a small humpback—and towed it home as proudly as if it were worth its weight in gold. Alex and the others, amused at his youthful enthusiasm, wouldn't discourage him.

''Having got a taste of blood, he'll drive his poor crew like slaves now, I suppose,'' Alex remarked.

''If he can drive a couple of those darkies, he's a better man than me,'' was John Davidson's comment.

Alex had expected the boss to be wildly excited about George's first kill and was slightly puzzled at his calmness until it occurred to him that John was not anxious to make too much fuss lest the praise went to George's head and he became too cocksure. The whole family came down to see George's capture brought alongside the tryworks, and if George wanted hero-worship, he certainly got it from the three girls—Margaret, Elsie, and Jean. For their benefit he staged the kill over again, standing up in the boat and hurling a lance into the dead whale. His younger brothers—Boyd, Archer, and little Charlie—were quite impressed by the importance of the occasion, but not so full of hero-worship.

''Wait until you've killed as many as dad and then you can talk,'' Boyd chided him after George had lanced the carcass for the third time.

"I'll show you how to kill them myself next season."

"You?" George mocked with an air of importance. "You couldn't even catch a yellowtail."

"That's enough," John Davidson interrupted. "George, put that lance down and get out of the boat. Get the boat away from there and help them swing the whale over. If you want to keep lancing it, you'll have plenty of opportunity in a minute to lance the blubber off with a boat spade."

Blushing slightly, the young hero dropped the lance as if it were red-hot and sprang to do as he was told. The rebuke had achieved its purpose, reminding him that although he was in charge of a boat, he was still one of the team, and, at all times, his father was boss.

If George thought he was going to catch a record number of whales for the season, he was doomed to disappointment, because for many weeks afterwards they hunted in vain. Then came the evening when, just as they were thinking of leaving South Head to go home, there was a shout from the lookout.

Most of the men, who had been lolling about at the bottom of Boyd's Tower, sprang to their feet and raced for the boats. George cursed as he ran with them, because Alex and his father were down at the rock ledge with the boats and that meant they would probably have a start on him. When it came to a hurried takeoff for a chase, it mattered not who got into which boat.

"Give it to her, Bullock," George yelled as they rounded the point. "Come on, boys. Don't let the old man beat us. Sam, Charlie, into it."

They were both using five-oared boats, and although his father had got away with a lead of about eighty yards, George was determined to get fast before him if he could. He wished he had four others like Bullock on the oars. How that big Swede could row! Charlie Adgery and Sam Haddigaddi were doing their best, Tom Earl was sparing no energy, and Bert Penrith seemed to be putting every ounce into it, but their efforts were not good enough. They were not breaking down that lead at all. Not that it worried John Davidson. He didn't care who got there first, as long as they brought home the whale.

"Don't lag, Whitty," he shouted. "Keep stroke with Alex. You're upsetting Bobbo. Pull evenly. That's better."

Alf Gardiner's hat fell off and rolled into the bottom of the boat.

"Never mind, Alf," John Davidson consoled him. "You're lucky it didn't go overboard."

Alf consoled himself, knowing only too well that had it gone overboard neither boat would have stopped to pick it up. Twice the whale surfaced and blew. The second time it was only about a quarter of a mile away.

"It's a black whale," George told his crew. "A beauty, too. Keep her going. We might beat them yet."

George veered his boat slightly to starboard, his keen eyes having picked out the fins of two killers following the whale's course. Then two more fins appeared between the two boats—one sharp-pointed with a little round knob and the other just an ordinary fin dropping sideways.

"We've got company," George remarked. "Tom and Hooky."

The killers were swimming furiously in a big circle round the boats. George could see two more a few hundred yards away cruising on the surface. Instinctively he slewed his boat towards them. Other killers, he knew, were down below tussling with the whale, trying to force it to the top. He saw Alex Greig ship his oar and stand up in the bows of the boat ahead.

"Get ready, Sam," George shouted to Sam Haddigaddi, and the darky was on his feet with the harpoon ready in a matter of seconds. Then there was a noise like a volcano erupting and in the boiling turmoil of water about a hundred yards ahead a huge black shape broke surface, rolling from side to side in its endeavours to shake off the five or six killers snapping at it from all angles. Tom and Hooky streaked away from the boats to join them. Now Alex had his harpoon poised. He steadied himself, took aim, and the shaft flashed across the water. But it was an unlucky shot, the harpoon merely sticking in the tail instead of embedding itself in the whale's expansive back. Down went the whale as John Davidson's crew backed away smartly.

"Stay there, Sam," George told his boat-steerer. "Keep her going. They've only stuck him in the tail. We'll try to get another iron in."

Penrith cursed and the looks on several others were expressive enough as they dug their oars fiercely into the water. If they were going to chase that whale now, it might mean much hard rowing before they could get within harpoon range. George was quite aware of what the men were thinking, but, apart from the fact that they would have to act as a pick-up boat in any case, he was wondering whether that harpoon would stay fast. Alex had taken a fairly long shot and the harpoon's grip might not be too secure.

George decided to take a long shot himself by veering at an angle to the course on which the whale was towing his father's boat. If the whale swung out to sea, as they often did, he might be lucky enough to be somewhere near its next breathing spot. He was bargaining, too, on some guidance from old Tom, who had cut across that way.

"I wouldn't mind betting Tom's right and he'll head that way," Sam shouted from the bows when he realized what George had in mind.

"A very smart character," George agreed. 'I'll back Tom any day."

"Wish he was smart enough to row this damned boat," Penrith growled.

"Throw him a towrope," Tom Earl suggested with a laugh. "He might tow us."

"Oh, shut up," Bullock snapped. "Save your breath and get stuck into it."

"He's turning," Sam remarked.

"Right. Keep watch."

For a few more minutes they pulled steadily, George gauging the course by his father's boat and Tom's fin until he saw two more killers appear on their starboard bow. Then Sam took his chance as the whale surfaced and the harpoon thudded into it just behind the head.

"Back, quick," George yelled. Besides avoiding the possible antics of the whale with a second harpoon pricking it, he had also to keep clear of the other boat.

"Let him take plenty of line," he ordered. "We're going astern of them."

The line began to rush from the tub, rasping its way through the cleat on the gunwale, and then, when the other boat was clear by a safe enough distance, they took up the strain on the line and settled down for the tow.

"This feller got plenty guts," Sam remarked after a while. "He play up. You see."

The way in which the whale was dragging the two boats and still making out to sea, despite the efforts of the killer pack to wheel him, suggested that they might be in for a bit of trouble. By this time it was nearly dark. In the boat ahead of them John Davidson and Alex Greig had already decided that they didn't like the trend of things at all.

"He's kept to a sou'easterly course and doesn't look like being wheeled," Alex said. "We must be four or five miles out now."

"He's a determined swine," Davidson agreed. "We're going to be a long way from home, I think, and it's going to be damned dark too when we're finished with him."

Instead of tiring, the whale seemed to go faster, and as the boats raced ever farther from land, the last shades of twilight blurred into the darkness of night. Sometimes the men in the boats could see the phosphorescent trail streaming away behind the whale when he came to the surface or as he swam not far down. At other times when he dived to the black depths they saw only the phosphorus flashing from the ropes. They must have been about eight miles out to sea when George realized how far from home they were; he was thinking about food when, suddenly, his nerves tensed at a cry from his father in the darkness ahead.

"George, cut your line. We're crossed."

There was a dull thud for'ard and the boat instantly slackened speed. Sam, quick as a flash, had grabbed a tomahawk and chopped through the line.

"Start pulling," George ordered, striving to peer into the darkness. "We've got to—"

What he had intended to say was cut short by a terrific crash, followed within a fractured second by a violent splash and yelling voices. The men paused in the act of dipping their oars and peered, almost petrified, in the direction from which they had heard the noise. George felt his blood racing madly and a terrible fear chilled him as he tried to picture what had happened. Nobody knew exactly. They could not see through the starless moonless darkness. It was quite obvious, though, that the whale had smashed the other boat and its occupants were in the water. George and his crew could hear one or two swimming now, a voice bellowing like a wounded bull—Bobbo, unmistakably—and somebody else singing out for help.

"Pull!" he screamed. "Steady. Steady. Watch out in front there, Sam."

Slowly the whaleboat moved towards the spot where George thought he could hear the cries.

"Where are you?" he shouted, seeking direction from the replies.

"Here's one," Sam advised. "Back."

A scuffle for'ard and the sound of slopping water told of one saved. The language identified him as Bobbo. No time for questions. Others were still out there, if they had not gone down.

"Keep together," George yelled.

"Over here, George." It was Alex Greig's voice. "Quick."

Somebody had the sense to keep splashing and the phosphorus guided the rescuers. They grabbed one dim form and hauled it in over the stern. Another found the boat himself and willing hands helped him over the gunwale.

"Darky, Whitty, and Alf Gardiner," somebody said. "That leaves the boss, Alex Greig, and Peter Lia."

George was nearly frantic. He hadn't heard his father's voice. Again he shouted into the darkness, hoping his father would answer, and listened carefully.

"Quick. Over here." It was Alex Greig once more.

They swung round and a patch of phosphorus glowed in the sea.

''Get him in,'' Alex gasped.

Dropping the steer oar, George caught Alex's arm while others hauled somebody else aboard.

''It's the boss,'' Bobbo muttered. ''He's hurt.''

''I'm all right,'' John Davidson moaned. ''A bit of the boat hit my legs. Get Alex in.''

With Alex Greig aboard and John Davidson seated as comfortably as space would allow, they counted heads.

''Peter Lia,'' George said even before the count was finished. ''He's still missing. Peter, are you there?''

Others shouted too, but no answer came back. The deathly silence was broken only by the lap of the water on the boat's planking.

''Looks bad,'' Bert Penrith remarked. ''He must have gone down, or he would've answered.''

''Never mind,'' said George. ''Pull slowly. We'll keep trying.''

For some time they cruised in the vicinity, calling out and with all eyes probing for some sign of the missing man, but in vain. They stared into blackness, grim in its silence. Peter Lia was gone.

''Better make for shore,'' John Davidson suggested after a while. ''There's no hope now. We've got no chance of finding the poor fellow.''

And so they headed, almost by instinct—for there was not even a star to guide them—towards the coastline. Now that he had a chance to think of their own predicament, George realized it was not so good. Here they were, eleven men in a whale boat designed to carry six, far out to sea on a night so dark that they could distinguish each other only by their voices. Fortunately the sea was very calm, because the boat's heavy loading did not give it much freeboard, the gunwale at times being just a couple of inches clear of the water. Gradually the story of what had happened unfolded itself. Apparently the whale had stopped dead, turned, then come up underneath them, and, feeling the contact with the boat, cracked down on top of it with his flukes.

''He must have sliced the boat through like butter,'' Alex said. ''John caught me as we went out and one or two pieces of the boat hit the water with us. I heard John sing out as if he was hurt and stuck to him. What happened to Peter I don't know, but I'm afraid the flukes might have got him. He was sitting just about where the whale belted us.''

Nobody else knew either, because none of them remembered seeing Lia after the whale struck. Alf admitted he had been too busy worrying about himself. Bobbo said it was too dark to see anybody; he had thought it was the Devil himself coming up from hell and had taken one leap overboard. Lia might have been killed outright, or he could have been caught in the line and dragged to his death behind the fleeing whale as it dived after smashing the boat. Many a whaler had ended his days like that. George knew only too well how that manila rope, flicked viciously by a maddened whale, could entangle a man or throw a noose round his leg—even his neck. With a smashed boat and coiled rope being dragged out at lightning speed, anything could happen.

For what seemed like ages, the gloomy boatload struggled toward the coast before they heard the sea's surge on the rocks and knew they were near solid earth once more. George did not need Alex's warning to keep well clear. He turned north, listening intently to the noise of the sea, for it was breaking only softly and intermittently, and watching for the light that old Jim should have on South Head. He thought they must be slightly south of Leatherjacket Bay, and if this were right, they should see that light any time now. Once John Davidson moaned as if he were in considerable pain, but he said nothing, and when Alex questioned him insisted he was all right. George wondered. He might be badly hurt for all they knew, and the five victims must have been nearly frozen in their wet clothes. Bobbo remarked once that it was "plenty damn cold." Otherwise there were few complaints. All considered themselves lucky to be alive, even in wet clothes—besides, they couldn't help thinking of poor Peter Lia.

"I'd reckon we hit the coast near Mowara," Alex Greig said after they had been rowing for some time, listening to the occasional spread of a wave over the rocks. "Judging by the time we've crawled up the coast since then, we should see a light any time now."

It was almost eerie in that darkness, knowing they were so close to land, yet not knowing exactly how close. Sometimes the sea would be very quiet and they would listen anxiously for its next guiding sound. George was beginning to feel the strain on his nerves after the night's happenings.

"I wish that damned sea was bigger," he growled during one brief period of silence. "We might hear it louder and more often."

"If there was any sea running, we wouldn't be hearing anything now," Alex Greig commented dryly, and John Davidson added, "Yes, if any of you ever said a prayer in your lives, you should be thanking the good Lord now."

Probably every man in the boat said a fervent prayer when in the distance they eventually saw a light break through the night. When it first appeared they all swung round to stare. Then the rowers turned back to their oars.

Old Jim and a black boy were waiting with a lantern on the rock ledge at South Head. There was no need to tell them something had happened.

"I had a feeling," Jim muttered before they were even out of the boat. "Yes, I had a feeling. Is John hurt bad?"

"Got a bit of a crack on the legs," Davidson told him. "Nothing to worry about though."

"We'll see. Where's that boy? Here. Run up and put plenty of wood on the fire. Big fire—quick."

The black boy scampered away up the hill and Jim held the lamp while Bobbo and Bullock lifted John Davidson from the boat. He could not stand when they put him gently on his feet, so they laid him on the ground and felt to see if there were any bones broken. Nasty bruises and several deep cuts seemed to be the sum total of injuries, but he had to be carried to the top, where the boy had a fire started outside Boyd's Tower; while the other sodden victims clustered eagerly round the blaze, Jim went to work with some of the ointment and bandages they always kept in the tower for such an emergency. Now, in the light of the fire—the first time they had been able to get a good look at each other for hours—more cuts and bruises were discovered, though fortunately nobody was crippled, as John Davidson seemed to be.

"It was one of the biggest black whales I've ever seen, Jim," he told the old fellow when he had been propped up on some bags near the fire. "I'll guarantee he was well over sixty feet, and a wicked damned swine, too. Old Tom and the pack couldn't stop him. He just kept going away to sea, though I'd reckon he'd be just about beat when he smashed us up. That might've been his last run."

"Could've been," Alex agreed. "Although he still had plenty of energy left by the way he came at us."

"He's probably dead out there now," said Davidson. "Anyhow, if he's not dead, he can't be far from it. We ought to wait until daylight and go out after him."

"I'll go," George said.

"You're not right in the head, but I'll go with you," said Alex.

There was silence, broken only by the crackling of the fire. No further volunteers offered.

"That whale is worth a few hundred quid," Davidson said temptingly.

"Not for me, boss," Bobbo announced firmly. "No damn good go back there. No, boss."

"I think I've had enough for one day," Penrith admitted. "Where's that boy with the tea? Come on, Joey. Hurry up."

"You're not going out after any whales," old Jim snorted. "Have some sense, John. You can't even walk now."

Davidson grumbled, but it was no use. Apart from the lack of enthusiasm after their ordeal only a short while before, most of them were too upset over losing Peter to have sufficient interest. Tom Earl had stood gazing almost sullenly into the fire without saying a word until he mumbled "thank you" for his mug of tea. He took it in his left hand, wandered over alongside the tower sipping at it, and leant against the stone wall.

"We've lost a good man and a good friend, Mr Davidson," he said thoughtfully.

"Yes, Tom. Poor chap. We'll miss him. I wonder if he has any relatives?"

"I don't think so," Earl replied. "He told me quite a lot about himself. He was not married and both his parents are dead. Now, strange as it may seem, Peter is dead too. I've never realized until tonight the significance of something I once heard a clergyman say at a funeral. Something about in the midst of life we are in death. How true it is. There was a fine young fellow with everything to live for and in a matter of seconds he is gone . . . not living any more. If a man dies in a bed or is killed in a hundred different ways, you can see him go and realize that he is going, but poor Peter just disappeared without a sign or a sound—without us being able to help him—into that horrible black water. I shall never forget it as long as I live."

Earl emptied his mug of tea, and picking up a sharp iron spike, chipped at the stone wall of the tower. Nobody took much notice. Earl had said concisely what was roughly the sum total of their own morose thoughts. The fire crackled and the spike grated on the stone surface until Earl finally threw the piece of iron away. The noise startled George, who had been half dozing, and as he looked up, a sudden flaring of the fire revealed what Earl had chipped in the tower:

In Memory of Peter Lia, who was killed by a whale, September 28, 1881. Aged 22 years.

"I'll keep this land after Father, if I can," George said solemnly. "That will always be a memorial to Peter."

Chapter 10

When John Davidson was well enough to take stock of things properly, he realized that in addition to one of his men, he had lost a valuable boat, and another smash, leaving neither a spare nor a pick-up boat, would virtually put them out of business. Whaling with only one boat would be courting suicide or, even with the best of luck, very difficult. The problem was where to get another whaleboat and how to get it in a hurry. The hurry was the real problem. Only money could overcome that. After a few seconds of mental arithmetic, Davidson knew that he had not been doing well enough lately to finance the purchase of a new boat. Then he thought of putting all hands to building one, but that would take time, and some of the hands would be pretty useless. Pondering on the situation brought him back repeatedly to an alternative he did not relish, but might have to embrace—get the money from Solomon.

So it was that John Davidson took his crews one morning and set off for town in the two boats to get a load of stores, but mainly to talk finance with Solomon. He had discussed it with George and Alex, who both agreed it would have to be done. "After all," said Alex, "he's your partner and it's up to him to pay some of the expenses as well as collect his share of the earnings. These accidents happen in any business. We didn't want to get the boat smashed."

That was what they told Solomon, but he didn't see it in the same light. His head sank into his shoulders and his brow was blacker than the darkest corner of his shop.

"Another new boat," he muttered. "No, I won't have it. They cost money. Too much money. It's extravagance."

"It's not extravagance," George countered. "It's a necessity. How could you do business without a shop? Is this shop extravagance?" George refrained with difficulty from adding that it would take a great stretch of imagination to see extravagance anywhere about Solomon's premises.

"No," Solomon replied. "This shop is not extravagant because it is only one shop. It would be extravagant if I had two or three shops in this one main street. I don't need three shops. Why do you need three boats?"

"Oh, don't be so childish," said Alex. "You know why. If we lose another boat we're in trouble, and you know too that in our business it's always likely to happen.''

''Yes, but it seems to happen too often,'' the storekeeper moaned. ''We can't afford it. They cost money. It's too much of a risk.''

''Listen,'' John Davidson said somewhat aggressively, ''the main risk is to our necks—every time we go out there to catch whales. You at least don't have to risk your life—only your money.''

George grinned to himself. He wondered which would seem the more important to Solomon. He was not surprised when Solomon exploded, ''Only my money? And you don't think that's important? I work hard for it and I don't intend to part with it easily.''

''Well, we're prepared to build a boat, which would cost less,'' John Davidson informed him. ''But that would take time, and in this business time can be money.''

''That doesn't impress me at all, John. Now look here. You owe me for your last lot of stores and—''

''Yes and we want some more now,'' Davidson cut in, extracting the list from his pocket and spreading it out on the counter.

''Are you going to pay cash?'' Solomon asked warily, whereupon John Davidson reminded him that he didn't pay cash for everything he bought for his store. Tempers were becoming very strained. But it was Solomon himself who saved the situation. He was a businessman at heart and here he was confronting a good customer who owed him for one order and was presenting another. Business—his own—must come first. This awkward question of the boat had to be put aside. The light that dawned inside Solomon shone through him, his brow brightened, and a smile broke across his lips.

''You know, John,'' he said softly, ''we are being childish. You and I have done business together for many years. Why quarrel like this? I'll get you these stores and I'll think over your idea about the new boat. Yes, I'll think it over.''

George glanced quickly at Alex. Both were unanimous in their suspicions, but for the time being they were in Solomon's hands. After all, he was entitled to time to think it over.

''You know,'' Solomon said after a pause, ''I've been pretty busy lately with one thing and another. And then there's these experiments. They've taken up a lot of my time.''

''Experiments?'' John Davidson asked.

''Flying,'' Solomon answered casually, not bothering to look up from Davidson's list of stores. ''I'm going to be the first man in the world to fly. Now that's a secret. Nobody else in Eden knows anything about it. I'm letting you know because you're my very good friends.''

Boyd's Tower on the south head of Twofold Bay. Built for a lighthouse by businessman and adventurer Benjamin Boyd, it never showed a light. Its only use was as a lookout for the whalers, some of whom can be seen in the windows and in a shelter at the base of the tower. Getting the huge blocks of Pyrmont sandstone there and building the tower must have been a massive task. Today, a sealed road enables visitors to drive to the tower, where the superb scenery is as untouched as it was when the whalers were there.

—Photo by C. E. Wellings

Getting a tow home. The whale hunters being towed home by a launch after chasing a whale. George Davidson is standing in the bow of the whale boat. Alex Greig is sitting on the side of the launch, partly obscured. Unfortunately, he looked away as the picture was taken.

A consignment of whalebone on the wharf at Eden for shipment to Sydney. The bundle lying on the decking contained 9 cwt from one whale.

Stripping the blubber from a whale at Davidson's tryworks.

—Photo by C. E. Wellings

"Oh, yes," John Davidson replied, his tone indicating that he was amused rather than being satirical. "The only chance you have of flying is to repent and see the light before you die."

"No, I'm quite serious," Solomon told them. "I'm going to fly and you're all going to see for yourselves. I'll be famous and make money—lots of it. It's true."

Alex turned slowly from the shop window and Solomon straightened up behind the counter, aware that he had their interest now in something other than the question of a new boat.

"Sol, old fellow, you're all right, aren't you? You're not sick?"

The query, from John Davidson, made Solomon smile benignly. "No," he said. "I'm quite all right. I'll tell you what it's all about. I've invented wings that'll work. I strap them on and I can fly like a bird."

"He's as mad as a snake," Alex Greig snapped.

But Solomon ignored the remark and continued, "You know that man has dreamt for hundreds of years of flying like the birds and many have tried in vain. I've been reading about it in a book I got from Sydney. Well, I think I know why they all failed. It's in the shape of the wings. They must be curved in front to scoop the air instead of being flat like a bat. The ones I've made are curved. If this is a success, and I know it will be, I'll patent the idea and make a fortune."

"Perhaps we'll get a new boat then," Alex grunted.

John Davidson knew the old storekeeper well enough to realize that he was serious. "Where have you got these wings?" he asked.

"Out back of the store. Come and I'll show you."

They followed Solomon out into the backyard and saw two winglike contraptions made of canvas on light wooden frames. George wanted to laugh, but restrained himself and asked Solomon whether he had tried them yet.

"No," Solomon said seriously. "But I'm willing to try now and let you see for yourselves. I'll have a go from a height first and come down with them."

"I'll bet you will," commented Alex. "Quicker than you think. What about making the jump from the cliffs near the headland? You wouldn't have to spend the rest of your life a cripple then. If you weren't killed outright, you'd at least drown and your sufferings would soon be over."

But Solomon's enthusiasm was really aroused now and sarcasm was wasted on him. Small beginnings first, he explained. He showed them a huge pile of crates and boxes he had stacked against the side of the building as high as the roof. This was to be the jumping-off point for his first flight. He would try the cliffs next. Solomon picked up a piece of rope, tied the wings behind his back, and began to climb the heap of boxes. When he reached the top, he untied the rope and strapped the wings on his forearms.

"You see," he called down to the watchers. "Just like a bird."

"Good God!" George said to his father. "We'd better stop him. He'll break his neck if he jumps from there."

"Too late now," Alex muttered. "But don't worry. He won't jump. This is just a lot of damned rot. He'll climb down in a minute."

"Will he?" George spoke with some concern now. "Look, he's standing on the edge like a high diver. Hey, Sol, don't be a fool. Take off those things and come down."

Solomon either didn't hear or didn't want to hear. He waved his arms with wings attached, bent his knees, then straightened up and catapulted himself into space. At least that was what he intended to do, but the kick-off he gave himself threw him down head first and pushed the top box into a violent rocking motion which disintegrated the stack from the top down. The three men on the ground had a split-second picture of Solomon turning turtle in the air, waving his wings furiously, and boxes and crates toppling after him. Solomon's one agonized scream preceded the crashes of the wooden avalanche. The storekeeper was unconscious when they turned him over on his back. Mrs Solomon ran from the back of the store and collapsed in a faint immediately after she saw what had happened. Alex sat her up and tried to revive her, while George and his father looked for signs of life in the fallen birdman.

"No," John Davidson answered George's anxious suggestion that Solomon might be dead. "He's alive. But he's probably broken some bones. Get those silly damned wings off him and we'll carry him inside."

Mrs Solomon came to and broke into wails of anguish. "He's dead. He's killed himself."

"No, he hasn't," John Davidson tried to assure her. "He's just knocked himself out."

"Why did you let him?" Mrs Solomon shrieked. "I knew he was trying to do this. I should have burnt those wings."

"Well, he won't try again, missus," said Alex. "I reckon he'll be put off flying for life after he recovers."

George and Alex carried Solomon inside and put him on a bed. George went for the doctor. John and Alex agreed that a small sip of brandy might help him recover consciousness, and while John held the glass to the storekeeper's lips, Alex poured himself out a stiff nip. Solomon was conscious, but moaning with pain when Dr Jones arrived.

"He's broken his left arm, sprained his right wrist and both his ankles," the doctor announced solemnly after a while. "He's also very badly shaken up. The shock will probably be worse than anything else. It looks as if he'll be in bed for a time, but he can think himself lucky he wasn't killed. I'll bandage him up and come and see him tomorrow."

The news was already the sensation of the day in Eden when the two Davidsons and Alex entered the Commercial Hotel to round up their boat crew, but before they left, something else had happened to spread mild excitement in the town. A big Norwegian whaling ship had come up the coast and was entering the bay. Davidson got his men together quickly and was alongside the ship in his boat before she anchored.

Christian Larsen, the captain, offered Davidson and his men the hospitality of the ship. Not that it was much, he said, but from one lot of whalers to another, what they had was there to share. Larsen was not anxious for his men to go ashore. They had only put in for the night, he explained. Shortage of water was their only worry. They probably had enough, provided they didn't strike bad headwinds going up the coast to Sydney. Larsen proposed to spend the night at anchor in the bay and take on water before sailing again in the morning.

"No, I don't want the boys ashore tonight," he told Davidson. "They find trouble enough when they get to Sydney. I want to get the ship there first."

But the inevitable compromise happened. The shore whalers stayed aboard to sample Larsen's rum, and it was nearly dark before John Davidson bundled them over the side of the ship and headed for home. He waved cheerily to Larsen and the Norwegians as the two boats pulled away from the ship, although inwardly he was far from being at ease. Between what they had bought in the hotel bars in the town and what they had accepted aboard the ship, at least half of his men had guzzled more rum than was good for them. Worse still would be the alcoholic impact on those who had drunk beer in the pubs and then the ship's rum. Davidson didn't need to tell Alex what was in his mind when he growled, "I hope we get across the bar into the river before dark." Alex thought so, too. Several oars were hitting the water with splashes that normally would have made the whaler responsible for such poor rowing blush with shame. The blushes might have been there in the form of flushes, but shame did not even stir their thoughts.

The wind had been blowing fairly hard from the south-west for a few days, and when it had eased away during the afternoon, Davidson knew that the sea would come up. It would be the usual pattern. South-west winds were cold winter winds that frequently had an after-effect like the rum his men had been drinking. While they blew from that direction, it could be choppy in the bay and off the coast, but there would not be much sea in close for two or three days. Wide out it would be different, though. But, if the wind swung round to south-east, in those seas would come. Or if, as had happened in this case, the wind dropped off, the seas would come rolling in to the coast and across Twofold Bay in the form of a big ground swell. Davidson often thought of the winter westerly winds as defenders of the shore from the onslaught of the sea—defenders while their strength lasted to flatten out the waves. Tonight the air would be calm, but the sea would be troubled. Already the swell was building up and the surge was foaming across the Kiah River bar. That they made the crossing safely, John and Alex agreed, was due more to providence than the usual skill and care of the boats' crews.

If John and Alex were glad to step ashore, some of the others were delighted to tumble out of the boats.

"Half of them are rotten drunk," Alex mumbled, though the thought occurred to him that his condition might have been no better had he spent in a hotel the time he'd been with Solomon. John remained silent. He hoped nothing would happen that night to need the services of the men. Young George was thinking likewise as he helped pull one of the boats up the slipway. What Effie Davidson thought when she saw the company staggering into dinner was not left in any doubt.

"Don't concern yourself about their condition now," she told her husband acidly. "It's a bit too late."

Of course, it had to be. Most of the crew were snoring the rafters off the bunkhouse when the killers began to sound the alarm outside the bar. George heard them first. He grabbed his father by the shoulders and shook him from his fireside doze.

"Come on," he said. "They've got one bailed up."

John Davidson heard the crack of a tail hitting the water. "Get Alex and enough for one crew," he snapped, beginning to exchange boots for slippers. "Effie, we're going out. Leave a light on the point."

Both men dashed from the house. John Davidson made for the waterfront to get a boat ready while George ran across to the bunkhouse yelling for Alex. There, the sight his hurricane lamp illuminated was even worse than he had expected. Two of the men had been sick alongside the bunks on which they had passed out and most of the others were in no state for immediate action. Alex was pulling on some clothes. Only Bert Penrith and Alf Gardiner blinked at the light.

"Rusho," George shouted. "Get a leg out there."

Somebody groaned in the far corner. Penrith and Gardiner started to slide to the floor, though not with their usual alacrity.

"Dad said only one crew," George told Alex. "I'll get Bobbo."

"Lucky to get one," Alex mumbled, his head in a heavy sweater.

"Bobbo," George panted. "Heave ho!" He pulled fiercely at the bedclothes, then at the big darkie's exposed legs. Three tugs were enough to bring Bobbo tumbling, cursing, to the cold floor. He knew instinctively rather than consciously what was on and in a couple of minutes the five men were running down to the water, where John Davidson had one of the boats afloat. Not a word passed. Five grabbed an oar each, slid them through the rowlocks and pulled for the rumbling river mouth. Before John concentrated on guiding them through the treacherous opening into the bay, he took one hand from the steer oar to douse the lantern he had brought.

The rowers saw two lights high up on the point after they had crossed the bar and then there was only one. Effie and Margaret had gone to place the light as requested, taking with them another lantern to light their way back home. The quarter of the moon showing intermittently through the clouds made light enough on the sea for the whalers, who were now riding the long swells in the phosphorescent wake of three killer guides. Across towards Eden wharf they could see the riding lights of the Norwegian ship, but Davidson had no desire to draw attention from that quarter. If Larsen knew what was afoot he might put three boats into the chase and take their whale, just when they wanted a whale urgently to help buy another boat. Davidson knew he had taken a risk in coming out at night with only one of his boats, but it was a risk he had to take. Better one sound crew than two half drunk, or one completely drunk. He noted that the swell had built up slightly since evening, though it was still not very big and the rollers were not moving in with the speed usually associated with bad weather. Nor was there any wind. What would come tomorrow would probably be just an ordinary, varying westerly breeze. If they got this whale fairly close by, conditions should be good for handling it.

The luminous trail veered through the dark water ahead and the men in the boat heard the familiar sound of a humper in trouble with the killer pack breaking surface. "Inside South Head," John Davidson remarked, moving the steer oar slightly to follow the source of the sound.

"Hope they keep it there," Alex said with obvious fervour. None of them wanted to row any farther than was necessary on this night, so cold, so cheerless, on a venture begun with much less than the usual amount of enthusiasm. The fulfillment of Alex's wish depended entirely on good luck and the degree of enthusiasm displayed by the killers. As it turned out they were in luck. Their allies had apparently been herding the whale into the bay for some time and were determined it should not escape to the open sea again. The arrival of the whaleboat only made the killers redouble their efforts. Bobbo stood up from the bow oar and threw the harpoon. Most of them heard a faint smack, but saw little, and were backing water with their oars a split second before the command. The sting of the harpoon and the realization that it had a new foe made the whale turn on the killer pack in another desperate burst to get out of the bay. Down it dived, dragging the rope from the tub in a scuffing stream. But lack of deep water hampered its manoeuvres here, and in no time the killers turned the course back towards the encircling beaches and shores from which there would be no escape. Round and round the boat was towed above the ever-weakening struggle, until at last the combatants surfaced and John Davidson went forward for the kill.

He must have lunged the lance almost immediately after he reached the bows, probably before Bobbo in his half-sleepy state had grabbed the steer oar properly, and when he called, ''Lay me off,'' Bobbo thought he heard, ''Lay me on.'' Most of the others at the oars heard correctly, but Bobbo's repeated instruction, ''Lay on,'' was enough to induce a fatal fraction of a second of indecision. The dying whale thrashed skywards and the edge of its falling tail, sliding along the gunwale, held it under an incoming roller side on. By the time the slimy carcass had plunged free the boat was swamped, though still upright, and its occupants were gasping in the cold dark water.

''You bloody fool, Bobbo,'' John Davidson bellowed. ''It's your fault. If you weren't half drunk or stupid it wouldn't have happened.''

''I'll kill him,'' Alf Gardiner spluttered. He was clutching the side of the boat, hatless, spitting out the mouthfuls of salt water he had swallowed when he had dived overboard as the whale struck. They pulled Alf in to join the gloomy company.

''Never mind your hat,'' Alex told him. ''Think yourself lucky you didn't go in with it.''

Fortunately for them all the rope had run free to allow the whale to sink to the bottom, only about seventy feet below on the sandy harbour bed. Had it caught on any obstruction, the boat would have gone down too. John Davidson made them lash the oars across, the usual custom to minimize the risk of capsizing a swamped boat in a sea, although there was not much danger of that with only a swell; then he paid out lots of rope to allow their waterlogged craft to ride easily in case the whale had a few last kicks left on the bottom. A glance at their situation showed that they could not expect help for some time at least. They were more than half a mile from home and more than two miles from Eden wharf and the Norwegian ship. In any case, thanks to their pains to hide their mission from the ship, nobody aboard her would know of their plight until morning. If they waited long enough, Davidson thought, Effie might get worried and rouse out those left behind to bring the other boat. But who could tell how long that would be? She was used to them dashing off at night and being away until morning when a whale took them far out to sea or down the coast. If they waited until morning, they might die of cold and exposure. It was no use, either, trying to call for help, because nobody at home would hear them above the noise of the surge on the rocks and the Kiah bar.

George offered the only solution he could think of in the ensuing discussion. He would swim home and bring out the other boat.

"You're mad," his father objected. "You'll never get there. Stay here and you've got some chance. Swim off and anything can happen to you."

"Stay here and we've all got no chance," George argued. "We'll be frozen to death before morning. Now, listen. I'm a good swimmer, but I'm not silly. I've thought this out. Empty that little water cask and lash it to my back. It'll keep me afloat if I want to have a rest, and I won't lose ground because the tide's running in for two hours yet. That'll help me over the bar, too. I reckon I'd be warmer swimming, anyhow, than sitting here."

They let him go. Alex groped for the cask, removed the bung, and held the cask above his head while the water ran out. John Davidson cut the painter from the boat and with this they lashed the cask through two small rings at each end, to George's back. "Good luck, son," John Davidson said when he was ready. Alex shook the young fellow's hand and then George splashed off into darkness. What thoughts the others had, they thought better to keep to themselves; they had no wish to add to the worries they knew must be plaguing John Davidson.

George soon found that he had undertaken something more difficult than even his practical mind had considered. At first he just kept going in the direction of the Kiah, not wasting his energy frantically, but swimming with slow steady strokes. He estimated that he would have to swim slightly southwest across the roll which was going straight down the bay towards Boydtown. When he paused for his first rest and took his bearings again from the light on the point, it seemed that he was as far away as ever, although he must have covered some distance from the boat. He set off again, then stopped suddenly in fear, looking about him in the darkness. He thought he had heard a swirl in the water nearby. Was it a shark? Horror chilled him colder than he had felt from the water's freezing bite. But the sound was not repeated and he went on his way, trying to console himself with the thought that sharks were not usually about at this time of the year. He thought of transferring the cask to his stomach, which would enable him to float on his back and row with his arms like oars, but abandoned the idea because swimming would keep the blood circulating in his legs and lessen the possiblity of cramp. How long he swam before he became conscious of the noise of the surge on the shore he never knew. Nor did he care at the time, because a new problem presented itself—how to get ashore and where.

Trying to get through the bar could be very awkward. It was not a nasty sea, but the swell was breaking up and its splurge could be running about strongly. He could hear an occasional crack and a following boom as a wave flattened out. George thought it better to bypass the bar by going ashore on Whale Spit beach, then swimming across the river inside. That way, too, he was not so likely to get knocked about on the rocks at the point. He took another bearing, sensing as he did the quickening of the roller as it reached its crest, then pushed off strongly at a tangent away from the direction in which that wave was rearing. He could feel the pull of the water round him now and the din of the surf was getting louder. On he went until he thought he could make the beach safely. The following wave went right over his head and diverted his attention from the shock he got when his feet first scraped the sand, but the next one pushed him forward and, struggling upright, he waded onto the beach.

If it had been cold in the water, it was freezing in the chill night air and his wet clothes clung to his goose-fleshed skin like frozen flypaper. But it barely troubled him as he ran across the sand, walked into the river, then swam across to the tryworks landing. Breathless from his exertions and reacting to it all with slight shock now that it was over, his thoughts were more than ever with those left in the boat and he pounded up the dark track to the house.

George's mother shrieked with horror, the immediate result of his half-drowned appearance at the door.

"They're all right," he assured her quickly. "They're out in the bay. But I've got to get the other boat to them. I'm going to fetch the men."

"You're not," she said sternly. "Margaret, come here quick. Take those clothes off at once, George. I'll get the men. Margaret, get some dry clothes for George."

Margaret in her nightgown took one look at her brother and disappeared. She was back with towels and dry clothes before he had stripped himself in front of the fire. Across the yard Mrs Davidson's voice was cutting hell through the booze-thickened atmosphere of the bunkhouse. "Come on, you lazy swine. There's men out in the bay in trouble. Get out of your drunken beds for God's sake."

The rest of that night doesn't matter much now. Forgetting their headaches and hangovers, the whalers sprang to it faster than they had ever done for any humpback and, with George at the steer oar holding a lighted lantern, set off to the rescue. John Davidson agreed that they would not waste time towing in the waterlogged boat. It could stay as a marker for the whale and they would get both in the morning.

"We'll get our new boat out of it, anyhow." He grinned as he sat shivering on the way home. "As for a drop of salt water, that never hurt anyone."

This dramatic picture was taken from an old newspaper photo, thought to have been the Sydney Evening News, but its origin is unknown. It could have been a painting by Oswald Brierly, Benjamin Boyd's artist, who had a ride on a whale's back in Boyd's time and narrowly escaped injury when the whale smacked the boat with its tail, chopping it in two. A similar thing happened later to George Davidson and his crew, although they were more fortunate. Their whale carried them like the boat in the picture for about 60 metres. Then it submerged quite gently and the boat floated off safely on an even keel.

Chapter 11

For George Davidson, the next few years included more than the ordinary excitement of whaling. There was his twenty-first birthday, which brought him a quarter share in the whaling business as a present from his father. Then his sister Margaret married Rene Bragg from Green Cape—an event which was to play no small part ultimately in George's own life, for the wedding drew to Eden many relatives and friends, including the Galli family of Bega, and George met Sarah Galli.

When Sarah returned to Bega with her parents after the wedding, more than an odd thought of her remained in Eden with the young whaler. As the months passed, he began to find frequent excuses to go to Bega. Sarah—dark-haired, with brown eyes and an olive complexion—soon became the only excuse for those trips. There were attractive girls in Eden, and George, like most young men, was not immune to attractive women, but Sarah soon became his only feminine interest. Perhaps the slightly domineering, yet kindly, firm manner in which she curbed his recklessness had something to do with it; perhaps it was because she seemed to see things so clearly and definitely.

Yet it was nearly six years before the intermittent courtship climaxed in Sarah becoming Mrs George Davidson. They made up their minds in the logical way that Sarah did most things, and then she decided just as logically that she would work in Eden pending the marriage to save George the time and expense involved in his Bega visits.

"Well," John Davidson said when they told him, "you're twenty-seven now, George. It's about time you got married. Good luck to the pair of you."

"Thank you, Mr Davidson," Sarah said while George beamed his pride at her.

"You know," John Davidson added, his eyes twinkling, "if it took George as long to harpoon a whale as it has taken him to pop the question to you, we'd all be broke in no time. I suppose he spun you a great yarn, did he?"

"No," Sarah said simply. "We just made up our minds to get married. I think we knew we would all along, though it's only since I came to Eden that we've really seen much of each other."

Mrs Davidson gave them her good wishes too, although she thought it appropriate to warn Sarah that life might not exactly be a bed of roses. "When you marry a man you take him for better or for worse, Sarah," she said. "Sometimes it's for better; sometimes it's for worse."

"The same thing applies when a man marries a woman," John Davidson interrupted. "Don't forget it turns out worse for him sometimes."

"Keep quiet, John," she said, glaring at him. "This is no time for jokes. I was telling Sarah—and I should know after all the years I've been married to you—that her life with George might bring a lot of hardships and a lot of worry. You've seen some of the glamour of whaling, Sarah. You have yet to learn that for those who engage in it life is often very hard. They have good seasons and bad seasons, which can mean plenty of food and other things you need, or just scraping along, as the case may be. You'll sit home for hours many a dark night while your husband and the crazy fools who work with him are somewhere out at sea risking their necks for a whale. You'll hear the wind howling outside and the waves breaking on the beach and wonder if he is going to come back to you in one piece . . . perhaps wonder if he is going to come back at all. I know. I've done it. And you will too. Many a night you'll stand up on the cliffs in the wind and the rain, staring out into the darkness, watching for a glimpse of a light or the sound of men's voices or the noise of oars, and if you don't keep a firm grip on yourself you can go nearly mad imagining all sorts of things. It's no use telling you not to worry, because you will. I can only hope that as the years go by you might become hardened, as I have, and then, when you have resigned yourself to the fact that your husband is a reckless maniac and all the worrying in the world won't do any good, your sons grow up and he takes them with him and you start all over again."

"I'm not afraid, Mrs Davidson," Sarah told her. "If I am to share with George the happiness our married life will bring, I must share the dangers and hardships that might go with it. We all come from people who pioneered this district. If our mothers had been afraid of a few hardships we . . . well, we wouldn't be here, would we?"

Mrs Davidson looked up from her chair and smiled. "You're a brave girl and good girl, Sarah," she said. "George couldn't have found a better mate."

"When do you think you'll have the wedding?" John Davidson asked.

"Don't know," George replied. "Sarah doesn't want any fuss made about it. We reckoned we'd just get the parson and a couple of witnesses and—"

"But when?" John Davidson insisted.

"Pretty soon," Sarah said.

"Yes," said George. "After all these years we've been courting, there's no sense in a long engagement."

"But you must have somewhere to live before you rush off and get married," Mrs Davidson remarked.

"I know," George said. "We thought about that. We were wondering if we could live in the old place over the hill—Brierly's cottage."

"Needs a bit of work doing to it."

"I'll fix it up," George said enthusiastically, and the deal was made.

If George and Sarah thought their wedding was going to pass unnoticed they were mistaken. John Davidson went over to Eden with George and they collected the Presbyterian parson (the Reverend Forbes), Sarah, Bill Axam, and his daughter Betty. Because Mr Forbes did not have a church building in Eden, George had engaged the big upstairs lounge room in the Great Southern Hotel, which, he reckoned, was as good as anywhere for the ceremony, and there they were married, as George's mother had said "for better or for worse." But someone had spread the news, and as they came down the stairs and entered the hallway they were greeted by the whaling crews and a swarm of other well-wishers.

"We couldn't let you get married without wishing you and the bride good luck, George," said Alex Greig, grasping his hand firmly.

Sarah stood by shyly while everyone crowded round.

"You can't keep these things a secret in a small place like Eden," said Alf Gardiner. "The boys want to drink your health."

"Well, I suppose any excuse is good enough for a drink, isn't it?" George taunted.

"Never mind," Alf insisted. "Come on. Who's getting those drinks?"

"Here. Take this lot." It was Bullock pushing forward a tray of foaming glasses.

"You fellows must have moved to get across the bay," George remarked. "There wasn't any sign of another boat coming when we left the wharf."

The gathering laughed. "We never chased any whale faster than we chased you when we saw you were clear of the wharf," Bert Penrith explained. "The boys nearly lifted the boat out of the water coming across."

"Well, here's good luck to all of you," George said, lifting his glass.

"No, you don't," Alex reprimanded him. "You don't get a drink yet. Come on, boys. To Mr and Mrs George Davidson.''

George grasped Sarah's arm and they stood quietly while the whalers responded to Alex's toast. George's emotions were stirred as he had rarely known them to be and he looked inquiringly at Sarah. She smiled happily as the men lowered their glasses—most of them empty—and said, ''You know, I don't drink myself, but I'm sure George would like to drink his beer. We're really very happy to have your good wishes. George will reciprocate by drinking for both of us.''

''Good on you, missus,'' somebody roared from the back and they cheered George as he emptied the glass.

Sarah knew she had won the hearts of these men from that day, and she was glad. Aware that a man's wife could often make him or ruin him, she realized that she could help George a lot. She didn't know much about whaling, though, and it caused quite a few laughs from time to time, but they all said, as Mrs John Davidson had forecast, that she would learn.

Sarah had her first real taste of the business when they brought George home one afternoon nearly crippled. Womanlike, she had a premonition that something was wrong, and when she saw four dripping men coming up to the house carrying George she stifled a scream and ran towards them as fast as she could.

''It's all right, missus,'' Alf Gardiner said in his blunt way. ''He's not dead.''

Sarah glared fiercely at him, and then she saw that George was smiling.

''I'm all right, Sarah,'' he said. ''We just had a little bit of an accident. No bones broken.''

''Get him inside quick,'' she snapped.

''We lost the whale, missus,'' Bullock informed her.

''Never mind the whale. Get him into the house.'' Sarah was rattled, but she was learning.

Then there was the night when they were away for hours chasing a whale. Somebody had knocked on the door and yelled, ''Rusho,'' and George had dashed out like a madman. She heard something about the killers coming up to the Kiah, and then they were gone, leaving her alone in the house. It was so quiet. The minutes spun into hours. She took a lantern and wandered up to the cliffs, but beyond the small sphere of light cast by the lamp everything was a terrible blackness, as cold as the night itself. Sarah shivered as a light breeze rustled the trees and whispered through the long grass. Out at sea the tiny, pale stars seemed to shiver with her. Down below on that pretty little beach where the waves played on sunny afternoons, there was nothing but the dark night. The waves were still playing—there was only a gentle surge—but the swish and gurgle as they tossed themselves on the sand and ran through the crevices of the rocks sounded frightening in her imagination. Sarah stayed there she knew not how long, and she remembered what her mother-in-law had told her, "Many a night you'll stand up on the cliffs in the wind and the rain, staring out into the darkness, watching for a glimpse of a light or the sound of men's voices or the noise of oars, and if you don't keep a firm grip on yourself you can go nearly mad imagining all sorts of things."

Go nearly mad! How true. She must go down to the other house with Mrs Davidson. She wanted to run all the way. But, no, that would not do. She had told Mrs Davidson she was not afraid. She would walk down. She must walk.

"Come in, Sarah," the older Mrs Davidson greeted her. "I thought you might come down."

"They've been gone such a long time and I thought I might wait here for George," Sarah tried to explain, feeling a tinge of annoyance run through her embarrassment.

"Yes, I know, dear. Sometimes they stay out much longer. But try not to worry. It won't bring them home any quicker."

Sarah looked at the clock over the fireplace, furtively she thought, but Mrs Davidson had glanced up from her knitting and read her mind.

"It's only half past eleven," she said casually. "That makes two and a half hours they've been gone. Some whales take about five hours to deal with, and then they have to anchor the carcass and fix marker buoys. They won't be back for a while yet. Put some more wood on the fire. It's in the big box behind the kitchen door."

Sarah brought the wood and then sat beside Mrs Davidson. The fire crackled occasionally, now and again a loose piece of iron hanging over the tanks would rattle in the breeze, and most of the time she could hear Mrs Davidson's knitting needles tapping together. Always there was the incessant ticking of the clock. When Mrs Davidson dropped her knitting and dozed for a while the clock seemed to tick louder every second, until Sarah could hardly sit still in her chair. But she had to keep calm. She was the wife of George Davidson. He was not to be worried over her panicking while he was engaged in serious and dangerous work. The clock must have ticked thousands of times before Sarah thought she heard them coming and roused the older woman.

"Yes," Mrs Davidson consoled her. "It's them."

George and his father were all smiles when they came in. "We got him, Sarah," George burst out. "A big black whale. Plenty of oil, plenty of bone, and plenty of money."

"I'm very glad, George," she said, handing him a cup of tea which

Mrs Davidson had made when they first heard the boats.

She was even more pleased when they walked home arm in arm and the lamplight flickered on the slate veranda around Brierly's old cottage. As they paused and George opened the door for her she heard the waves on the little beach. Yes. They were playing on the sand. It would be lovely to watch them tomorrow when the sun reflected from every ripple.

Early morning kill. George Davidson lancing a whale in Twofold Bay.

–Photo by C. E. Wellings

Chapter 12

George was out at sea killing a whale when their first child was born. It couldn't be helped if a whale chose to put in an appearance at such a crucial moment, and, after all, whales were their bread and butter. George's mother, who was looking after Sarah, was even glad to see the men out of the way, convinced they would be more hindrance than help. George had asked whether they should get the doctor from Bega, but his mother knew the doctor would only come those forty miles over rough roads if it were really necessary. Women in those parts looked after each other when their children were born.

The whale killed and anchored, George came home to find himself the father of a son, and, as in the Bible story, they called his name John.

Women sometimes do the most unpredictable things. With John scarcely big enough to toddle, Sarah startled George one afternoon by adding another member to the family. She collected him from the aboriginal camp—God knows why—but she did, and neither she nor George ever regretted their adoption. Arthur Ashby they called him.

"Good Lord, woman!" was George's verbal reaction when Sarah confronted him with the bedraggled little half-caste boy.

Arthur, no more than nine years old, clung timidly to her hand and awaited developments.

"I got him at the camp," Sarah said. "I told old Lucy we'd look after him—"

"Yes," George interrupted, "I can see you got him at the camp, but—"

"George, he's such a nice little chap. He's got no mother or father. I asked Lucy if I could have him. Don't know why, but there you are. Lucy said, 'Yes, missus,' and George—missus wants him."

George looked at his wife, then at the boy, who let go Sarah's hand and hid behind her back. George couldn't help laughing. "Very well," he said. "We'll look after him, as long as he behaves himself. You don't know these kids like I do. They'd pinch the eye out of your head. Anyhow, we'll see."

And so Arthur Ashby came to live with the Davidsons, who soon realized that the lad was not only honest but was keen to help in any way he could. It was obvious, too, that Arthur was going to be a handy man in the boats when he was old enough. Whenever they went over to Eden, Arthur managed to go with them, just for the sheer love of being in the boat. When they were deblubbering a whale at the tryworks, he would grab a boat spade and chop happily with the skill and energy of a much older hand.

As Sarah and George's family increased with the addition of Roy and Jim, and Arthur was growing up, the country, too, was going through its growing pains. For many years there had been talk of federation—the welding of the Australian colonies into nationhood. By 1899, with the beginning of a new century only months away, the talk was being taken more seriously and it looked as if federation might be more than a faint possibility, but that depended on the votes of the people in the various colonies, who were to decide the question by a referendum.

Looking back, many people could not help wondering at the irony of it. First a policy of separation into different colonies with different administrations; now, after all these years of going their own way, a move for unified administration. The first colony of New South Wales had included New Zealand at one stage and what is now Queensland, Victoria, and Tasmania. Gradually it had been carved up and, excluding New Zealand which was a long way over the sea anyhow, Australia had been split into six separate colonies, with different and obstinate ideas about such things as railway gauges, postal facilities, customs, excise, commerce, and navigation. Then there was the question of defence, brought home to a few thinking people over the last decade when rumours began to spread that Germany had designs on New Guinea, that Russia had definite imperialistic ideas in a southward direction, and that France was thinking of taking the New Hebrides for a criminal transportation colony.

In Sydney, men like Sir Henry Parkes had been arguing for years that trade and commerce between the colonies should be absolutely free and unrestricted, that there should be Federal control of customs and defence, a High Court of Appeal for Australia, and a Federal Parliament. But there were many people who did not want federation, and for several years the fortunes of its possibility had fluctuated with the conferences and conventions arranged by the men who firmly believed in their ideal of nationhood.

In Eden, the move for federation did not interfere much with the ordinary course of the town's life. The steamer—usually the Illawarra Steam Navigation Company's S.S. *Eden*—arrived from Sydney twice a week and sailed for Sydney on Wednesdays and Saturdays, the Union Company's *Wakatipu* called on her Sydney-Launceston run, the Davidsons caught a whale sometimes, John Hopkins slashed at the carcass of a sheep in his tiny butcher shop, the postmaster (Mr Kebby) discussed the weather with anyone who had nothing else to talk about, Tom Ramsey beamed at customers over the counter of the Eden Stores, or some misguided individual staggered about the streets after a session in one of the hotels until he was invited to spend the night in the lock-up as the guest of Constable Thompson. Then came suggestions in some Sydney newspapers that if federation became a reality the Bombala district should be selected as the site of the Federal capital with Eden as the Federal port.

John Hopkins drove his chopper right through a leg of beef and embedded it deep in the chopping block, as he told a customer that if Eden was to be the Federal port it was a damned good idea and he would certainly vote for federation. Old Cappy Russell, now retired, did not have to convince the new pilot, Captain Newton, but he spoke often and emphatically on the subject. On the street corners, in the bars, on the wharf, those who thought of it talked of it and agreed it was a good idea. Twofold Bay had been neglected since the early days of the colony when Ben Boyd had tried to develop it as the harbour of what he dreamt would become one of Australia's finest cities, and this neglect, Eden folk agreed, was not accidental. It was, they said bitterly, the planned scheming of big business interests in Sydney. Why else should Eden remain just a small town on the edge of one of Australia's finest and most beautiful deep-water harbours? Sydney interests, they said, did not want Twofold Bay developed as a port because it was the natural outlet for the whole of the Riverina district and the Monaro as well as portion of northern Victoria, and if Eden had become the busy maritime city it should have been, millions of pounds' worth of produce would be passing through there instead of Sydney. That was why, they said, certain interests had stopped the Government from building the railway south of Nowra and that was why no railways from the inland districts came anywhere near Eden. They were proud of their harbour and, with all the indignation of local pride, resented the way it had been either neglected or sabotaged all these years.

"Why," old Cappy Russell told a group in the Commercial Hotel, "the largest ship afloat could come in here without any trouble. You could get the whole British fleet and the American fleet in here together and there would still be plenty of room left. There's sixty feet of water sheer alongside each of the two headlands and from ninety to a hundred and thirty feet all the way across. It's about two miles from the lighthouse to East Boyd with an average depth of sixty feet and you'll find the sheer depth round the shores averaging about thirty-five feet. I know, because they're the official soundings on the Admiralty charts and—besides, I know damn well enough myself."

But so far the selection of a Federal capital and Federal port was still only talk and any names were only suggestions. The first question to be resolved was federation itself. Eden had its share of the campaigning for the referendum. Politicians found their way to the little township to blast the ears of the inhabitants and slogans began to appear on buildings, fences, and shop verandas exhorting voters, "Strike Out the No," "To Be or Not to Be—A United People," "Federation or Repudiation," "Shall It Be Union or Disunion?" On the evening before the taking of the referendum, there was a gala Federation Ball in the School of Arts, arranged by the Eden Progress Association.

Far into the night the sounds of revelry emanated from the long rambling hall on the slope down to the high cliffs. Willing hands had spent most of the day decorating the walls and crisscrossing the ceiling with festoons and evergreens, and to lend a truly patriotic air to the proceedings Captain Newton had brought along the entire collection of flags from the pilot station to drape among the other decorations on the walls. Nearly everyone in Eden went to the ball. Those who were too old to enter actively into the spirit of things went along to watch the younger folk enjoy themselves. Most of the whalers cleaned themselves up and donned collars and ties, and George and Sarah came across with them in the big whaleboat. It was a real fashion parade for the women, some of whom had been carefully nurturing for weeks a new dress creation with which they hoped to stun local society.

As the evening wore on and the arguments over federation began to wear out, it was inevitable that one or two revellers, stimulated by more than a few good "stingers" of rum, should become boisterous. Bullock, roaring like his namesake, nearly caused a stampede by challenging some young fellow in the middle of the floor during a waltz. Right or wrong, Bullock wanted him outside to fight, or, better still, to fight on the spot. Nobody knew what it was all about, but respecting Bullock's temper and the possible menace of his clenching fists, the dancers scattered. Several women began to scream when Bullock grabbed the victim of his attentions. The music had hardly stopped before George sprinted across the floor and barged between them.

"Cut it out, Bullock," he appealed, grappling with the Swede's huge bulk.

"I'll kill him, boss," Bullock roared.

"Let him go," George shouted.

Bullock relaxed his grip and those who had scattered began to form a meekly advancing circle, staring curiously at the tough, wiry little figure of George Davidson pushing the big Swede away.

"He insulted us, boss," Bullock insisted, but George with the assistance of Alex Greig, who had pushed his way through the crowd, led the still furious Bullock outside before he asked what it was all about.

"I heard him say something about stinking whalers," Bullock told them. "He was trying to be funny with that girl."

George and Alex quietened him, and then, hoping rather than satisfied that Bullock would behave himself for the rest of the evening, they went inside.

"What's the matter with Bullock?" Sarah asked anxiously.

"Oh, nothing to worry about," George assured her. "He's just had a few rums too many. That's all. He'll be right now."

And so the Federation Ball continued into the early hours of the morning, the piano tinkling and the violin scraping to the faint accompaniment of the sea swishing over the rocks below the cliffs.

Of course the referendum was carried, and as the months passed, Eden people read of plans for the first Commonwealth Parliament. But it was two years later—9 May 1901—before the parliament assembled and met in Melbourne with the question of a Federal Capital still the subject of vague discussions. The first Federal member for Eden-Monaro was Mr Austin Chapman, who had represented Braidwood in the New South Wales Legislative Assembly for ten years. Eden had a very distinguished visitor for Christmas that year in Mr George Reid, Leader of the Opposition in the Federal Parliament, and the people of the town and district could not let the occasion pass without notice. They arranged a banquet in the School of Arts for Mr Reid and his family.

As is the usual custom, Mr Reid had to reply to toasts and say nice things about Eden and its people. Not that he found the task very difficult. Like everyone else who came to Eden, he was captivated by the beauty of its harbour and surroundings, and he said so. But Mr Reid said more. He said he could not understand why Eden had not put in a claim for the Federal capital site.

"This wonderful harbour, situated about midway between Sydney and Melbourne, is only one qualification," he said. "There are a hundred other good reasons why Eden and Twofold Bay should be brought under notice. I must confess I did not know there existed such a magnificent port capable of taking the largest ships and set in such beautiful surroundings. Your town has been aptly named."

This was something for which many public-spirited souls in the little township had waited long years, and believing that at last they had found a strong champion, they added cheers to their vigorous applause—poor simple souls, happy in their insolation from politics and the cunning of politicians which was mainly responsible for their isolation. There was no doubt Mr Reid meant what he said about Eden, but had one or two been suspicious enough, it might have occurred to them that a shrewd politician like Mr Reid never loses the opportunity to take a trick. He was Leader of the Opposition this Christmas of 1901. He hoped to be Prime Minister by Christmas of 1903.

His words, though, acted like timely rain on the seeds of thought already sown in the minds of many in the little community. Larry O'Toole, proprietor and editor of Eden's newly established newspaper, the *Eden Propeller*, gave the speech great prominence and added emphasis by quoting from a speech of Sir Henry Parkes, who some years back was reported as saying:

> It does not follow that because this very fine port [Eden] has from one cause or another been neglected that it will continue to be neglected. When that district is opened up by railway construction, to which in my opinion it is richly entitled, Eden, which is a very fine harbour, will become the site of a very important maritime city. Twofold Bay has been the victim, if I may so term it, of singular neglect. I do not say whose fault it is. It is difficult to distinguish. But before many years Twofold Bay, where the town of Eden is situated, will become one of the most important places in New South Wales. I have no doubt whatever of that. As far back as 1873 I advocated construction of a railway to the port to bring the traffic of Monaro to the Bay.

Such hopes! Only a few weeks after Mr Reid's departure, indignant Eden people were reading in the *Propeller* that the Public Works Committee of the New South Wales Parliament had refused to sanction the construction of a railway line connecting Eden and Bega. What they said then about Reid, Parkes, and politicians in general was quite different to what they had said about them at that banquet in the School of Arts.

"The dirty rogues," John Davidson roared through his black beard as he thumped an empty glass down on the counter of the Pier Hotel bar. "They kept this place back in Boyd's day and they'll always keep it back. You don't think they're going to build a railway to bring trade to this port at the expense of Sydney, do you? Mark my words, none of us or our children or even their kids will ever see the railway line come past Nowra. Those big pastoral companies in Sydney want the lot."

"But the Government was talking about it and I thought they would build the line," Cappy Russell argued.

"The Government," John Hopkins snorted. "When the Government ever does anything it promises to do except collect damn taxes I'll cut my throat with a meat chopper."

"The railway would've made this place," George Davidson said thoughtfully. "We have to depend on shipping—what we get of it. Now they reckon the *Wakatipu* might be laid up for some time."

"Where did you hear that?" his father asked.

"Somebody told me on the wharf a while ago."

"That's right," Cappy Russell said. "It's in today's *Propeller*. She collided with the Adelaide Company's *Eurimbla* near Bradley's Head in Sydney Harbour on Saturday night."

"What about my new whaling gear?" John Davidson moaned. "It was coming on the *Wakatipu*."

"Don't worry, John," the old pilot assured him. "You'll get it. I saw a wire from the Union Company this afternoon. They're putting the *Kittawa* on the run while the old girl is laid up."

And so the politicians were reviled in the hotels, the shops, and in the street-corner discussion groups. Larry O'Toole sat in the *Propeller* office for two hours writing what he intended to be the most caustic editorial of his career. When he had finished, he tossed the pen across the table and gazed through the window at the ruins of Boydtown behind the long yellow beach in the south-west corner of the bay. Benjamin Boyd, he mumbled subconsciously. Had Boyd succeeded, Larry O'Toole thought to himself, the *Propeller* might never have come into existence, but there would probably have been several big newspapers. Yes, O'Toole thought, the politicians helped to smash Boyd in those days. Certainly several of the people Boyd employed in his enterprise robbed him right and left and were largely responsible for his downfall and the ruination of his plans, but the politicians and big city business interests who were frightened of Boyd helped too. Was the same thing happening again? He could not help thinking it was and that Eden and other places with similar claims for advancement would never emerge from their isolation until Sydney became so overgrown and saturated with population that it could absorb no more.

Chapter 13

Although they shared with other Eden residents their disappointment over the failure of the plans for the railway, the Davidsons, like everyone else, had plenty of their own worries to occupy their minds. The past two seasons had yielded anything but a fortune and future prospects did not appear much better. Deep-sea whaling was booming, with the result that prices were not. Oil—dirt-cheap oil—was coming in from Japan, and the tanners, soap-makers, and rope manufacturers who used whale oil in the production of their goods were naturally unconcerned over another local industry when they saw they could cut costs by using imported oil.

With disgust George watched his father sell thirty tuns of first-class oil on the Eden wharf for sixteen pounds a tun.

"What odds," John Davidson replied when George protested that it was absurd. "We've got to get rid of it, and the way things are we can't haggle over the price. They're not falling over us to buy it, you know."

George merely grunted. So did Sol Solomon, but with a long verbal aftermath. George walked out of the shop in the middle of it and waited for his father in the street.

"I'm getting more sick and tired of Solomon and his moaning every day," George said savagely as they walked down the hill to the wharf. "He wants every halfpenny he can get from us, and what does he do? Nothing. Just sits in his store and expects us to give him a fat share of the earnings from our hard work. I had to walk out or I'd have lost my temper with him. I tell you, I will next time."

"I could have got wild myself, but that won't get us anywhere," John Davidson remarked wisely.

They walked on without another word, until they turned quietly, as if instinctively, through the bar door of the Pier Hotel. Inside, both broke the silence, George to order two beers, his father to growl at Cappy Russell, who was sitting at a table near the window.

"You damned old loafer don't you ever do any work?"

"No more than I can help." The old pilot grinned. "No more than you do anyhow, John."

"Well, it's about time you did something instead of sitting here sipping beer all day. Every time I come into this pub you're here."

"Well, what of it?" the old fellow retorted. "I'm a retired gentleman now, I am, and I can do what I like with my spare time. I'm going to Sydney soon to buy a big yacht. You've heard them tell about Ben Boyd's yacht, the *Wanderer*. Well, I guarantee Boyd's yacht was a dinghy compared to the one I'm buying."

"You're wandering," George said, laughing for the first time that afternoon.

The barman, Bill Holden, slapped a cloth on the counter and mopped up the beer he had spilt. Bill was a very fastidious barman, particularly when it came to keeping his counter clean.

"Old Cappy's been telling everyone about his yacht all day," he said. "He's nearly driven us mad. I've heard about it at least three hundred times today. For Gawd's sake, don't start the old devil talking again."

"You mind your own business, Bill Holden," Cappy roared, leaping from the table with the agility of one much younger. He was at the counter in a few strides, thrusting his white beard almost in George's face. "So I'm wandering, am I? Well, you wait and see, young fellow. You wait and see my yacht. And as for you, John Davidson, when I want to come into the Pier Hotel I'll come in, and I'll drink as much beer as I want to. I'll have more time than you will next season, anyhow, when this new bloke starts in opposition to you. He reckons he's going to show you how to catch whales."

"What new bloke?" John Davidson asked casually, but curiously.

"I don't know much about it yet, but he's coming here," Cappy told them. "Archie J. Boyd is his name. At least that's what he signed himself in the letter he wrote to a certain person in this town—and don't ask me who the certain person is because being a gentleman of my word I'm not at liberty to say. He's supposed to have sugar plantations up in the islands somewhere. All I know is that he is coming and bringing a couple of boats and some gear. I shouldn't have told you that much, but being old friends I thought—"

"You thought what?" George snapped.

"Oh, shut up, George," his father interrupted. "Listen, Cappy, don't take any notice of either of us. We've just had a little discussion with Sol Solomon and it's made us a bit cranky."

"I can quite believe that," Cappy remarked, wiping his mouth. "I was cranky myself after a discussion with Sol yesterday. He reckoned I didn't pay my last bill for stores and I know damn well I did pay him. I'm sure the old devil forgets sometimes who's paid and who hasn't and just asks everyone to make sure. Like his blasted hide, though, to infer that me—a gentleman of honour what doesn't owe a soul a halfpenny—would try to take him down for a lousy fifty bob or whatever it was."

"You'd never take anyone down, would you, Cappy?" Bill Holden asked.

"Certainly not," the old fellow roared. "Now don't you try to be smart, Bill Holden. You know me well enough—"

"Yes. Well, give us some money now and I'll fill those pots up again."

Cappy gaped. "What?" he parried. "Give you some money?"

"Yes, you heard me, some money. You're shouting, aren't you?"

Cappy regained his composure quickly. "Oh, yes. Who said I wasn't?"

"Nobody. Only wanted to hurry you up, that's all. You've been too busy talking. You're a terrific talker, you know."

"Never mind," said John Davidson, laughing at the expression on the old fellow's face. "Here's your good health, Cappy. And good luck with your yacht."

"Thanks, John," he replied. "I hope you have good luck against your new opposition when it starts."

"We'll see," John Davidson said. "Anyhow, we can't be worried."

George and his father drank their beer and turned to go.

"Have one with me," Bill Holden invited them. "We don't see much of you over here lately."

"No thanks, Bill," the older Davidson replied. "I think it's going to blow pretty hard out of the south-east before evening and I want to get back across the bay. Sam and a couple of the boys are waiting with the boat at the wharf. See you next week probably. Good-bye."

"Have one with me then," Holden called after them as they passed through the door.

"Thanks," Cappy Russell muttered, but loud enough for the barman to hear. "I'll have one with you now, Bill. I mightn't be here when they come over next week."

"Nobody would be more surprised than me," Holden remarked flippantly. "Cappy, I don't think you're ever out of the place. In any case, I didn't ask you to have a drink. I asked the Davidsons. You've had too much already. Next thing you'll be rushing off to Sydney and ordering a four-masted barque instead of your yacht."

That did it. The yacht was becoming a sore point with old Cappy and he was just at the stage when jokes about his dream boat were beginning to irritate him. He tossed his empty mug across the counter, partly because of the vicious turn his mood had taken, partly to show unmistakable contempt, and partly in the hope that it would spill a few drops over Holden's clean oilcloth, and then stamped out without another word. Holden stood clutching the mug, which he had fielded neatly on the edge of the counter as it was about to roll to the floor, and stared for a little while from behind a mischievous grin before he put the mug under the counter and relaxed. A less experienced barman might have worried at the prospect of losing a good customer like the old pilot. But not Bill Holden. He knew Cappy Russell and he knew Cappy would be back.

If John Davidson had been inclined to forget the threat of opposition to his whaling business, he was reminded of it less than a week after the discussion in the Pier Hotel when Bill Glover called at the house one evening and said he was leaving to take a job as Boyd's manager.

"I don't really want to go, John," he said, "but it's a good chance for me. It'll hurt leaving the boys, too. I've been with them and with you a long time."

"Must be about ten years," Davidson remarked. "Well, Billy, I don't want to lose you, but if you think you can better yourself all I can do is wish you good luck. When do you want to go?"

"Oh, I don't know. Soon as I can, I suppose. Anyhow the season's a little way off yet. I thought I'd tell you now, John, instead of leaving it until the last minute."

John Davidson pulled his pipe from a coat pocket and stuck it into his mouth while he went through other pockets after tobacco. "I'm glad you did, Billy," he said. "Gives me a chance to get another man in time. Well, you please yourself and make whatever arrangements you like about going."

Mrs Davidson had heard from inside, but, womanlike, she still had to ask her husband when he came in what it was all about.

"Nothing much," he said. "Billy Glover is leaving. That's all."

"Well I gathered that," she said. "About this fellow Boyd starting, though. You didn't tell me anything."

John Davidson looked thoughtful. He was standing near the fireplace puffing his pipe and twirling the dead match in his fingers. "No, Effie, I didn't. To tell you the truth I hadn't given it much thought. You know the way these rumours get around sometimes and—"

"Never mind rumours," she said purposefully, sitting up straight in the armchair which she always occupied in the evenings after dinner. "Sounds more than a rumour to me. Billy Glover wouldn't be leaving if it wasn't right.

"As if things weren't bad enough," she remarked, relaxing again. "Here, John, put that match in the fireplace. Don't throw it on the floor.

I'm sick and tired of cleaning up this place.''

Davidson tossed the match into the fireplace. ''Oh, stop growling, Effie,'' he said, grinning.

''Stop growling?'' she retorted. ''You'll all be growling if this Boyd fellow beats you for a few good whales.''

''He won't, though.''

''Won't he? How do you know? You've lost them before when other boats have been working here and if that happens again it'll be the same old story—no money, no nothing. And that reminds me. You'd better get some stores over from town tomorrow, too. I suppose we've got no money, though. Or have we?''

''Yes, we've got money, but not much. I'll go over to town tomorrow in any case because I want to see Solomon.''

''See Solomon,'' she snorted. ''Fat lot of good that'll do unless you've got plenty of money, and you'll need plenty for the list of things we want here.''

John Davidson bent down over the fireplace and knocked the ashes from his pipe, grunted an indication that he had heard the comment, straightened up, and then yawned. ''All right, Effie,'' he said. ''I'm going to bed. Must get some sleep.''

But he didn't sleep for a while. Instead he lay and turned over in his mind several things that had been worrying him. Effie had stimulated his thoughts, too, as she often did in her direct way, and had hit one nail right on the head when she referred to money. John Davidson didn't need his wife to tell him that unless things improved money was going to be a very scarce commodity as far as they were concerned. This opposition, too, would involve him in more expense with the possibility of less reward. His boats and crews would have to be maintained more carefully than ever, which meant there could be no cutting down on expenses.

The longer he turned the problem over in his mind, the more involved it became. This was not like most other forms of business, where a man could budget on estimates. Everything worked on chance and possibilities. He thought he might ask Solomon for a better financial arrangement, which seemed the only way out. Then, as he became drowsy and dozed, his thoughts went round and round in circles again, and he was no nearer the solution than when he had first pondered over it. Finally John Davidson just gave up and let sleep claim him, but he had made up his mind to talk with George in the morning. Then they would see Solomon.

George did most of the talking next morning and he was still talking when they climbed from the boat to the wharf at Eden and headed for Solomon's store. ''We're going to have words with Solomon this time,'' he said. ''Don't just listen to him, as you always do. He's a pretty shrewd old bird, particularly when it comes to money.''

''But just what are we going to put to him?'' John Davidson argued.

''Tell him we want more for our work than we're getting. I've been boiling for years over this arrangement. Look. What did Solomon put into the partnership in the first place? Nothing—well, practically nothing. And what has he got out of it ever since? Nearly the lot. From what I can make of it you let a clever businessman like Solomon come into partnership with you under a more or less unwritten agreement, he sits back and does nothing, we do the work and he collects most of the profits. Did either of you put any money into it?''

''Well, not much. The main thing we did was to pool some whaling gear.''

''Yes,'' George remarked cynically, ''and for that privilege Solomon has had almost a mortgage over our livelihood ever since. He's a shrewd financier and you don't really know what he's been doing. I tell you, Dad, I've been worried about him for some time. There was that oil we sent to Sydney last year—or rather the oil Solomon sent in his name. We didn't see a penny from it.''

''No,'' John Davidson agreed, ''but we bought stores from him on credit on account of it.''

George snorted. ''Very generous,'' he remarked. ''Solomon wasn't giving anything away and we paid for what we bought—actually paid for it in advance. Now listen to me. You tell him we want something better. If you don't, I will, and pretty quick too.''

Solomon was beaming over the counter the instant he saw them walk through the door. George didn't like that. ''Good morning, gentlemen,'' he greeted them.

Never mind, George thought to himself. They would wipe that smile off his face. They returned the greeting, somewhat less affably though no less politely, and Solomon straightened up, leaning against the edge of the counter with his thumbs dug into his waistcoat pockets.

''Fine day, John,'' he remarked, looking through the door towards the headland, where an occasional line of white foam edging the rocks was the only interruption to the deep blue of the sea. ''Yes, a lovely day. Makes a man restless to be indoors. But then, John, business is business and a man never got anywhere by neglecting it.''

''Quite right, Sol,'' John Davidson replied. ''That's what we came to see you about really. We wanted to talk about arrangements for the whaling season. In plain words, we must have some better agreement—financially, I mean—or we can't carry on. There's opposition starting this season you know.''

''Opposition. Yes, I know. I heard the other day.'' Solomon looked at them blandly, as if waiting for them to make the next move, and when nothing came promptly, he made it himself. ''Funny thing, John,'' he said. ''I've been thinking more or less the same as that.''

''The same as what?'' George cut in quickly, wondering what Solomon was up to, but never dreaming the truth.

''Oh, about the financial side of it,'' Solomon explained. ''You see, prices for oil and bone aren't as good as they were and if I'm going to finance you with opposition competing, I want a bigger share—say, at least two-thirds of the returns.''

''Two-thirds!'' John Davidson gasped. ''You're not serious, are you, Sol?''

''Business is business,'' Solomon said, shrugging his shoulders and spreading his hands out in a sideways movement.

''Wait a minute,'' George said curtly. ''If anyone is entitled to more of the business it's us. You've sat on your tail for years dragging profits from our work under a tinpot partnership which I don't think counts for anything. Dad has been too easy. If I had my way, Solomon, I wouldn't give you even a chunk of blubber. I'd—''

''Now talk sense, Sol,'' John Davidson interrupted, pushing George behind him.

''I'm talking sense,'' Solomon insisted. ''I've still got to finance you to the same extent, if not more than previously, and if it were possible for you to catch, say, fifteen whales in the season without opposition you might get only eight or so with other boats working. That means that if it were possible for you to earn, say for argument, five hundred pounds in the season without opposition, you might earn only three hundred with opposition, and if I'm financing you to the extent of two hundred for the season, I'd be battling to make ends meet—in other words to balance the books. Then again, if results aren't any better than they have been over the last couple of years—''

''But, Sol,'' John Davidson queried, ''just exactly what do you mean by financing us? You don't even provision us in the proper sense. We buy everything from your shop and pay for it the same as any ordinary customer.''

''You often buy it on credit and payment depends on money coming from the whaling,'' Solomon explained. ''That's financing you.''

''Well, we've bought our last from you,'' George told him, pushing forward again. ''We'll deal elsewhere and then there'll be no need for you to finance us.''

Solomon shrugged his shoulders again. ''You have no money,'' he said. ''You just have to deal here.''

George was furious. He could see his father was losing patience too.

At first he had thought Solomon was bluffing, but it was apparent now that this was no bluff, because Solomon was under the impression that he had them where he wanted them and if it was a bad season he was not going to lose by it. The situation looked grim. Solomon was right. They had no money, or very little, and unless they got money from somewhere, Boyd might easily have the whaling to himself before long. George took a chance, even if it was an impetuous one.

"That's where you're wrong, Sol," he said heatedly. "We don't have to deal here, and if you think we're going to starve, think again. Anyhow we don't care what you think. We're through with you. Come on, Dad."

"George is right," his father said sternly. "If that is your attitude, Sol, we won't buy another thing in your shop."

They turned and walked out, leaving Solomon to shrug his shoulders again.

"You shouldn't have done that," John Davidson said as they started to walk down the road. "We couldn't carry on under those terms, but I'm hanged if I know what we're going to do now."

"I do," George said.

"What?"

"We can do without Solomon. I'm going to Sydney to get finance, and we'll be much better off. You see, this gives us the chance to get rid of a useless partner. Solomon's partnership with us is finished."

"Yes, but where are you going to get any money in Sydney?"

"I'll go and see Mr Nicol."

"That tanner's agent who was here a couple of years ago?"

"Yes. Remember when we couldn't sell that oil anywhere and he came and bought the whole lot in the shed? Tanners want whale oil all the time. I'll tell him I don't want money—only provisions and whaling gear—and in return he is guaranteed our season's catch. Sarah can stay with you and mum while I'm away."

John Davidson laughed. "All right," he said. "It's worth trying."

Two days later, George stood on the deck of the coastal ship *Eden* as she steamed out of Twofold Bay, headed for Sydney. When the ship berthed at Darling Harbour on the Friday morning, George booked a bed for the night at a hotel, changed into his best suit, and went looking for Charles Nicol's office on Bathurst Street. Nicol remembered him, which helped considerably, because George had been feeling slightly nervous while he waited for the clerk to announce his presence.

"How are you, Mr Davidson?" Nicol greeted George pleasantly, rising and dragging a chair alongside his office table. "Sit down."

"Thank you," George said, wondering as he settled himself in the chair how to lead up to his proposition. He was well aware that Nicol represented probably his only chance of success in Sydney and, if he bungled this, the outlook would not be very bright for the Davidson family. His mind was racing quickly—too quickly to allow clear thinking—but Nicol soon put him at his ease.

"How are things down in Eden, Mr Davidson?" he asked while George was still wondering what to say.

"Oh, just about the same," George replied. "Nothing much ever happens. We're waiting for the whaling season to start."

"Nothing much ever happens?" Nicol repeated. "Don't tell me you fellows lead a dull life, although I suppose what looks so thrilling and glamorous to the onlooker is only hard work to you. How did you do last season?"

"Not bad, but not so good," George answered truthfully. "We can only catch whales when they come along, and last season there didn't seem to be so many about."

"Yes, that's true. Tell me, have you still got that big islander with you? What do you call him?"

"Bobbo."

"Oh, yes. Bobbo. He seems to be quite a character. Strong as an ox, too. How's your father?"

"Quite well."

"I see. I don't suppose you have any more oil to sell?"

"No," George replied. "I wish we had."

"Yes. You would sell it easier than when I bought that lot in your shed. Funny thing how sometimes there's a surplus of a particular commodity and then there's not so much about; prices jump and prices fall and other commodities are affected too. Not that there is any shortage of whale oil at the moment. There's plenty of it coming in from deep-sea whalers, although some of it is not good oil. I know for our business I'd rather have a regular supply of good oil all the time."

George saw his lead and took it. "That is actually what I came to see you about, Mr Nicol," he said. "Dad and I were wondering if you'd be interested in a regular contract for the purchase of our oil. If you were, it would suit us too because we'd just ship it to you whenever we had some ready."

Nicol sat back in his chair and reached for a tin of cigarettes. "Have a smoke?" he asked, opening the tin and extending it to George. "A contract," he said with the first puff. "Well, I might. What would you propose?"

"I don't know. You could make us an offer." George waited, almost holding his breath.

"I can't state a fixed price," Nicol said, "but I'll tell you what I will do. I'll pay you ten shillings a tun over the ruling price, whatever that happens to be from time to time."

"That would suit us," George said, feeling quite happy about developments so far, but now came the most difficult part of the negotiations. Nicol, perhaps unwittingly, saved the situation for him.

"Do you want any money on account?" he asked.

"No," George replied, "I don't want any money. I just want a start in provisions and whaling gear. If you could give me an order to get a few things to take back with me, that would do."

"Certainly. Make out your list and I'll give you an order to go to Lassetter's and get your provisions and an order on Broomfield's for your whaling gear. When are you going back?"

"The *Eden* sails at noon on Monday and I'd like to go then if I could."

"Nothing to stop you. See the clerk outside, tell him what you want, and he'll make out the list, I'll sign the orders, and you might get the stuff delivered to the ship this afternoon. It should be there by tomorrow morning anyhow."

"Thank you very much," George said. They shook hands and Nicol walked to the door of his office.

"Stewart," he said to a clerk, who sprang up from the desk where he had been working. "Take a list of stores and provisions from Mr Davidson on an order form—two, rather, one for Lassetter's and one for Broomfield's—then bring them in for me to sign. Good luck, Mr Davidson. Give my regards to your father."

"Good luck to you, Mr Nicol, and again thanks very much," George said, trying to hide his excitement. Inside a quarter of an hour he was walking along Bathurst Street, whistling to himself, with the two orders in his pocket. Now, he reflected, he could go back and forget about Solomon. In his pocket he had orders for seventy pounds' worth of provisions and every piece of whaling gear they wanted. They could start the season confidently, opposition or no opposition, and there would be no more profits for Solomon.

George was pacing the deck impatiently when the ship entered Twofold Bay on Tuesday morning, and he sprang on to the wharf almost before the mooring ropes had been made fast. He wanted to get home quickly with the good news. The stores could wait until he sent a couple of the whaleboats over for them later. Cappy Russell was standing on the wharf sucking his pipe, as he always was when a ship arrived or departed. George nearly knocked the old fellow over rushing up to shake his hand.

"Good morning, Cappy," he almost shouted. "Do us a favour?

Yes, I knew you would. Lend me your dinghy. I want to get home quick.''

Cappy removed his pipe from his mouth with the disengaged hand and stared at him inquiringly. ''All right, George,'' he said. ''Take the dinghy. But why all the fuss and excitement?''

''Oh, nothing. I'll bring the dinghy back before lunch when I come with the whaleboats to get some stuff from the ship. Thanks, Cappy.''

George bounded across to the other side of the wharf, threw his bag into the dinghy, threw himself in after it, untied the painter, grabbed the paddles, and set off across the bay. As he rowed he whistled an occasional few bars of a song he had heard somewhere in Sydney. Those few bars were all he could remember, but he liked as much as he knew of the tune and didn't mind giving himself a few encores. It was a lovely morning. The water about the boat was a pleasant green and where it gurgled away behind were mottled lace patterns of white. Out at sea it was so blue, except where the little waves kicked up by the light nor'easter caught the sun and reflected its brightness. It seemed no time before George was guiding the dinghy across the Kiah bar towards the landing-stage at the tryworks, where Bobbo and Alex Greig were waiting to meet him.

He thought they didn't look as pleased as they might have been, even when he told them to cheer up, that he had done ''some good business'' in Sydney. Then it occurred to him that his father had not come down. Somebody must have seen the dinghy coming across the bay. Perhaps his father did not know and Alex and Bobbo had been at the tryworks by coincidence when he came into the river. Never mind, George thought. He would run up to the house and tell them the good news.

''Get two of the boats ready to go over to the wharf,'' George called back as he ran up the path. ''I brought back a lot of gear and provisions on the ship.''

''Why didn't you tell young feller George?'' Bobbo muttered to Alex.

''I couldn't, Bobbo,'' Greig answered, and walked away.

George had reached the flat land on top when he saw Sarah and his mother walking down the path. He broke into a grin as he called out to them. Evidently they had seen him coming in the dinghy after all. He met them in the middle of the little orchard in front of the house, threw his bag on the ground, and kissed them both. Then, as he drew back, he saw their faces. Alex and Bobbo had looked almost like that. Something was wrong, he knew now. His father should have been the first to meet him.

''George,'' his mother said very quietly, ''your father is very ill. We've had the doctor.''

George glanced from her to Sarah. "That's bad," he said. "Dad never had a doctor unless it was really serious." He knew, too, that his mother was not a woman to send for doctors indiscriminately. George picked up his bag. "Come on," he said. "I want to see him."

Bad as the shock had been, there was worse to come when George entered the bedroom and saw his father. John Davidson, lying as if in a coma, apparently saw nobody and recognized nobody. It was no use. They closed the door and went into the kitchen, where George flopped dejectedly on a chair.

"What happened?" he asked. "What's wrong with him?"

"We don't know exactly," his mother told him. "He got up on Sunday morning to light the fire for breakfast and it seems that when he stooped to put the match to it he collapsed. I heard a funny noise and went out and found him lying on the floor. Sarah and I got him into bed, but he couldn't talk to us. He's been like that ever since. The doctor says he took a stroke and his brain is paralysed."

"Good God," George said, "I can't believe it. He was never sick in his life and he was so well and hearty when I went to Sydney. When is the doctor coming again?"

"He should be here this morning," Sarah told him.

"Isn't there anything he can do?"

"He's quite honest. Says he doesn't think so."

"Who is it?"

"Dr Storey from Bega."

George got up and walked to the window, merely because his nerves would not allow him to sit still any longer. "I had some good news for him, too," he said. "I saw Mr Nicol in Sydney. He gave us a contract for all our oil and made me out an order for seventy pounds' worth of provisions and gear on account. I brought the stuff back with me."

"He would have been very pleased," Sarah remarked.

"Yes," Mrs Davidson added in a soft voice. "He would have been."

It was well after midday when Dr Storey landed from the boat that brought him across. His visit to the patient was brief. "You'll have to get him to Sydney," he told George and his mother. "He's pretty bad and I tell you frankly there's nothing I can do. He has one chance. A specialist might be able to save him. I'll send a wire to Dr Gordon Craig and make arrangements if you like."

"We're guided by you, doctor," George said.

"Well, get him to Sydney as quickly as you can."

"But how? The skipper of the *Eden* told me coming in this morning that he's not going out until Thursday evening."

"The *Corrina*, a Tasmanian ship. She berthed while I was waiting for the boat to bring me over here. She is going on to Sydney tonight. If that man is to have any chance at all, he must be on board when the *Corrina* sails. I'm sorry I can't do anything. It would be foolish—worse, even criminal—for me to tell you otherwise.''

They thanked Dr Storey and George saw him off in the boat.

''What did the doctor say?'' Alex Greig asked.

''Looks bad, Alex,'' George said grimly. ''We've got to get Dad to Sydney on that Tasmanian ship for specialist treatment. Dr Storey as good as told us there's no hope for him, but he wouldn't recommend rushing him to Sydney if there wasn't a slight chance.''

''No, that's right,'' Alex agreed. ''By the way, how about the stores from the *Eden?* Two boats can go any time you like.''

George thought for a minute. ''Hold on a while,'' he said. ''I'll go with you and see the skipper of the *Corrina*. I think mum and Archer had better travel with dad.''

His mother had the same idea and she and Archer were already packing some clothes into bags when he returned to the house.

''The only thing I'm worried about is that we haven't much money,'' George said. ''You might need a lot. You don't know how long you might be away.''

Mrs Davidson stopped her packing and looked up. ''I've had forty pounds stowed away for a long time that even your father didn't know about,'' she told him. ''I put it away a little bit at a time thinking that some day it might be needed. That day has come, George.''

When it was time to leave, Bobbo and Alex Greig carried John Davidson down to the boat as gently as they could, and those who were staying behind stood silently on the landing to see them off. At the wharf they carried him up the steps and across to the *Corrina*. There was quite a little gathering. George noticed Cappy Russell, John Hopkins, Bill Holden, and Billy Glover. But they waited until the patient had been taken on board before they approached George, knowing there was nothing they could do. As the ship cast off and began to draw away from the wharf, they stood with him.

''I hope he pulls through,'' Glover said. ''He's one of the best blokes I've ever known.''

''Of course he will,'' said John Hopkins. ''Nothing could kill Johnny Davidson.''

But George was not so sure. Something told him as he watched the *Corrina* swing clear of the wharf and begin to move slowly ahead that he would never see his father again. John Davidson, he knew, was going to sea from Twofold Bay for the last time—not in the stern of a whaleboat.

Never again would his black beard shudder in the breeze as he tugged at the steer oar and shouted directions to his men. John Davidson was going through the heads in a bed on board ship, a helpless and dying man.

The end of the chase. Getting ready to lance a humpback whale in Twofold Bay. One of the killers can be seen to the right of the whale.

–Photo by C. E. Wellings

Chapter 14

John Davidson died in Sydney about a month later and was buried in Botany Cemetery. As much as he wanted to go to Sydney when his mother wrote and told him that the end could not be more than a few days, George knew no good purpose would be served by going, and, besides, he had too much responsibility now to leave home at the beginning of the whaling season. The opposition—Boyd—had brought two good boats, well fitted with plenty of gear, and Billy Glover and his crews were very keen. More than ever, George felt his position as head of the family, although Archer, Boyd, Harry, and Charlie were no longer mere youths.

Archer and Boyd stayed with him in the boats, but he was grateful to know that he also had Alex Greig, Bobbo, Charlie Adgery, Sam Haddigaddi, Bert Penrith, Peter and Albert Thomas (father and son half-castes), Dan Parsons (a good aboriginal whaler), and most of his father's old team. Perhaps that was why they finished the first season with ten whales and the opposition got none. Within three months, George had cleared the seventy pounds advanced by Mr Nicol and was sending him plenty of good oil.

Two of the whales were killed in one day. The first one, harpooned in the morning near Leatherjacket Bay, played merry hell before the killers drove it ashore on the rocks outside South Head in its dying struggles. Billy Glover and his crew, badly beaten in the chase and left as mere spectators, laughed, but George didn't. There was no chance of getting that whale off and towing it into the tryworks. They would have to deblubber it on the spot and ship the blubber in the boats—deblubber it quickly, too, before any bad weather blew up. By lunchtime they had the second boatload ready, and George decided to boil some in the trypots, leaving one boat and crew to continue the deblubbering, at the same time watching and ready should another whale come along. Uncle Jim was helping by keeping a lookout from the old tower.

They had just unloaded the last of the blubber when young John came running down from the house. "Daddy," he panted, scrambling over the rocks, "Uncle Jim's coming on his horse. I saw him over the hill and ran down to tell you."

"Good on you, John," George said. "That was very smart. Now go back up to your mother and be careful along the edge of the water."

Uncle Jim was yelling "Rusho" from the top of the pathway by this time, but the boat was already gliding back from the slipway into the water, and the men were tumbling aboard.

"That kid's learning," Alex remarked. "He knew damn well what Jim was coming for."

"So do you blokes," George retorted for the benefit of the crew. "Get stuck into it. They may need a hand out there."

The oars thrust at the water and the long, lean boat skimmed towards the river mouth. Across the bar George swung the boat's nose for South Head. Then, to the surprise of his crew, he scowled to them to slow down.

"Ease down," he repeated quietly. "Put your coats on, boys."

"What's up?" Bobbo mumbled. "Boss gone mad?"

Something certainly was wrong, but George set their minds at rest with one word—"opposition." The rowers looked round and saw, about three hundred yards away on the port bow, another whaleboat in which Billy Glover and his crew were making back towards Eden wharf. Coats donned, the Davidson crew resumed rowing at a steady pace while George stood in the stern trying to look as poker-faced as a sly grin would allow. Glover evidently was not aware that Davidson's other boat was chasing another whale outside the harbour and, if he didn't know, they were not going to tell him. Ashore, opposition whalers were usually good friends, but afloat they were deadly enemies and "don't get in my way or I'll go over the top of you," was understood as an unwritten law.

"Good day, George," Glover called as the boats passed about a hundred yards from each other. "Going out after more blubber?"

"Yes," George answered. "Might as well. If the weather blows up this evening, there'll be none left by morning."

"Good on you!" Glover laughed. "Hope you break your backs dragging it in."

George grinned, but mumbled profanely as he turned for'ard again. Glover had no doubt seen the crew's quick-change act and they would not be able to increase their pace without arousing his suspicions until they rounded the headland. Meanwhile anything might be happening out there, and another boat to help could make all the difference between catching the whale or not catching it. George's growing impatience made the trip down the bay seem almost endless. He looked back when they were nearly to South Head, saw Glover's boat still heading towards Eden wharf, and then his impatience got the better of him.

"Righto," he said. "Give it to her. We can't wait any longer."

Coats were tossed off and the boat's prow began to thump harder and louder into the choppy tops of the rollers. George looked again to see what Glover was doing, satisfied himself that he had hoodwinked his rivals, and then turned his attention to the open sea. He saw the whale blow before they had cleared the headland, but looked in vain for his other boat.

"Funny," he remarked to Alex. "Where the hell is Archer's boat? I can see the whale. Can't see any boat."

Greig glanced over his shoulder. "What's the matter then?" he grunted. "They must've been smashed up."

"The killers are giving that whale some curry," George remarked, although he feared that what Alex had said was only too true and his eyes squinted as he searched the surrounding sea. "There they are," he shouted suddenly. "They're in the water. Lift 'er, Bobbo. Pull your guts out. Quick."

The men needed no urging. Some of them had been in the same plight themselves on more than one occasion and they knew the spine-chilling feeling of struggling in the sea with their clothes on, hoping fervently that no prowling sharks were in the vicinity. The whaleboat literally bounced across the waves, George Davidson steering it towards the specks of men's heads he could see rising and falling with the swell. Soon he could count the heads. One, two, three . . . six. They were all there.

"None missing," he told the rowers. "One of them's waving. They must be hanging onto the boat."

George was right. The men in the water were clinging to the boat—two battered halves of it. Boyd Davidson was supporting Archer Davidson, and Dan Parsons, looking almost pale beneath his black aboriginal skin, was quite limp between the two half-castes, Peter and Albert Thomas. the men were quickly hauled aboard over the bows and as fast as the rowers could shift a five-oared boat carrying twelve men they made for South Head. George could see Archer and Parsons were in a bad way and he knew the boat was beyond any hope of salvage. But that whale wasn't, and George, despite concern for his injured brother, could not help looking to see what the killers were doing with it. The whale was trying to break out to sea, while the killers were edging it into the bay. He saw in a quick glance old Tom's fin moving round in circles, and could imagine what the other killers were doing down below.

"What is it?" he asked Boyd Davidson.

"A humper, and she's vicious," Boyd told him. "She's got a calf with her. We were going to lance her and got too close."

"You blasted idiot," George snapped at him. "Don't you know

better? The old man taught you and the rest of us when we were in damned napkins to keep well clear of a whale with a calf. What happened?''

''Oh, she just swung on us and belted us clean in the middle with her flukes while Archer still had the lance in his hand. The boat . . . it was like chopping a leg of mutton with a meat chopper. You saw the pieces.''

''You're damned lucky you blokes weren't the meat,'' Alex Greig reminded him. ''Glover held us up or we'd have been there sooner.''

''But didn't you know it had a calf?'' George persisted.

''Oh, shut up,'' Boyd growled. ''All you think about is stinking rotten damned whales. Your brother and another man are badly hurt. Get us ashore and you can do what you like. You go and get her.''

''I will,'' George said, and for the rest of the dash shorewards the only sounds were the creak of the oars and the thudding of the waves against the boat.

They landed the wet and injured men on the big red rock at the foot of South Head and sped seawards again to where George could see the whale blowing. His language as he urged the crew on was more vigorous than usual. One boat smashed up and two men badly injured was enough to make anyone swear, and now, to make things worse, Billy Glover and his crew were coming out, rowing like fury towards the harassed whale, which, tormented mercilessly by the killers, was being shepherded slowly into the bay. Glover had thought hard about one or two things before his suspicions crystallized and he had ordered his crew to ''pull like blazes'' for South Head. He knew that if his suspicions proved to be wrong his men would not be overjoyed at having to row full tilt over the ground they had just covered, but he knew, too, after long association with George Davidson and George Davidson's father that there had been something ''fishy'' about George's sudden departure for another load of blubber. Anyhow, he had taken so long to act on these suspicions that George, after depositing the rescued men ashore, still had a good lead.

George trailed the killers and found their quarry, still with the calf, going for her life with fifty fathoms of rope trailing behind, although the killers had taken most of the life out of her. He picked the trailing rope from the water with a grappling hook, made it fast, and soon they were closing on the beaten whale. George steered in, more cautiously than the others had done, went for'ard and lanced her. He was preparing to lance again when Glover brought his boat close by.

''You've got him, George,'' he said. ''Mind if I give him a lance?''

''Please yourself,'' George replied. ''It isn't a him, though; it's a pretty savage her and she's smashed up one boat already.''

Glover gave his boat-steerer the steering oar and scrambled to the bows to pick up the lance, but he had not even straightened for the throw before the whale swung round, kicked its flukes wickedly, and nearly upset them. The edge of her flukes caught two oars, tearing them from the rowers' grasp and tossing them high into the air, and the boat rocked almost on its beam ends in the backwash from the whale's hind quarters as they crashed back into the water.

George's patience, worn thin by the day's events, would not spare him a laugh. "Keep out of the road," he snarled. "You'll get killed."

With Archer and Parsons laid up and likely to be convalescent for some weeks, George found himself short-handed, especially as Boyd, badly shaken by the latest smashed-boat incident, had very little enthusiasm left. What enthusiasm he still held disappeared altogether a week later when another boat with Alex Greig in charge had a hole thumped through its planking by a blow from a black whale, which, had it hit squarely instead of grazing the side, would have made pulp of the boat and its occupants.

"I'm finished," Boyd told George that night. "I'm turning in my share of the business. It's no good to me."

"But I'm short-handed," George said. "You know how things are."

"Listen," Boyd said firmly, "it's no use arguing with me, because I don't want to go whaling any more. The season is nearly over and you'll get more men for the next. Besides, I want a steady job. There's a Government job going at the lighthouse in Eden and I'm taking it. This game offers no future for a man and certainly no comforts for his wife and family. What have we got this season? Ten whales. Next season we might get none, next season one or two, and a man is scraping and battling from one year to another—unless his life happens to end suddenly a few miles outside the heads one of these days."

"The Davidsons have whaled from Twofold Bay since Ben Boyd's day and—"

"Well, here's one Davidson who's turning it up right now," Boyd interrupted. "A steady Government job in the lighthouse may lack a bit of excitement, but I'll turn that over to you and Archer with my share in the business."

There was no more excitement for anyone that season because there were no more whales. Boyd moved across the bay to take his job at the lighthouse. George and Sarah changed residence to the old family home, and Effie Davidson moved to a small dwelling nearby. With no whales to catch, the men returned to their summer occupations. Bobbo and Bullock worked five days a week at timber-cutting—to keep themselves fit, so they said—and relaxed in the town's hostelries on the other two days. George, relaxing in a hostelry one afternoon, found himself piloted to a meeting and appointed a member of the committee arranging Eden's first agricultural show. Somebody suggested that one day would be enough for the show, especially since it was Eden's first venture. George challenged him that one day would not be enough, that Eden was not a one-horse town and it should be a two-day show. Local pride won and the show was scheduled for 17th and 18th March. A very wise choice, old Paddy O'Rourke told the meeting when the dates had been decided. They could not do better than open their first show on "the good St Patrick's day."

George's argument for the two-day show was borne out, mainly because those who went the first day were there again on the second and over the two days sixteen hundred people paid for admission to the picturesque little area which the committee had leased on the cliffs overlooking the northern fold of the bay. Paddy O'Rourke was there for the opening, in a resplendent green tie which became more and more beer-stained as the day wore on. Farmers from the surrounding district paraded before the judges with their horses and their cattle, local lasses paraded themselves before the local male youth, sideshowmen rang bells and shouted themselves as near hoarse as is possible for sideshowmen as they exhorted the public to "see the fat lady" or "stay two rounds with the basher and win a fiver."

Each night of the show there was a ball in the School of Arts and Eden celebrated gaily. Far up the street, those strolling in the moonlight could hear the voice of Charlie Wellings, who was master of ceremonies, "Gentlemen, your partners please for the lancers. Come on, gents. Don't stand round the door. There's plenty of pretty girls just waiting to be asked." Then the piano, coaxed by the local maestro, Angus Young, would strum the tune and feet would shuffle across the floor. George Davidson and Alex Greig danced until their feet could stand no more. Sarah was busy both nights helping in the supper room and did very little dancing herself, but she reckoned George was far better off exercising his feet on the floor than he would be outside exercising his elbows drinking rum. She saw Bullock once, swaying somewhat unsteadily near the door trying to catch George's eye, and promptly warned him off.

"You too, Bobbo," she told the big islander, who was standing back outside the door. "No rum for the boss."

Bobbo grinned sheepishly. "Rum, missus? No. Rum's firewater. None for Bobbo; none for boss, too."

"Well, you be sure there's none for boss," she emphasized.

Apart from one minor fight on the second night between four of the town's youth, Eden's biggest social event since the Federation Ball went splendidly. Then, the show and the show balls over, the town returned to its normal placid life—as placid as life was in 1903. But that was how Eden folk liked it, except those who were disappointed at the town's slow progress.

George Davidson, like others, saw the same old ramshackle buildings dotted about Imlay Street, Mrs Crichton still beamed from behind the scratched and stained counter of the Commercial Hotel bar, and Shelley and Company, general agents and tea merchants, still guaranteed to supply anything from a needle to a haystack—or rather needles to steam engines. They advertised in the *Propeller*: "No rubbish put onto customers. Machinery, from sewing machine needles to steam engines provided on shortest notice. Dealers in livestock from chickens to Durham bulls."

Mrs Crichton, too, believed in the power of advertising and paid the *Propeller* each week to tell its readers that her Commercial Hotel "by acknowledgment occupies a choice position in scenic Eden, facing the dawn over the Pacific, and being centrally situated is found most convenient. The first and second-class tables are the most liberal throughout the South Coast." And because potential customers in those days had a good deal of thought for their horses, her advertisements added, "Good stabling, honest and attentive groom. We have a regard for horses—they cannot speak for themselves."

The Union steamship *Wakatipu,* back on the run again after its mishap in Sydney Harbour, churned its way into Eden a month after the show, and half the town wandered along to the wharf to watch her berth. To Captain Livingstone, waving from the bridge, it was almost a homecoming. He loved the calls at Eden and, almost as much, the Pier Hotel's beer.

"Good God!" he exclaimed when he walked into the bar, accompanied by his first mate, Bill Green, and escorted by old Cappy Russell. "What's happened here? Did a tidal wave hit you?"

"No," Cappy reassured him. "They're just renovating the place."

"Good day, captain," barman Bill Holden intervened as they stopped at the counter. "No. We weren't hit by any tidal wave. The boss is having the place done up, dividing this big bar into two and making a bar parlour. Quite flash, too, it'll be when it's finished. Look at this. Stained Californian redwood and kauri panels for the counter and them ornamental shelves like they have in the flash city pubs."

"H'm" Captain Livingstone commented. "Well, get us a few flash beers, Bill. I suppose we'll get better measure now. You won't be game to spill it on the nice new counter."

"Ah, he'd drive a man mad," Cappy Russell sneered. "You won't be able to move in the damned place with Holden running round wiping up every spot that gets on the counter, besides insulting gentlemen what drink here and help pay his wages, and then. . . . Look at this notice they've got over there—'No spitting.' Where do they think a man was brought up? I don't know. The hide and the damned cheek!''

Everyone laughed, but old Cappy only snorted when Bill Holden retorted, ''Well, old boy, you won't have to worry much longer. The police tell me they're going to get a prohibition order issued against you when the court sits again.''

The party was growing. George Davidson and Alex Greig had come in with John Hopkins.

''Good day, George,'' Captain Livingstone greeted him. ''Have you got Hopkins carving up the whales now?''

''Wish I did have,'' George said, tossing two shillings on the counter. ''He's a good man with a knife. Although I suppose most of the blubber would disappear into his butcher shop.''

''Couldn't be much worse than the meat we took on in Launceston,'' Captain Livingstone remarked. ''No wonder most of the passengers were sick coming up.''

''You missed us out on the way down?'' Greig asked.

''Yes. Went straight through because we were a day late getting out of Sydney. Made up for it on the trip back, though. We left Queen's Wharf, Launceston, at seven o'clock yesterday morning and berthed here at ten this morning. That's an average of thirteen knots on the run up from Tassie. Not bad for the old ship.''

''Not bad,'' George agreed. ''It's pretty good.''

''Wait till I get my yacht,'' Cappy Russell chipped in. ''Did I tell you I was getting the most magnificent yacht they've ever seen in Eden, Captain?''

''No, but you've told everyone else,'' Bill Holden reminded him. ''Shut up and drink your beer. These other gents are waiting. Are you going to shout this time?''

''Well!'' Cappy's face reddened. ''I'll have you know, Bill Holden, that I demand a bit of civility in this hotel or I'll speak to the management. The likes of you insultin' a gentleman—and a good paying customer at that—every time he comes into the place. The hide and the cheek. I'll have you know—''

''Come on then,'' Holden said, picking up the glasses. ''If you're a good paying customer, sling us the coin for these drinks.''

Cappy fumed. The company laughed. Cappy dived into his pockets, but George was already pushing his money across.

''All right, Cappy,'' he said. ''We'll let you get the next one.''

The old fellow snorted again, glaring straight ahead into the mirror at the back of the shelves. He knew they considered him fair game, particularly Bill Holden with his too-ready wit. Never mind, Cappy mused. The day would come. He would show them when he brought his yacht to Eden and moored it near the wharf. He could see in the bar mirror the exact place where he would put down the mooring and as Bill Holden strutted up and down behind the Pier Hotel counter, he would have to look at the yacht all the time, would look enviously as she glided past when Cappy took her to sea. Yes. Holden and all these others laughed now. He would show them.

Chapter 15

It was nearly eighteen months later before Cappy Russell's dream came true. He went to Sydney in the *Wakatipu* and a couple of weeks afterwards sailed his dream boat into Twofold Bay, standing in the stern like a proud father admiring his first-born as he steered her past the end of the wharf. He knew curious eyes were surveying every inch of her graceful thirty-foot hull and tall mast and he was enjoying it. Cappy, literally bouncing with excitement inside, tried to look very calm and dignified when he waved to the onlookers along the wharf. Through the corner of his eye he saw Rochfort, the publican; Alan Jamieson, Bill Holden, and John Hopkins' son Jim. That was enough. It was a completely rejuvenated edition of Cappy Russell that made its appearance in the bar of the Pier Hotel after the yacht had been safely moored. He pushed the door open, stood for a dignified two seconds scanning the interior, then strode proudly to the counter, aware that today he was really a person of importance.

"Well," Holden greeted him, "if it isn't Captain Kidd himself."

"Captain Kidd!" The old pilot almost exploded, but quickly remembered that he was master of the situation today—the day he had been awaiting so long. "What do you mean, Captain Kidd?" he asked, grinning slyly as he leant one elbow on the counter and tugged a cigar from his top pocket.

" 'Struth," Holden gasped. "Cigars and all now. Anyhow, don't pretend innocence. Where'd you get the yacht? Piracy is still an offence, you know, and you'd look lovely dangling from that tall mast."

"Oh, so that's it." Cappy relaxed and lit the cigar. "Well," he resumed, "it's just as I've been trying to tell you for months—"

"Years," Holden emphasized.

"All right then, years. But it's just as I've been trying to tell you. Now you can see for yourselves. And ain't she a beauty? As for your slighting remark about piracy, Bill Holden, a gentleman of my standing can afford to ignore such trashy witticisms. It's no business of yours where I got her, although I'll satisfy your curiosity enough to tell you she's paid for and she's mine, and seein' as how I'm a gentleman what doesn't owe any man a damned halfpenny, let alone the likes of you—"

"Now, now, Cappy," Holden said, backing beyond range of the

glowing cigar end, "don't get all steamed up. I was just going to shout you a drink to celebrate."

"What!" Cappy was flabbergasted. "You . . . you . . . "

"Yes. I said to Jimmy Hopkins out on the wharf a while ago when you were mooring the yacht: That old Cappy Russell, I said, he wasn't pulling our legs after all and I'm going to break all my resolutions and buy him a grog when he comes ashore. Didn't I, Jim?"

"That's right," Hopkins agreed.

"Well, of course, if you insist—"

"A pleasure, captain," Holden said, smiling as he reached for three glasses. "Jim and I must drink your good health with you and wish you every happiness with your yacht."

"It's very good of you," Cappy said, still not knowing quite what to make of the situation. Holden had been teasing him for so long that he couldn't believe there was not a catch somewhere.

"And I'll shake hands with it," Holden said when the glasses were lined up on the counter. "Good luck, Cappy."

Cappy beamed as he gripped the barman's hand and then they tossed off their ale.

"I'll tell you what I'll do," Cappy said when they had finished. "I'll shout for the bar."

"Good idea," Jim Hopkins grunted, his eyes blinking from under the upturned brim of his hat.

"Yeah, a good idea," Holden added, looking round the bar—empty apart from the three of them.

Across the bay at the whaling station they had seen the yacht come in and Alex Greig suggested it might be Cappy's, but George Davidson gave the matter only half a thought—the half he could spare from much more serious thinking. This year—1904—had been grim financially and unless something turned up very quickly with the start of the whaling season, their position would soon become desperate. It would have been already, he knew only too well, but for the few pounds that Sarah had strung out so carefully. Last season they had not taken even one whale. Sarah said nothing, except when she had to remind George that they could not afford one or two things he wanted, and his mother, realizing that he had enough on his mind, tactfully left the subject alone.

By the time the killers made their first appearance in Leatherjacket Bay, George was beginning to feel the strain—more from inaction than anything else—and although she would not let him know, Sarah was quite worried about him. She was probably just as glad as he was when she knew that the killers had come back, as they did every year at the beginning of the season, and even more pleased a week later when George and the others left their lunch half-eaten and dashed for the boats. The hours rolled by and she waited patiently, as she had learnt to do over many years. But she no longer watched from the cliffs beyond the house, mainly because she knew that young John—now a very energetic fourteen-year-old—was perched there and would let her know when the boats were coming home. He did, and she ran with him down to the tryworks.

"Two, Sarah," George yelled to her before his boat was over the river bar. "Two beauties."

"I'd better go and get your father and the men something to eat," she told John and, after waving back to the boats, walked briskly up the path to the house.

That night they celebrated. Over in the bunkhouse Bobbo and Charlie Roberts—a half-bred Kanaka who had joined them the season before—each produced a bottle of rum and Uncle Jim rummaged among his belongings until he found a small drop of whisky that he had been hoarding for such an occasion. George's mother soon reminded him that his father would never have allowed the darkies to drink in the bunkhouse. But he didn't care.

"Hang it all, woman," he said. "We've been going round with long faces for months. It's time there was some joy about the place. Let them be. Those two whales should bring us in anything from seven hundred to a thousand pounds at least, the way the market is now for oil and bone. Think what it means to all of us. We want food and stores. Sarah could do with some new clothes; I want new gear. We don't have to hang up our hats to any blasted tradesman or storekeeper and with the season only just starting—"

"Yes," she said softly, but there was an underlying firmness in her voice. "I know. I've heard your father talk like that so often. But those darkies shouldn't be filling themselves up with rum."

"Why shouldn't they?" George snapped. "They can't have enough grog over there to get even merry on, which is the reason I've been saving up a bottle of rum for them in a secret hiding place, and I'm taking it over and having one with them."

"As you please," she said, looking up from her knitting and arching her eyebrows. "Like your father, you can't be told anything."

George lit his pipe, strolled from the room, and the door closed behind him.

"Huh," the elder Mrs Davidson snorted. "I've never known any good to come of drinking yet, and mark my words it never will."

Sarah, sitting by the fireplace patching Jim's trousers, merely smiled to herself. Even without that rum George would sleep well tonight, and so would she.

They did sleep soundly, until just before daylight, when a door slammed with a terrific crash and Sarah, startled, awoke to hear the wind roaring and a piece of loose iron slapping madly on one of the tanks. She tugged at George, and kept tugging while he grunted and mumbled incoherently for a few seconds.

"George!" she almost screamed. "Wake up."

"What's the matter?" he asked, rubbing his eyes.

"Listen," she appealed.

"Good God!" He sat upright in bed. "Sounds like a sou'easter."

They looked at each other, listening to the noise of the wind and the crash of waves on the rocks outside the river mouth.

"Are the boats all right?" Sarah asked, although she knew only too well that there was no need to worry about the boats. The look on George's face answered her real fear.

"The boats?" he gasped. "Yes. What about our two whales, though?"

"They'll be safe enough, won't they?"

"As to that," George replied miserably, "the good Lord is the only one who can answer, because he's the only one who knows how long this will last. But if you ask me . . . well, I don't like it at all. Looks as if we're in for a nasty gale—a very nasty one. Anyhow, we can't do much about it."

Neither of them slept again, and although George did not say much more, Sarah knew what was going through his mind and left him alone. She knew that if the gale lasted several days, as they usually did, the whales would come to the surface when the gases brought them up and the floating carcasses would be like derelicts at the mercy of the sea.

For three days the gale blew its hardest and the white-topped, greyish-green rollers boomed and split asunder on the rocks and the little sandy beaches around the bay, while rain pelted from misty skies. On the fourth night the rain lifted and the wind eased away, but Sarah was not as relieved as she should have been, knowing only too well that it might be a couple of days yet before those terrible seas calmed down and George would not wait so long to go out after the whales. Apart from the thought of them working on the heavy ground swell that would remain, she dreaded what might happen to the boats while crossing the bar, leaving or entering the river mouth.

"The sand-spit is just boiling mad," she said to George in the morning. "You won't go out until tomorrow, will you?"

Appreciating the cunning of woman, he parried the apparently innocent remark with male evasiveness. "Don't know," he said. "The sea might go off by this afternoon. Don't think so, though."

"George," she said firmly, "you're not going. You know very well it would be even madder than all the other mad things you've done in your life to try to cross that bar with the seas breaking like they are."

"Very well," he said, a slight trace of impatience showing. "Very well, woman, if it'll please you."

But she didn't trust him and her suspicions grew as she watched him become more and more restless all the morning. She was quite prepared for it when he got up after lunch, grabbed his hat, and announced, "We're going out."

"I suppose I can't stop you," Sarah said resignedly. "You know what I think of it, though."

"I know." He stopped at the door for a minute, taking longer than usual to tug his hat on. "Now listen to me, Sarah. We can't afford to let about a thousand quid slip away and, besides, don't you worry, we'll be quite all right."

That was the end of it. The door closed behind him. It opened about ten minutes later to admit George's mother.

"They're going out, Sarah," she said. "I saw them getting the boats ready and came across."

"Yes," Sarah almost snapped.

"He's mad. God knows his father was mad enough, but he's worse. Those seas are rolling mountains high."

"Well, what are you going to do about it?"

"Nothing, I suppose. Make a cup of tea."

Sarah got up and put a woollen jacket round her shoulders. "Not yet," she said. "Coming with me?"

They walked up behind the house and stood on the edge of the cliffs, Sarah trying to calm herself and the older woman keeping a tactful silence. Beneath them the big swell smashed on the rocks and surged away again, leaving a thick foam like beer froth. The river bar was a seething barrier. They could see the two green boats hovering inside the entrance awaiting their chance, George standing with the steer oar in the stern of one and Alex Greig, shading his vision with one hand, peering from the stern of the other. Then George's boat moved forward, racing like a streak through a break in the seas, and slowed down to keep her head just into the roll in the deeper water outside. It seemed ages before the other boat took its opportunity and joined them and the pair began to head out to sea. George saw the women standing on the cliffs and waved to them as they turned back to the house.

Sarah was alone when George returned just on dark. He took off his hat and sank quietly into a chair near the fireplace, looking at her sheepishly, almost boyishly, as he often did when something was wrong, but this time she didn't need to ask.

"You've lost them," she said softly, standing alongside him and letting her arm fall gently about his shoulder. All her anger at his foolhardiness had vanished instantly when she saw him. It was not so much the money. She was not even thinking of their financial loss now. Her main concern was George's disappointment—almost like that of a little boy fishing for tiddlers who catches a big fish and loses it at the top of the water.

"Yes," he answered, "they're gone. Lines and gear and everything. Not a damn trace of either one. We searched until the sun was going down and we had to come in to get over the bar before dark."

"Never mind, George," she tried to console him. "You'll get others."

"Of course, we will. But when? You know we're broke and I can't keep those men working indefinitely for nothing, except for what food we can give them."

"Have you spoken to the boys?"

"No, I was too disgusted to say anything to them when we came in. Anyhow they know without being told."

Sarah moved a kettle of water across to the fire and reached for the tea caddy.

"Why don't you talk to them this evening?" she suggested. "I think they would've said something before this if money meant so much to them."

"Yes, but they've been paid so far. The worry will be from this week on, when we can't pay them and there's no sign of money to come."

"Well, if you don't do anything, you'll just worry yourself to death."

Sarah was right. George ceded the wisdom of her argument and agreed to speak to the men after dinner. He saw them in the bunkhouse when by all rights his dinner should have settled, but it was still like a lump in his stomach. He didn't waste words. These men talked bluntly and liked to be treated the same way.

"I suppose you know what the loss of those two whales means?" he began. "They would've brought us in enough for a long while, but—"

"It's all right, George," Alex Greig interrupted. "The boys know and they understand. As for me, well, you don't need to be told my attitude if we're on the rocks."

"We are. That's the position exactly. I'm broke. I've got nothing and I can't pay you."

The silence lasted only a second or two, but George knew from their faces what the answer would be. It came from Charlie Roberts.

"We'll stick to you, boss," he grunted.

"Me too," Alf Gardiner said. "If we can't stick together in bad times, what's the use? I whaled with your old man and he was broke more than once. We didn't leave him."

"No damn fear," Bobbo added. "Bobbo only buy grog anyhow. No grog, no fights. We stay, boss. All us broke, too."

George smiled with the others. "I hope we won't be broke long," he said. "There has to be a turn of the tide some time and as long as we have enough to eat we can live until then. I'm going over to town tomorrow to see if I can get some credit."

"You'll get it," Alex assured him. "I'll go with you."

"Well, there's no need to tell you blokes what I think of you," George began. "I hope I can more than make it up to you."

"Never mind trying to thank them," Alex said. "They'd made up their minds when it looked a hundred to one on the gale carrying off the whales."

Next day George and Alex, with Arthur Ashby, Bobbo, Bert Penrith, and Alf Gardiner, rowed across to Eden in one of the whaleboats. Because the sea was still running fairly high, they decided to stay in town if business delayed them until dusk and they could not cross the river mouth before dark. George gave Bobbo the usual instructions as they parted in Imlay Street—no pubs and no fights.

Bobbo grinned. "No money, boss. No pubs, no fights—no choice."

"You couldn't keep out of mischief, but keep out of trouble," George retorted. "If you land in the cooler, I haven't enough to bail you out and you'll have to do time."

Bourn Davidson, a cousin, who had opened a small business in Imlay Street, seemed their best chance of getting the stores on credit, although George didn't like taking advantage of relatives. But he need not have worried.

"You'll get something soon, George," Bourn said when he heard the position. "What credit do you want?"

"Oh, just enough stores for a month or so until we get another whale."

"Good. Make out a list of what you want."

Darkness was settling round the hills when they were ready to leave, and Bobbo was nowhere to be found. Not that it made any difference because they would have to stay overnight in Eden, and Bobbo would be sure to turn up at the wharf in the morning. Jim Hopkins said he had seen Bobbo at the other end of Imlay Street with a gin from the aborigines' camp—Lucy, he thought her name was. She had been round town a lot lately with a darky named Jackie Cooper and Jackie's missus, Maria, didn't like it. If Bobbo was trying to go for Lucy, Hopkins reckoned the eternal triangle would probably become a badly buckled rectangle. George was annoyed, but beyond remarking that Bobbo should have more sense, he kept quiet, hoping fervently that if Bobbo got himself into any trouble, he did so well away from the darkie's camp at Cattle Bay and the firewater they drank there.

Everyone in town knew of George's misfortune with the two whales and he could have drowned his sorrows in ample drink had he accepted the many invitations from sympathizers, but George did not feel like drinking, even when he walked down to the School of Arts hall later to look in on the Convent Ball. Inside the door he saw Father Kenny standing with a stout, clean-shaven man and one of the town's young bloods.

"And it's ashamed of y'self you should be," Father Kenny was saying to the youth in his Irish-tinged, best reproachful voice. "If drink it has to be, then drink like a man and not like a young hooligan, and keep some spark o' respect for women, whether they be young or old, or mark my words, I'll kick you out faster than you come in here again. Be off now."

George grinned as the sullen youth shuffled away. Father Kenny, he knew, could give even the toughest man the father of a hiding with his tongue, and, if need be, could supplement it more than efficiently with his fists. Everyone, Protestant or Catholic, liked the genial Irish priest from the nearby town of Pambula. A middle-aged man, fairly stout, of dark complexion, and a bright and happy disposition, he was a familiar figure in Eden, Kiah, Towamba, and other parts of the district, which he visited in his buggy drawn by a fiery chestnut horse.

Father Kenny was usually happy and joking, but his anger knew no bounds if he sensed a wrong, even if its victim was the most bitter Orangeman. George remembered when some of the local farmers had been having a bad season and Eden storekeeper Matt O'Brien had stopped their credit and was going to summons them. Father Kenny came to town and saw Matt after he had spoken to some of the farmers on his way from Pambula.

"I hear a few of the farmers are up against it, Matt," he said.

"Eh?" Matt parried. "Oh, you mean they can't pay their bills. Yeah, that's right. But I've got to pay mine, and I can't go on giving them stuff without the coin. Who do they think I am—a damn millionaire?"

"What are they going to do, Matt?"

"I don't know," Matt retorted, "but if they don't pay up, I'm going to summons them."

"You're not," Father Kenny remonstrated with him. "And would you think, Matt, a noble action it'd be to do that? Think of those poor men with their wives and children and without anything to eat. If they could pay fines, they could pay you, but they can't, at least until they get on their feet again. What good will it do to summons them?''

''I don't care,'' Matt insisted.

''But I do and so does the good Lord,'' Father Kenny roared at him, his patience gone. ''If those people come to you, give them what they want or your backside I'll be kicking—and I'm just the man to do it, too.''

All Eden knew of the incident because it had happened in the middle of Imlay Street. Some said Father Kenny should have minded his own business, but there were few who did not admire him all the more.

The priest had caught sight of George at the hall door and turned to meet him. ''Well,'' he remarked, smiling broadly, ''if it isn't George Davidson himself. I didn't expect to see you here tonight, George. By the holy saints themselves you had bad luck with the weather, getting two beautiful big whales and then losing them.''

Peter Murphy and a couple of the good father's flock who were in the vicinity looked rather surprised by the expression, but Father Kenny didn't even notice.

''I see you've been giving one of the lads a dressing-down,'' George remarked.

''Oh, him. Just a young hoodlum who doesn't know when enough is enough. But tell me about yourself, George, and your good wife. How is she?''

''Quite well, Father.''

''You must be getting a little family round you now, though not enough to make a crew for one of the boats, I suppose?''

George laughed. ''No, not yet. Young John, the eldest, is only fourteen, you know. Then there's Roy, Jim, Effie, and young Sarah.''

''I see. Oh, by the way, George, do you know Mr Morgan?''

''No. How do you do, Mr Morgan?'' He held out his hand to the stranger who had been standing with the priest when he came in.

''Glad to know you,'' Morgan said. ''Jim Morgan is my name.''

''He's here to take over the *Propeller,*'' Father Kenny explained.

''Yes, I've bought out Larry O'Toole,'' Morgan told him. ''I'm going to rename it the *Observer* and see if I can build it up a bit.''

''Well, I wish you luck,'' George said. ''Larry did what he could to help put this place on the map and I'm sure you'll try to do the same, but it's a pretty hopeless battle.''

''I know that and you can be sure I'll do what I can,'' Morgan replied. ''By the way, Mr Davidson, I've heard a lot about you and your whalers and I was wondering if I might have the chance of going out on a chase with you one of these days. I'd like to write something firsthand for the *Observer* and probably for one of the Sydney papers."

"We'll see," George answered. "I'll keep it in mind, but remember you go at your own risk. Good night. Good night, Father."

"A most remarkable little fellow," Father Kenny said thoughtfully. "Most remarkable. Strong as a whale himself and not a fear in him. Well, Morgan, I'd better leave you and see how the ladies are getting on with the supper. You know," he added with a twinkle in his eye, "I'm getting kind of hungry myself."

When George and Alex wandered down to the wharf with their stores in the morning, they found a bedraggled Bobbo seated on a timber trolley, staring down into the water.

"Well, look who's here," Alex remarked. Bobbo sprang up and turned to face them.

"Where've you been?" George asked, eyeing him curiously. Bobbo's curly mop of hair was tousled, his shirt was torn, and his trousers were covered with mud. "Didn't I tell you to keep out of trouble? Where did you get the grog?"

Bobbo looked very sheepishly at the decking of the wharf. "Grog, boss? What grog?"

"You've been down to the camp at Cattle Bay drinking that lousy firewater. It'll rot your blasted inside out—that's what it'll do to you. And if you take my advice you'll keep away from those gins. They're no good—at least not the one you look as if you've been with all night."

"Gins, boss? Bobbo no trust any woman. What gin?"

"Oh, you know as well as I do you can't do anything in a small town like this and get away with it. Come on, anyhow, dump these stores aboard and we'll get home before we lose you again. And in case you're thinking of going over to Cattle Bay to clean up Lucy's boy friend, forget it, because we haven't got time."

Bobbo, stooping to grab a bag of provisions, straightened up again and gaped at George Davidson in amazement, but said nothing and climbed down into the boat.

"I've never seen him so flabbergasted," Alex observed. "He won't admit anything, though."

"Good for him," George said. "It's more than some of the white men round here would do."

With stores and food for a month assured, George spent most of his time with the men on South Head watching the sea for whales and keeping an eye on the killers, who would often give the first clue long before any whale spouts could be seen in the distance. Bobbo and Bullock amused themselves by fishing from the rocks and feeding the killers with some

Imlay Street, the main street of Eden, in the early 1930s. The Hotel Eden, formerly the Great Southern Hotel, where George and Sarah Davidson were married, is still there, but the town has grown with new shops and shopping arcades. Gone are the trees, which not many years ago provided shade for stray cows. Cars are parked now in the middle of the road as well as the kerbsides, and parking space is often hard to find.

—Photo by C. E. Wellings

Launching the whale boat. From left: Charlie Davidson, Albert Thomas (aboriginal), Bill Adgery, Jack Davidson, Bill Greig and George Davidson (steer oar). Note the rough and ready slipway made of tree trunks and branches.

—Photo by W. T. Hall, Eden

of the fish when they came in close. Old Tom and Hooky came every morning for their fish and made a great fuss when it was thrown to them. George used to boast that he could almost make old Tom eat out of his hand, and he could, too. The big killer whale would wait a few feet out until George threw him a fish. Then he would toss it in the air, catch it again, and play like a cat with a mouse before eating it. They had been on the lookout for only three days when George's impatience got the better of him.

"Stop feeding those killers, Bullock," he roared from the cliff. "It's time they chased up a couple of whales instead."

Back at the house, Sarah Davidson had lost her patience too. John—they called him Jack mostly now—had disappeared and had been missing since about seven o'clock that morning. It was eleven o'clock now. She could hear the faint sound of church bells battling across the bay against the stiff south-westerly breeze that had sprung up. She had wanted Jack to help her with a few things about the house. Wait until he came back, she told herself. She would give it to him. Effie had mumbled something about Jack going away into the bush with Charlie Adgery, Jnr., but became suddenly dumb when she saw the stern look on her mother's face. The stern look was still there when Sarah walked out to the tank later and saw Charlie Adgery running down the hill with Jack some distance behind.

"Come and see the big whale, missus," Charlie called to her. "Big humpy, missus."

"You wretch," she scolded him when he stopped at a discreet distance from her. "You know you're not to take Jack away into the bush."

"Come and see the whale, missus," he insisted, still eyeing her fearfully. Jack arrived and joined them.

"It's right, mum," he said. "Charlie can run faster than me and I sent him on."

"I'll give you whale with a whip if you don't stop this nonsense."

"It's true, mum," he pleaded. "Come and see for yourself, just up on the cliff at the back."

Sarah realized then that it was not merely an attempt to avert her wrath, and ran with them to the point overlooking the river bar. To her surprise she saw two big whales near the mouth of the river, but there was no sign of the boats. How the whales had got into the bay past the killers and the men on the lookout she could not imagine, unless they had worked down from the northern entrance and cut across near Cattle Bay unnoticed in the choppy waves made by the wind. She knew that whales would not spout in shallow water, that they moved along slowly, coming up quietly at intervals, and might not be seen from a distance. Anyhow, it didn't matter how they had got through the cordon. She turned to the two boys.

"Charlie, you can run faster than Jackie. Now, listen, I'll forget the whipping if you see how fast you can run to the lookout and tell the men about the whales. Go for your life."

The black boy did not need any more instructions. He was off like a flash through the bush.

"Can I go too, mum?" Jack asked.

"You certainly cannot go," he was told firmly. "You can go inside and stay in for the rest of the day, and if I catch you going off with Charlie again I'll . . . Jack, come here at once." She screamed another command for him to return, but the boy was disappearing over the hill. Fearing he was in for it already, he considered he might as well be skinned for a sheep as a lamb and if his mother kept him in all day he would miss the whale chase. Not if he could help it. He was hiding in a good vantage point when the two boats came speeding down the bay with the pack of killers and intercepted the whales near East Boyd.

Over the water in Eden other eyes had caught sight of the boats and cries of "Rusho" were echoing through the town. Father Kenny, saying Mass in St Joseph's Church, heard signs of restlessness. Then he began to hear the sound of tiptoeing feet and, turning to face the congregation before the last gospel, he saw with a start that the church contained only a few women. Without losing his composure, he faced the altar again. It made no difference, he thought. Most of them never stayed for the last gospel anyhow. He said the final prayers, entered the sacristy with slightly more dignity than usual, removed his robes with more haste than usual, and hurried off to join the excited crowd on the hillside leading down to Snug Cove.

Chapter 16

Capture of these two whales and seven more in less than three weeks ended the financial worries that had weighed so heavily on the Davidson family during the last year or so, but the whales nearly cost George and some of his men their lives and resulted indirectly in the death of poor old Cappy Russell. For all the mishaps that occurred in these troublesome weeks, the aboriginal whalers blamed the wanton slaughter of the killer, Jackson. It was only natural that the darkies should think so, bound to so many legends and superstitions about the killers. They believed that when a whaler died he was reincarnated and came back to earth as a killer in the Twofold Bay pack, many of whom even bore the names of aboriginal whalers who had passed on. Before the white folk came to Twofold Bay, the killers had hunted the grampus—a porpoiselike cetecean—and frequently ran these creatures ashore, where the blacks would feed on them, strengthened in the belief that the killers were sacred because they even provided food for their faithful.

Jackson was chasing a grampus on the afternoon he met his death. He had rounded it up in the surf off Aslam's Beach in the northern bay, out from where the little cemetery stretched back from the edge of the beach's creamy sand. Jackson dashed in too fast and too far and ran himself ashore in shallow water. He flopped about frantically, probably aware that the tide was running out fast. But it was no use. George and his crew, on their way out to inspect a buoyed whale, had been watching the chase, saw what happened, and began to row in quickly to float Jackson off. With only a light surf running, George was not worried about taking the boat in. The darkies' only fear was that they would not get there quickly enough, and they rowed like demons. But somebody else had seen Jackson's plight. George, standing in the stern of his boat, could see a man walking along the beach, and as they drew nearer to the shore he recognized Harry Silks, a fellow who had been loafing round Eden for some time, living more or less on his wits. Had it occurred to George that Silks meant to do Jackson harm, he might have saved the stranded killer. But he did not dream of what was to happen, even when Silks, seeing the boat coming, ran the last distance, stopped on the edge of the water, and began to take off his boots.

"That fellow Silks is going in after him," George remarked. "He'll never shift him."

The rowers glanced round and saw the man walking into the water towards where Jackson was still floundering. "Keep him away, boss," Arthur Ashby puffed. "We'll get Jackson off without hurting him."

"Hey," George shouted, "leave him alone. We're coming in."

Ignoring the warning, Silks waded to within a few feet of Jackson and stood looking at the killer. Suddenly, to George's horror, Silks took a big sheath knife from his belt.

"Good God!" George gasped. Then he yelled at the top of his voice, "Hey, you, leave him alone."

The rowers stopped their oars in midair and looked round just as Silks buried the knife in Jackson and darted back beyond reach of the threshing tail.

"You dirty rotten swine!" George roared furiously. "What did you do that for?"

George's anger was nothing to that of the darkies. Bobbo grabbed a spare harpoon and hurled it with a force remarkable even for him. It landed well short of Silks, who realized it was time to get going and took to his heels into the bush.

"We're going after him, boss," said Sam Haddigaddi. "We'll cut him in bits."

"Bobbo fix like island boys," the big islander growled, reaching for a small tomahawk which he often carried stuck through his belt. "Pull." He dug his oar viciously into the water and the boat slewed round. George knew these were not idle threats and the thought of Silks being carved up by the infuriated blackfellows sobered his own anger slightly.

"Lay off, Bobbo," he ordered. "You're not going ashore—none of you."

"If you don't let us ashore, boss, we'll jump over," Sam threatened.

"I'm boss here," George told them firmly. "Have some damned sense. Never mind that swine. He'll get what's coming to him. Now take her in gently . . . easy, Bobbo, easy . . . we'll see if we can do anything for poor old Jackson. That's more important."

They rowed carefully through the small breakers past where Jackson was still struggling feebly in the blood-darkened water. Arthur Ashby remarked that he was still alive, but they could all see that the end was near and nothing they could do would help Jackson now. Sam was in tears. So was Albert Thomas, who had remained grimly silent. George couldn't bear to look at Jackson's dying agonies any longer. Perhaps even more than the others, he knew they were losing a good friend, and it hurt as much as if Jackson had been human.

"Come on," he said when he could bring himself to speak again, "we've got work to do." He wanted to keep the men busy as long as possible, hoping that meanwhile Silks would have enough sense to get out of town.

But Silks was still there that evening when the news had spread, and white and black man alike would have cut his throat with the greatest of pleasure. Constable Walz went looking for Silks, satisfied that it would be wiser to get him out of the way than have to find somebody to charge with his murder.

"Why did you do it?" he asked Silks when he found him in a room at the Commercial Hotel.

"I was going to sell his skeleton to the museum in Sydney," Silks replied. "They would've paid good money for it."

"Well, I don't know," the policeman remarked. "Some people do the silliest things. Fancy killing one of those in a place like Eden. You must be mad."

"But I'm not going to take the skeleton, though."

"I shouldn't think you would," Walz told him contemptuously. "Anyhow, if you take my advice, you won't stay in Eden a minute longer than you can help, or I won't guarantee your safety. George Davidson's darkies will tear you to pieces if they get their hands on you and the same applies to plenty more wild blackfellows about the place. Get going right away. If I were you, I'd disguise myself too. I'm not joking. I'm serious."

Silks was beginning to realize that. The look on his face indicated enough. "But how?" he asked. "Where can I go tonight?"

Constable Walz walked to the door and opened it. "I don't know and I don't care," he said. "That's your problem. But, remember, if you don't go somewhere, I'll have to be disposing of your skeleton, and it won't be to the museum."

Later that night, while dark-skinned searchers were combing Eden for Silks, a scared figure was walking briskly along the road to Pambula.

George Davidson, sitting by his fireside, was writing a letter to the Eden Progress Association, suggesting that the Government be asked to protect killer whales and make it a criminal offence for anyone to harm them. Destruction of killers, he wrote, would ruin Eden's whaling industry.

Although Sam Haddigaddi and Charlie Adgery insisted that "plenty bad luck" would come of Jackson's death, and George partly believed them, he was inclined to forget their forebodings when another week brought in four more whales. One came right up to the Kiah River bar while they were deblubbering two previous catches. Within an hour it had joined its dead mates. George was in even better spirits when he received a letter from the Bank of New South Wales, advising that whalebone was bringing sixteen hundred pounds a ton on the London market and high prices were being paid for oil. The first two catches of the previous week had yielded seventeen hundredweight of bone and twenty tuns of oil.

Then things began to happen. George quarrelled with Bobbo, who had taken the dinghy and gone away to Eden one night to see Lucy. He quarrelled again when Sam left some of the whaling gear lying about the slipway, and Sam wouldn't speak to him for the rest of the day. He was still sulking next morning when they went out after a whale, leaving Alex and his crew to go on with the deblubbering job, even though it meant they were going without a pick-up boat.

Tom and his killer pack had the whale—a humpback—cornered off South Head, but it broke away and made off to sea before they could get within harpoon range, and they chased it for more than two miles before they finally got fast. Down went the humper and charged out to sea again, shaking off the killers—Tom, Stranger, Humpy, Hooky, and Cooper—like a gigantic footballer tossing aside smaller opponents in a determined rush for the goal line. The two small-fin killers, Charlie and the Kinscher, had even less chance, but the pack stuck to its prey, Tom swinging onto the flukes, Stranger and Hooky snapping at the blubber, and Charlie and the Kinscher throwing themselves over the blowhole when the whale came near the surface.

Usually the killers worked with almost military strategy, one division harrying the whale while another division waited farther out, ready to take up should the whale break free. Then the first division took the outside patrol. They seldom attacked collectively until the whale was well into the bay or, as in this case, was refusing to be turned back. Like a scientifically trained army they divided into squads, each squad relieving the other, until they had worked the whale into shallow water and there, with his back to the wall as it were, the combined force attacked him. That was what they were doing now—leaping on the whale's back, fastening to his lips to prevent him from sounding, and tearing off yards of blubber. Sometimes when the whale surfaced it cried in pain, shook itself free of its tormentors, and dived again seeking whatever escape the dark-green depths might offer. In the midst of one of these dives it turned sharply. Arthur Ashby, his eyes following every move of the rope line, saw in a split second that the whale had gone down below and swung the steer oar to whip the boat round quickly onto the same course. But one of those freak accidents happened. George was standing in the bows, the rope running between his legs, as was the usual practice. The rope caught round a bollard as the whale came up sideways, sprang like a taut bowstring let loose and, catching one of George's legs, tossed him into the air and over the side. Sam Haddigaddi and Albert Thomas sprang to free the line while the whale dashed away again with the boat in tow.

George didn't know exactly what had happened. He could only think, in the split second that such incidents usually allow for thinking, that the line must have coiled and caught his leg. More than one whaler had been dragged to his death under the sea by a harpooned whale. The weight of the whale dragging on one end of the rope and the boat on the other end would tighten a noose from which there was no escape. Perhaps the thought added to the horrible frantic sensation that ran through George as he felt himself going down for what seemed like miles. The bubbles gurgled louder and louder in his ears and he saw weird patterns of flashing lights, until it all stopped suddenly and he saw daylight, realizing with heavenly relief that there was no rope line round his leg and he had come to the surface.

Then, struggling to keep afloat while he kicked off one of his new shoes and tore off his coat, it occurred to him that there was no pick-up boat and his own boat was nearly a quarter of a mile away. But his men had cut adrift from the whale and were rowing back as fast as they could. George swam towards them, knowing it would be only a matter of minutes before he was aboard again, provided—the chilling thought flooded his mind—there were no sharks about. With this new fear gnawing at his stomach, he began to imagine that the water round him was hiding dozens of large sharks that would start to tear him to pieces at any minute. George was not one to panic, but the feeling that he was not alone grew stronger and, when he heard a swirl close by and saw a fin break surface, the shock hit him in the stomach with a thousand chills. This was it, his madly racing mind told him. One of the brutes had been hanging about like the cowards they were, waiting for the killers to finish off the whale. The blood and torn blubber often brought them for miles.

He had seen these treacherous big fish maul the carcasses of whales, had shuddred at the sight of their rows of terrible mincing teeth, their cruel, sly, ravenous eyes and had admired their sleek manoeuvrability. That was what he dreaded now. That fin was moving only slowly, but suddenly it would streak towards him and—already his nerves began to imagine the burning tear of razor-edged teeth. Then the fin rose farther out of the water and George's panic cleared enough to let him notice that it was too big for a shark's fin. It was sharp and had a round knob at the tip. It was Tom's fin. The big killer moved across and swam alongside, just keeping pace with the human swimmer, who didn't know whether he was any better or worse off than if it had been a shark.

In all the years George Davidson had been whaling, he had come to regard these killers, and Tom in particular, more or less as pet dogs, but he had only thought of them as such from a boat or on shore, never dreaming of swimming in the open sea with one as a companion. He had seen how they ripped a whale, had seen poor old Jackson deal effectively with a big shark on one occasion, and had thought he knew all about them. Now he wished he knew just one more thing—whether they would attack a man. George kept swimming. That was all he could do, apart from hope for the best. He didn't think Tom would harm him, although the self-assurance did little to allay his uneasy feelings, and while Tom watched him with one eye, George kept both eyes on Tom.

But nothing happened until George had been hauled back into the boat, and then Tom swam off to join the rest of the pack harrying the whale. George was almost speechless, even when Sam, quite recovered from his sullen unfriendliness, stripped off his flannel and gave it to him.

"By cripes, boss, we thought you was a goner," Sam said, a big grin deepening the wrinkles round his face.

"You're hurt," Arthur Ashby said. "Take that flannel off him again, Sam."

George dragged back a corner of the flannel and saw that his hip had been badly cut, evidently where the line had caught him. It was stinging too. "I didn't know," he remarked. "Had too much else to think about in the water." Then he laughed softly. "What do you think of that old devil, Tom?" he continued. "I nearly died when he came up alongside me and kept swimming there until you picked me up. He was looking out of one eye at me like Satan himself. Wouldn't touch me, though. You'd almost believe he stayed there to protect me."

"That's what he did, boss," said Charlie Roberts, and the others agreed solemnly.

"H'm," George grunted. "Well, anyhow, let's get going after that whale." They gaped at him, sitting in the bows shivering slightly. "Come on," George roared. "We're not going to let him get away."

They knew he meant what he said. Five oars churned the water and the long green boat was racing through the swell again. Less than an hour later the whale was anchored and buoyed, and down below Tom and the other killers were feasting on the tongue. As evidence of their dissecting operation, a big circle of sea had a coating of oil on the surface, making it as smooth as undulating green glass.

Sarah wanted to keep George convalescent for a while. She suggested it, knowing full well that she was wasting her breath; he refused to listen, knowing equally well that he could hardly walk. Two days later he was out after another whale, which he killed between the lookout and East Boyd. Night and day the trypots boiled on the edge of the Kiah River, the neighbouring air reeked with the putrid smell of blubber, and the oil that meant wealth to the whalers flowed into the casks. In nineteen days they had caught nine whales. George was a new man, freed from the terrible money worries that had been hanging over his head for so long.

Across the bay many had another topic for gossip when the Commonwealth Parliament put the Federal Capital Bill through both Houses. The Bill provided that the site must be within seventeen miles of Dalgety and must have an area of not less than nine hundred square miles, with access to the sea. This, everyone thought, meant that the Federal capital would be somewhere between Eden and Dalgety, and Twofold Bay would be its port.

''I told you so,'' Jim Hopkins reminded customers between flourishes of his meat chopper.

''I knew it,'' Commercial Hotel licensee, Dave Crichton, said wisely to all who mentioned the subject in his bar. ''Austin Chapman told me all along they couldn't overlook Eden. We did a good thing in electing him. He fought hard for it in the House.''

''You see,'' Cappy Russell assured the waterfront group. ''This harbour won't be able to hold all the shipping it will get in a few years.''

''It's railways we want now,'' Jim Morgan declared to a small group sitting on the edge of the footpath outside the *Observer* office. ''Link Eden up with Sydney and Melbourne, have another line going across from Bega through Queanbeyan and Yass to the Riverina districts, and the port is made. I don't think they'll do it, though. Not while Sydney business interests control politics.''

''But this is a Federal matter,'' Captain Newton argued. ''What did we get federation for? It's nothing to do with Sydney.''

''Isn't it?'' Morgan replied. ''You wait and see. Why do you think the New South Wales Government has refused to develop this part of the country ever since Ben Boyd's day?''

''I know. To keep the trade of the whole State centred on Sydney.''

''Yes. And another thing. This place is just as close to Melbourne as it is to Sydney. Work that out.''

''But,'' Captain Newton asked, ''why do they want to grab everything? It doesn't make sense to me. Sydney would be nothing without the wealth of the country behind it.''

''Listen,'' Morgan continued. ''In the first place there is no sentiment in business and those who control business are concerned with only one thing—what they can get out of it for themselves and their shareholders. They don't give a damn about the development of the country as a whole. As a matter of fact they'd rather see it not developed. Take, for instance, a big city firm making soap. Do you think it wants to see places like Bathurst, Goulburn, or Wagga with soap factories? Not on your life. I've seen city industry squeezing the very breath out of smaller concerns in the country by cutting prices in those particular areas. But wait until they've choked the smaller country industry and see how long the prices stay cut."

"But can't the Government do anything about it?" John Hopkins asked.

Morgan smiled to himself at the old fellow's credulity. "The Government is big business," he said. "Politicians smile at the people who vote for them with one side of their face and wink at their real masters with the other eye. The people might say who gets into Parliament, but the people haven't really much say about what these men do when they get there. That's one of the dangers I see in this federation. State rights will eventually be whittled away until one day the people of Queensland, Western Australia, and Tasmania wake up to the fact that the Commonwealth Government doesn't even know they exist—isn't even allowed to know by those who control politics in Sydney and Melbourne."

"They say Queensland could be one of the best States of the lot," Captain Newton remarked. "The skipper of a timber ship in here a few months ago told me they don't even know the undiscovered wealth it holds in minerals and other things waiting to be dug up. He says the country will grow anything and there's coal—plenty of it—but hardly anyone knows it's there."

"He's probably right," Morgan said. "I don't know. I've never been in Queensland. But that only goes to prove what I said a minute ago. Out of sight out of mind, and business combines and monopolies in the big cities will keep it that way."

"But these Sydney blokes you talk about," Hopkins said thoughtfully. "They can't do this forever or we'll give the rest of the country back to the blacks."

"No," Morgan replied. "It won't go on forever. Only until Sydney becomes so big and cumbersome that it contains more than half the people in New South Wales and nearly all the State's secondary industries. Then they'll have to spread some of it elsewhere."

John Hopkins got up and stretched his arms. "Better go and get the mailbags—and have one of them Sydney beers." He yawned. "Have one, Jim?"

"No thanks," Morgan replied. "I've got to write a leader—an editorial, you know."

A few weeks later, Morgan was writing another editorial with a copy of the *Sydney Morning Herald* alongside him. What he wrote was inspired by the *Herald*'s leading article, which emphasized what he had been telling everyone in Eden.

In the Eden *Observer* of 7 October 1904, the bewildered and indignant townspeople read:

> It would appear from the tone of the Sydney press that an effort is being made to alter the site of the Federal Capital from Dalgety to Lyndhurst. A leading article in the *Sydney Morning Herald* of October 1 makes no secret of the reason which inspires its advocacy of a different site from that selected. That newspaper says: ''We must, if the Dalgety site be expropriated on the lines proposed by the Act, give up an irregular slice of territory, set up at Eden a rival port to Sydney and give up not 100 but 900 square miles of the area of this State.''
>
> The cloven hoof is visible at once. ''Set up in Eden a rival port to Sydney.'' It is not the ''irregular slice of territory,'' it is not the 900 square miles but it is the fear that another port will be opened up—as it should have been 60 years ago—and so interfere with the trade of Sydney. The spirit of centralisation is still strong in Sydney, as it ever was, and there is nothing which has retarded so much the progress of this State as the successful efforts of the merchants and traders of the metropolis to attract the whole of the trade there. Why should another port not be opened up if it gives greater facilities to the people? Did the maker of the universe intend that Twofold Bay, Jervis Bay, and Port Stephens and other harbours should remain unused because they would be rivals to Sydney? The idea is outrageous.

Everyone in Eden agreed with James Morgan, though they knew they were not even the pawns in the game being played. What was the use? Letters of protest were written to Austin Chapman at Federal Parliament House in Melbourne and life round the shores of Twofold Bay went on as usual.

It had its tragedies too, just as any other little community, like the day when John Hopkins' son Henry was drowned at the wharf. Nobody knew just how it happened because Henry was alone at the time, unloading bags of wattle bark from a cart. Old John took it badly. Everyone could see that. The cheery look disappeared from his rugged face and he shook hands with a half-hearted grasp instead of the warm grip for which he had been noted. Even the way he greeted everyone with his familiar ''Good day, boy'' sounded different.

Then the whalers had another near tragedy when they got fast to a large humper which the killers had brought into the bay. When harpooned, it had decided to get out of the bay again as fast as it could, despite the equally determined efforts of the killers to stop it. They slowed the whale down a couple of miles off South Head and, when it surfaced again, George managed to lance it. Next time the whale surfaced it practically stopped, and before the speed of the boat could be checked, it was right alongside the whale and among the leaping and snapping pack of killers. George saw the huge tail going up in the air.

"Look out," he yelled. "Swing her, Arthur."

Ashby swung the steer oar smartly, but the flukes settled down across the boat, pinning George's brother Harry to the bow-oar seat. Instantly Bert Penrith jumped into the sea, followed just as promptly by Bobbo. Bullock, not so quick to dive, was caught going over the side by a slithering portion of the flukes, which pinned one of his legs to the gunwale, leaving half of the big Swede wriggling in the boat and the other half gurgling in the water.

While George was working frantically to release his brother, the massive barnacle-encrusted tail moved again, releasing Bullock, who dived for the depths. But, before George could push Harry overboard and get clear himself, the great flukes came down again heavily on the boat, hitting George across the back with a glancing blow which was sufficient to knock him, almost unconscious, up into the thigh-boards. Dazed, he lay there while the whale drew clear and tried to sound, but the killers forced it up again almost immediately, and it broke surface with its head within about a foot of the boat. George saw the whale looking at him through a blurred mist. He moved and shuddered at the pain it caused. His groping right hand found the lance and hurled it towards the dark bulk before everything about him blacked out.

He must have recovered his senses very quickly, because he came to just as the men who had gone overboard swam back and climbed aboard. The boat, he realized with some surprise, was still afloat, although the oars were missing. About fifty yards away, the dying whale was kicking feebly, surrounded by the tearing pack of killers, and coming towards them with the giant strides of its five oars was Alex Greig's pick-up boat.

"We're all right," George called to them. "Get that whale fixed."

George soon became aware that he was far from all right. His back felt as if it was broken. He was so sick he feared he would vomit any minute and he had to lie down on the floorboards before they turned for home.

Sarah was very distressed when she saw the men carrying him up to the house. Try as she would, she could never disregard the awful dread that some day they would carry him from the boat for the last time, and although George's mother tried to reassure her by saying that there were no bones broken, she knew he was badly hurt.

"This time he's not going out again," she said firmly. "Take him in and get him into bed, Alex."

"There's nothing wrong with me, Sarah," he pleaded.

"There will be unless you stay in bed for a while instead of running out and trying to kill yourself all the time."

George grinned. "Look at the money we're making," he taunted. "You can buy another new dress next week—two or three if you want them."

"Yes, all very nice, I'm sure. But I don't want to have to buy a black one. How did all this happen?"

"Oh, missus, big feller humpy go *bong-bong* with his tail *whack-whack* along boat," Bobbo hastened to explain, demonstrating with the palm of his hand. "We dive and swim. Big feller whale go *bong-bong* again, hit boss and—"

"Never mind," she snapped, trying to suppress a grin. "Get feller boss inside."

George was laid up for three weeks, and Sarah saw to it that he did not stir outside. But she couldn't watch him all the time and the inevitable happened one day when she went over to his mother's house. Archer Davidson and Sam Haddigaddi came in and said the killers had a whale off East Boyd.

"Well, what are you waiting for?" George said. "Why don't you get going?"

"We can't go without you, boss," Sam answered.

"What damned rot! Archer can take charge, or Alex. Where's Alex?"

"He's getting a boat ready," Archer replied. "The boys won't go without you, though."

"That's right, boss," Sam added.

"But I can't go. I don't think I could walk, or even sit up and, besides, the missus would be worried to death. I promised her not to go in the boat again until I'm better."

"Well, we won't go," Sam insisted.

George yielded to the temptation. "Quick," he said. "Get me out of bed before the missus comes back."

They trussed him up, carried him down to the boat and sat him on the bow seat. "Bring that thing, Sam," he called out, pointing to a whale-gun inside the door of the shed. "It's loaded, isn't it?"

"Think so, boss."

"Right. Hurry up and shove off."

George sat staring at the whale-gun while they rowed out over the bar. Heavy, clumsy things like miniature cannons, these guns had to be held up by two strong hands and the recoil when they were fired was terrific. The killers didn't like them either and that was the main reason why George always used the harpoon and the lance.

"Give me the gun and I'll have a shot at him," he said when they drew near the whale. He waited until the killers left a clear space and pulled the trigger.

Boom! The bomb broke the whale's back and the recoil of the gun nearly did the same to George. He dropped the cumbersome weapon and grabbed the edge of the gunwale, holding on tightly while the pain seemed to tear at his back like red-hot knives. The killers had disappeared with the explosion, but the whale, which had stayed on the surface, kept moving slowly backwards, evidently crippled and unable to swim ahead. George reckoned that it could not swing its tail at them either, so they went alongside, and he kept lancing until the whale was dead.

"Come on," he said. "Let's get home. I don't know what the missus is going to say."

Chapter 17

At the end of the whaling season, George's boat crews left for their summer occupations. Most of them were turning now to sleeper-cutting—an industry that was expanding rapidly with the demand for the high-quality sleepers from the big timber forests in the Eden district. It was becoming a common sight to see up to two thousand of these sleepers stacked on the wharf for shipment to Sydney.

Rumours that alluvial gold had been found on the Timbillica River near Mount Imlay seemed likely to cause a second Kiandra rush from Eden just after Christmas of that year. The story was that an old fellow named Bill Lang, who had been timber-cutting near Mount Imlay, had brought a quantity of gold into Towamba, but with a shrewdness that was not surprising he was keeping a very close mouth as to where he had found it. When a party from Lowamba dashed out to seach for themselves, they found Lang's camp, and although they could see where he had been prospecting nearby, they could not find a trace of gold in the working. Within a week dozens of fortune-hunters were prospecting about the mountain and in Eden dozens more were waiting to see what they would find.

John Hopkins, arguing with the Saturday afternoon crowd outside the Commercial Hotel, offered to bet "an even two quid" that nothing would come of Lang's gold discovery. Sucking his pipe fiercely, he recalled that somewhere way back about the sixties, an Auckland syndicate had sent out a party to prospect "them hills" and wasted its money. "Of course I'm not saying they didn't find gold, mind you," he said cautiously. "They found it all right, but not in payable quantities, and that's what counts."

"Old George Weston tells me different fellows have been prospecting in that locality for years," Constable Walz remarked.

"Yes, that's right, boy," Hopkins paused for a moment to continue puffing in an unequal battle with his pipe, which seemed doomed to go out at any minute. "I'll tell you where and then see if you don't agree with what I've been saying. It may be a—what do you call it—one of them coincidences, but the place is about three miles below the locality on Boggy Creek known as Skiter's Flat.''

The old mailman roared at his own joke until he had to cut it short to curse his pipe and borrow a match with which to get it going again. Cappy Russell was in the group when he looked up again.

''Good day, boy,'' Hopkins greeted him. ''You haven't got gold fever too I hope.''

''Who, me? On this prospecting business? No, not on your life. Out there in those hills all night with wild dingoes and snakes and things? Mind you it's not as how I'm scared, but—''

''Not much,'' John Hopkins' son Jim drawled from behind a veranda post.

''Is that so?'' Cappy retorted. ''Well, anyhow I think a gentleman of my standing in the community can afford to ignore a remark like that, and seein' as how I know the motives behind it—sheer jealousy—it doesn't matter a damn to me, Jim Hopkins. I'll say, though, that I'm as game as any man here. It's just that I don't like those things. Give me the sea any day and you can have your bush and them dingoes and snakes.''

''I see you've been painting your yacht, Cappy,'' Walz interposed, knowing that the old fellow would be more than delighted to change the subject and talk about his boat. ''She looks pretty good.''

''The niftiest craft they've ever seen in Eden,'' Cappy agreed. ''Of course, I haven't got her looking just the way I want yet, but give me time.''

''She sails well, judging by the way she was beating up into that nor'easter when I saw her outside the other day,'' John Hopkins remarked.

''Sails well?'' Cappy repeated. ''She'll show anything her own size I've seen two or three knots. I'm going to put her in an ocean race.''

Jim Hopkins pushed his hat back farther on his head and blinked hard. ''What ocean race?'' he asked.

''Oh, there's ocean races. Never you mind.''

As John Hopkins had predicted, the Mount Imlay gold rush fizzled out and the weather became the principal topic of conversation again.

Autumn was already turning to the first stages of winter when George's crews began to leave the timber camps and wander back to the whaling station. Alex Greig, too, was keen to start, especially after a big shark convinced him that whaling was no more dangerous than fishing. Alex had been fishing in the bay from a skiff when, he claimed, one of the biggest sharks he had ever seen in his life made a rush for his hand, which was resting on the gunwale of the boat. Luckily he saw the shark coming and drew back just as its charge nearly upset the craft. Alex decided to get going and started to haul up the kellick as fast as he could, but the shark charged that, missed, and again crashed into the boat. By this time Alex was quite annoyed, so he rowed ashore and came back with a boat spade and a shark line, determined to give the scavenger something to think about, but it had disappeared.

"The swine of a thing must've been at least eighteen feet long," he told George and a grinning bunch of darkies. "It's coming to something when a man can't go out and catch himself a few fish without his boat becoming a target for mad sharks."

"Better stay ashore for a while," Arthur Ashby suggested. "That's probably the one they've seen hanging about the wharf lately."

"Stay ashore?" Alex roared. "What the hell do you think I am?"

"Well, there'll be no more time for fishing anyhow," George said. "We'll get the boats ready and start the lookouts again. The killers should be back any day now."

The killers came back about a week later—at night—and celebrated their return for the season by hunting a whale into the bay. It was one of those clear moonlit nights and the air was so still that the whalers, sitting yarning on the steps of the bunkhouse, heard the killers snorting out in the bay like a herd of horses and were grabbing their coats before two or three of the killer pack started to floptail about at the entrance to the river. Down the slope they ran, through the little orchard, Bert Penrith as usual pulling on his trousers as he hobbled in the wake of the crowd, and Sarah screaming to them to mind her geraniums. They probably didn't even hear her. She stood looking down towards the river until she heard the squeak of rowlocks and the plop of oars. Then she heard young Sarah crying and went to attend to her.

Outside the river bar three killers were waiting to pilot the boats, which raced across the bay to where the main killer pack was tearing at the whale near the cliffs under the lighthouse.

"He's going some," Alex shouted across the space between the two boats.

"Looks like they're not holding him either," George called back. I'll keep after him, Alex, and you go down near the wharf in case he breaks through."

The boats parted, George heading for the sounds of conflict and Alex steering towards the wharf. But the chase moved fast and George was still trailing his quarry when it and the killers thrashed a phosphorescent path round the point into Snug Cove, where Alex's boat was waiting to intercept.

" 'Struth!" Darky Whitty gulped. "What is it? Greased lightning?"

"Never mind," Alex commanded. "Give it to her. Wake up, Roger." He was addressing Roger Whelan, son of their former opponent, who had signed on with them the previous week.

The boat shot forward, aimed for the area beyond the end of the wharf, where, Alex estimated, they might get the chance of a shot. They might have, too, had not the wharf intervened. Suddenly there was a rending crash and splintering of wood as the water at the end of the wharf went up like a silver volcano in the moonlight. The rowers stopped and sat gaping.

"Good God!" Alex remarked. "He's hit the wharf and taken one of the big crosspieces underneath clean out."

"I don't like the look of this one at all," Archer Davidson said. "He's too lively altogether for—'Struth Almighty—"

A noise almost like a bomb explosion drowned Archer's half-finished sentence. The maddened whale had careered across from the wharf and rammed Cappy Russell's yacht. They could see the gaping hole in the yacht's planking as she turned on her side and went down like a stone.

"My God!" Alex muttered. "Cappy's boat."

"Let's get out of this," Roger Whelan suggested. "That mad thing is likely to do anything. We'll be next."

"No, we won't," Alex said. "Come on. The killers are driving him up on the beach. He must be pretty stunned after those two whacks."

When George and his crew arrived, Alex had lanced the whale and it was nearly dead.

"A finback," George gasped. "No wonder it travelled so fast. I knew a humper wouldn't go like that."

"Yeah," Alex agreed. "I suppose you heard him hit the end of the wharf and Cappy's boat."

"Cappy's boat? That's what it was?"

"Look at it, or rather what's left."

George shuddered as he looked. All they could see of the yacht was the top of her mast sticking out of the water. "We thought it was you blokes at first."

"Only damn luck it wasn't," Archer remarked. "We'd have gone through the wharf with him if we'd been in tow."

The crowd of spectators on the beach was growing, and Jim Hopkins and Bill Holden, who had rushed out of the Pier Hotel to watch the drama, were telling latecomers what had happened.

"One of the nastiest whales I ever knew of," Jim was saying. "A finback, of course. They're all like that. Must be about eighty feet this one, although that's about their average size."

"Where's Cappy?" Holden remarked. "He'll die when he sees what's happened to his lovely boat."

Jim Hopkins shook his head sadly. "He won't put her in any ocean race now," he said.

Poor Cappy. He was nearly in a state of collapse when he reached the wharf and stood looking miserably at the top of the mast. Then he pulled himself together and raced down to the beach.

"You blasted fiends," he wailed, shaking his fist under George Davidson's nose. "You did this on purpose . . . I'll have the law on you . . . I'll make you pay . . . I'll . . . "

"Calm down, Cappy," Bill Holden restrained him. "They couldn't help it. They weren't even fast to the whale. The killers chased it into the bay and made it hit the wharf and your boat. You can sue the killers if you like. Sue Tom and Stranger. They probably did it."

"It's no joke," Cappy fumed. "If you think it is, Bill Holden, I'll take you—"

"I don't think it's a joke. I'm only trying to make you act sensibly about an accident that's happened—an act of God, you might say."

"An act of these lunatics," the old fellow roared. "They were chasing the whale, weren't they?"

"Cappy, listen," George pleaded. "We didn't even get near the whale and didn't touch it until the killers had it stranded on the beach here. How could we help it running into your yacht?"

Holden went over to the hotel and came back with a stiff rum for Cappy, and gradually they quietened the old fellow, but it was useless trying to lift him from the black depression that had settled on him.

"We'd better come and get the carcass tomorrow," George told Alex. "No good trying to tow it across tonight."

"Take it to hell with you," Cappy moaned. "Get it out of my sight. If it's there when I come down tomorrow, I'll put a charge under it and blow it up."

It was no use staying any longer, sorry as they were for what had happened. The whaleboats shoved off and gradually faded into the pale light over the bay, the crowd dwindled away, and Cappy, refusing to be comforted or helped in any way, sat in solitary misery on the beach, staring at all he could see of his beloved yacht.

The whalers arrived early next morning. George was not worried by Cappy's threat, even if he thought an explosive charge could have done much harm to the dead whale, but he knew it would take four hours of hard towing to get the carcass across the three miles of water to the Kiah River and they might as well start early. They were halfway across when the tow lines jerked and the boat began to slew round, and as the whalers looked, they saw a huge shark grabbing the whale's flukes. The shark tugged at the whale until it had dragged the boat in a complete turnabout. Ashby stood up and looked over the side.

"He's a terrific size," he gasped.

"Not an inch under twenty-two feet I'd reckon," Penrith said in an awed tone, pushing his hat rim up while he stared as if fascinated at the big shark, which, on the other hand, seemed to be taking little notice of them while it tried to drag the carcass away.

"That's the one I saw the other day I'll swear," said Alex Greig. "He's got the same ugly look on his dial."

"You said that one was only eighteen feet," Bullock challenged. "This one is easily twenty-two."

"I tell you it's the same one," Alex insisted. "I'd know him again anywhere, I tell you."

"You must be just about on speaking terms with the bloke by now," George suggested. "Tell him to lay off our whale."

Alex laughed with the rest, swung the steer oar, and brought it down hard with the flat side on the water. Like a flash the shark interrupted his mauling and darted away, but just as quickly he was back again.

"Come on," George directed. "Stop playing with the damn thing or it'll drag us all over the bay and chew every bit of blubber off that carcass. Take us alongside, near the tail. Easy . . . not too close."

"A couple of strokes just to give us steering way," Alex told the men quietly, hoping that they would certainly not get too close and the shark would clear off, but it had tasted the blubber and was munching it with relish, ripping out large hunks with each snap of its jaws. As the oars bit the water, the shark tugged fiercely at the carcass, dragging it and himself right alongside the boat.

Wide-eyed, the crew gaped at the big fin and high tail of the shark, whose body seemed to stretch for most of the whaleboat's thirty-foot length. His tail was near where Alex was standing at the steer oar and his nose was opposite where George was leaning on the thigh-board for'ard. But only for a second or two. George's eyes had narrowed, and instead of gaping like the others he was thinking quickly. He grabbed a boat spade, and almost in the same action with which he picked it up, drove the razor-edged blade across the back of the shark's neck like an axe. Blood spurted through the water as the shark dived, breaking the boat-spade handle against the gunwale, and the men looking over the side saw the writhing monster going down into the opaqueness of the dark-green depths.

They chaffed George and his boys all along Imlay Street, when the whalers went over to town on Friday, and with total irreverence towards the fate of Cappy's yacht, some groups joked freely about finback whales. Dave Crichton was laughing with Bill Holden when George and Alex went into the Commercial Hotel.

"Hullo," he greeted them, "the finbackers come to town."

"What, no excitement around the bay this afternoon?" Holden added. "No sharks, Alex?"

"No. Only one or two we've seen in town. Anyhow, what are you doing drinking up here? Out of your territory a bit, aren't you?''

''Maybe I am, but it's safer these days, I reckon. I said to the boss this morning, 'The job's not worth it,' I said, and that's quite right. A man never knows when he's risking his life working in the Pier Hotel with you and those wild blackfellers chasing finbacks through the wharf and smashing up people's boats. Last night, so 'elp me, I didn't sleep. Next thing, I kept thinking, they'll be driving one of them right through the pub. So the boss says to me this morning, 'Bill,' he says, 'you're getting a bit shaky on it; you're worryin' too much. Go up the road and hit yourself with a few grogs at Dave Crichton's.' That's what he said and here I am. But despite the worry you've caused me I'm ready to shout.''

''Thanks,'' George said. ''We don't mind if you do. How's Cappy? How's he taking things?''

''Oh, no good. The old boy's pretty cut up about it all. And to make things worse, the yacht wasn't insured. I haven't seen him since the day before yesterday when he was talking about getting a bullock team to drag it up on the beach to repair the planking. It's pretty tough on him, I suppose. He thought so much of that boat.''

''Yeah,'' they agreed and gave silent attention for a minute to taking the froth off their beer.

''To get back to these finbacks,'' Dave Crichton resumed. ''We were laughing about that when you came in.''

''Laughing about what?'' Alex asked.

''Have you seen the *Observer* yet?''

''No. Why?''

''Well, listen to this.'' Crichton picked up the paper from under the counter and adjusted his glasses. ''It's written, so it says, by a correspondent of *Chambers' Journal* who has had considerable whaling experience in the southern hemisphere. Listen: 'The loose finback is never attacked by boats. He is too dangerous for he will take out nearly 1000 yards of line and yet not abate his speed. On rare occasions finbacks have been killed by boats. Their layer of blubber is thin and the plates of baleen (owing to its shortness) would not be worth more than £300 a ton. At Twofold Bay (N.S.W.) there is a shore whaling station which maintains itself principally by finbacking. As the pods or parties of finbacks cross the bay on their way northwards, they are assailed by droves of killers (minor toothed whales) and these extraordinary creatures actually seize the monstrous finbacks, worry them as a fox terrier will a rat, and thus enable the boats to come up and despatch them with a bomb. No whaleman, however, ever hurts a killer. He is the whaleman's friend.' And then there is this bit in brackets, 'Finback whales are not, as stated above, sought in Twofold Bay. Ed. *Observer*.' ''

George and Alex, who had been grinning as they listened, burst out laughing. "Well, I'm blowed," George said. "Morgan must be hard up for stuff to put in that damn paper. What rot! What does he say—'despatch them with a bomb'? I guarantee he's never seen a finback in his life. Wait till I see Morgan."

"Not worth worrying about," Alex remarked. "Fill 'em up again, Dave."

"You know," George said, "we did get fast to a finback once—some years before my father died—and what a time it gave them. I wasn't in the boat, but Charlie Adgery reckons it went so fast he could see stars."

"Wouldn't be surprised what Charlie saw, particularly with a few grogs in," Holden commented.

"Well, the old man had opposition here at the time and that's probably why he did it. The killers bailed this finback up against the rocks near Cattle Bay, and our blokes thought they had him cornered, but as soon as they hit him, he turned and went off like a rocket and nearly swamped the boat with the pace he was doing. It ended up with the whale being driven ashore by the killers near the wharf, strangely enough, almost in the same place as they beached the one that hit Cappy's boat."

"Well, it's just as I said," Holden observed. "They're getting closer to the pub every time."

George bought another drink and they turned to go. "By the way," he said, pausing at the door, "have you seen John Hopkins about today?"

"John Hopkins?" Crichton answered. "Didn't you know? He went to Sydney yesterday by the *Wakatipu* to have an operation. Pretty serious, they say. He's cracked up badly since Henry was drowned."

"Oh, I'm sorry to hear that. Well, good day."

"I didn't like the look of Hopkins," Crichton remarked when the other two had gone. "These operations are not always a success and, besides, John must be close to sixty-five now."

"He is," Holden said. "He told me the other week he was sixty-five."

George and Alex met Cappy on the slope near the wharf. The old fellow greeted them quite cordially, though obviously he was feeling very miserable.

"I'm going to try to get the yacht up on the beach at high tide tomorrow," he told them. "I got a fellow—one of these timber haulers—with a team of bullocks. As long as we can drag her up past high-water mark it'll do. The keel is the only trouble, but I think she'll come up on her side. It's all good sand bottom. I've got a darky who's going to dive down to undo the mooring and fix the hauling ropes."

Alex thought of the big shark, but wisely refrained from mentioning the subject. "We're terribly sorry, Cappy," he said. "We wouldn't have had it happen for the world. You know that."

"Yes," the old fellow said, "I know that, and I know I was a bit unreasonable the other night, but you can appreciate it was a terrible shock to me. She took nearly every penny I had, that boat did. Still, never mind. These things happen."

"If there's anything we can do, just let us know," George offered.

"Yes, yes. It's very good of you, but it's too far to come across when I can get plenty of others who are handy to the wharf. Besides, the bullock team will do the work."

The bullocks did the work well enough when they were harnessed to the yacht at high tide next morning, and gradually the hull followed the mast out of the water, sliding on its starboard beam, the hole in the other side gaping at an angle skywards. Then the bullocks began to strain at the ropes as the yacht became more and more dead weight, and even with the help of the dozen or so aborigines Cappy had brought from the Cattle Bay camp, the haul slowed down and stopped.

"Give 'em a spell, Harry," Cappy called to the bullock driver, Harry Stevens. "She's got too much water in her. We'll turn her over on the port side and let it run out before we try to drag her any farther up on the beach."

Drained of most of the water that had been making her so heavy, the yacht began to move again and kept going until the keel started to burrow into the sand, and once more the bullocks were straining. Cappy was standing near the front of the boat yelling to Stevens to ease off, when there was a cracking sound not unlike the sound of Stevens' stock-whip, and Cappy rolled on the sand, moaning and clutching his left leg in both hands. One of the ropes had broken and, released like a catapult, had hit Cappy's knee.

Stevens stopped his bullocks and rushed to Cappy's assistance with a few onlookers from the wharf, but they could not get him on his feet. Every time his left foot touched the ground he nearly screamed with pain. The leg seemed to have lost all power and the knee was badly swollen. There was only one thing to do. Two men carried him home while another went for the doctor. That night everyone in Eden knew that Cappy Russell had smashed his kneecap and was more or less crippled. If he got about at all it would have to be on crutches. But not everybody knew that in addition to a broken kneecap he also had what amounted to a broken heart, and as the weeks passed, Cappy gradually lost interest in everything about him—even lost the will to live.

He must have known that he would never be able to repair his yacht now and would never be able to sail her again. No doubt that was why he spent hours brooding, sitting on his veranda, looking out across the sea. Perhaps that was what made him hobble down to the beach one night and set the yacht alight where she lay on the water's edge. Cappy was squatting on the sand, silhouetted eerily against the background of the yacht's blazing skeleton, when people began to flock to the beach to see what the fire was about.

"She's mine and I can do what I like with her," was all he would say. But he called Bill Holden over when the fire had died down and most of the onlookers were wandering off. "They probably think I'm mad, Bill," he said. "I'm not, though. I just know I'm finished, so what's the use of leaving her there to be in everyone's road?"

Holden picked him up and took his arm. "Come on, Cappy," he said, "I'll take you home."

A couple of weeks later Cappy Russell was dead. When Jim Hopkins came into the hotel for a drink and told Holden, the barman filled another glass.

"I'll have one with you, Jim," he said solemnly. "To a fine old bloke, who'll still be a gentleman of standing in the community he's gone to now."

Outside on the little beach the waves were lapping the charred keel and fragments of ribs of a yacht, and up on the hill beyond, screaming sea gulls hovered overhead while Captain Newton lowered the flag at the lighthouse to half-mast.

Chapter 18

Autumn came again, and as the leaves on the trees in the Davidson orchard turned from yellow to golden-brown, the westerly winds curled round the sides of Mount Imlay and sent the leaves fluttering to the shivering grass. Everything pointed to an early winter, particularly when the killers arrived in Leatherjacket Bay weeks before their normal time of returning from the Antarctic, indicating that the whales were already on their northward trek. There arrived in the bay, too, a small steamer named *Jenny Lind,* in charge of a typical seafaring type who introduced himself as Captain Young and told those who asked about the two whale-boats on the ship's deck that he had come to Eden to get a whale.

"He's come to Eden to get a whale, has he?" George Davidson said when he heard the news from a local fisherman who was passing the Kiah mouth. "H'm, we'll see. If there's any whales to be caught round here, I'll catch them."

"Is that so?" Sarah remarked when George told her. "I've been wondering what that funny-looking ship was doing in here. She doesn't look like a whaling ship and, besides, this fellow says he wants only one whale. What does he want one for?"

"Don't know until I go over to town tomorrow and find out. But if he's only pretending in the hope that I'll buy him off, he's got another think coming. I'm sick of buying out people who get an idea they'd like to amuse themselves by catching whales."

George went over to Eden next day in a slightly aggressive frame of mind, despite Sarah's reminder that he did not own Twofold Bay and the adjacent ocean. As he drew alongside the *Jenny Lind,* he glared at the man who greeted him and at his crew looking over the side, glared at one of the whaleboats, and then back at the man again.

"Where's the skipper?" he demanded.

"Gone up to town," the fellow replied. "You Mr Davidson?"

"Yes."

"Glad to meet you. Jones is my name. I'm mate. Cap'n Young was talking about goin' over to see you, but if you're goin' up town you'll probably bump into him—most likely at the Commercial Hotel. That's where he said he was goin'."

"Thanks," George said. "I might see him."

They beached the boat near the wharf and headed up the hill towards the hotel, George and Alex walking in front, followed by Bobbo, Bullock, and Bert Penrith. It was no coincidence that Bobbo and Bullock were in the party. George remembered occasions in his youth when similar discussions with crews of visiting deep-sea whaling ships had led to fierce scuffles. Not that he expected anything like that to happen now. But, if it did, Bobbo and Bullock would be handy support. Entering the hotel, George held open the swing-door to allow Bullock's huge frame to tower in the aperture behind him and Bobbo's tousled curls to block what space was left.

"Well, good day," Dave Crichton greeted them. "Haven't seen you blokes for a week or two."

"We've been about," Alex said casually.

"Come over here, George," the publican invited. "You too, Alex, and the boys. I want you to meet Captain Young. Captain this is George Davidson—the man you've heard so much about—Alex Greig, Bert Penrith, Bullock, and Bobbo."

"Pleased to meet all of you," Young responded, shaking hands all round. "And this here is Bill Freeman, second mate of the *Jenny Lind*."

George surveyed the stocky little captain and the tall, well-built fellow with him. Young was one of those red-faced, cheery types with twinkling eyes. His slightly booming voice conveyed an impression of sincerity.

"I hear you came down here to get a whale," George began.

Young threw back his head and laughed. "Pour us a round of drinks, Mr Crichton, with one for yourself," he said, unfolding a pound note on the counter. "Yes, that's right. They tell me, though, that you're not very fond of opposition, so I thought I'd like to have a talk with you."

"Well, that's good of you, but what do you want me to do? Here, Bobbo, none of that damned rum. Give him beer, Dave."

Bobbo, crestfallen, watched Crichton replace the rum bottle on the shelf. "Too cold for beer, boss," Bobbo grumbled. "One rum won't hurt Bobbo."

"No," George snapped, and turned back to face Young, who was watching with keen interest how this little fellow subdued the big islander. "What do you want a whale for?" George asked.

"Well, I suppose it does sound strange, but I'll tell you why. A syndicate has engaged me to get one for exhibition purposes. They think they can make a bit of money by putting a whale on show in Sydney."

"They'll have to make their money quickly, before the thing goes rotten."

"No doubt. But that'll be their worry. My job is only to catch one, and that's where you come into it. I want you to give me a fair go."

"I'll give you a fair go, if that's all you want," George agreed. "Provided, of course, you clear out after you get your whale. I'll tell you what I'll do. If one whale comes along, you'll have to get it—if you can. If two whales come, we'll take one apiece and I'll help you take yours, on the condition I've mentioned already, that it's only for one catch. When you get that you clear out."

"Let's drink to it," Young suggested. "The deal is made."

"Yeah," Crichton remarked, "the deal is made. But there's one thing you've forgotten."

"What's that?" Young asked.

Crichton lit a cigarette, and with the breath that expelled the smoke replied, "The killers."

"The killers? What about them?"

"Well, they're funny things and it's just occurred to me that they mightn't work for you like they do for George. You see, captain, George has them killers trained like hunting dogs and every dog knows its own master, as the saying goes."

"What rot!" Young roared with laughter. "Killers ain't like dogs. Come on, Mr Crichton. Cut out the fairy yarns and get us another round."

"He might be right, captain," said George, who had caught an almost imperceptible gleam in the publican's glance as he turned to fill the glasses. Alex had seen it too.

"You never know," he said. "Dave might be right. You'd better hope for two whales to come along, so that you can have one according to the deal."

"It's pretty hard work without the killers," Penrith added.

"Ah, rubbish," Young retorted good-humouredly.

"No rubbish about it," Crichton came back. "Listen, I'll tell you a story that'll give you some idea what you're up against, but bear in mind what I'm going to tell you first. Now these killers make their home here during the whaling season in Leatherjacket Bay—Killer Bay, some call it—just outside South Head, and sometimes whales have been anchored and buoyed there after they were killed. Well, the snapper come round the carcasses very thick, you see, captain, and all the old hands about here do a spot of fishing. Snapper—they get dozens of big beauties. But they're not game to put the kellick over. No fear, they're not. I'll tell you for why. It's because the killers would get the kellick rope in their mouths and tow the boat out to sea at a pace too fast to be comfortable."

Young laughed again.

"It's right what I'm telling you," Crichton insisted. "Now some say it's only that the killers amuse themselves and have a bit of fun—they're very playful devils, of course—and others reckon that the killers resent the intrusion of strangers into their domain, but whatever it is they'll soon shift anyone who anchors there to fish. Right. Now we come to the main part of the story. Some years ago George had opposition here, and one of the opposition boats was beating his boat to a whale a mile or two out from the lighthouse and it looked as if George's boat would never gain on them. Well, the killers seemed to realize this and several of them kept swimming back to George's boat as if trying to urge him on while others lashed the water in front of the opposition boat, trying to stop it.'' Crichton paused to blow a cloud of smoke to the ceiling and saw with obvious satisfaction that he had them all interested. ''It was then that George decided to try an experiment,'' he continued. ''Remembering the habits of the killers with fishermen's kellick ropes, he threw the painter over the bows of the boat. Instantly—'' Crichton's head jerked emphatically in a half-upward nod and his open palm slapped the bar counter—''the rope was grabbed by two of the killers, who took it in their mouths tandem-fashion and raced away towards the whale, passing the opposition boat like it was becalmed almost. Then, when they were about fifty yards from the whale, which was being harried by other killers, these two let go the rope and swam back to help their mates intercept the opposition boat, just to make sure. There's no need to tell you George got the whale, and that's what you're up against, captain.''

There was a split second of silence, during which Bobbo gaped at the publican with wide-open eyes, Bullock looked bored, George, Alex, and Penrith tried to keep straight faces, and Crichton gazed poker-faced at Young and his second mate. Then the grin that had been expanding on Young's face burst into another peal of laughter and they all joined in.

''Well, I've heard some pretty tall stories about these Eden killers, but that's the best yet,'' Freeman commented. ''I believe they're pretty near that good, though.''

''Pretty near,'' George told him. ''Although Dave ought to have more damn sense.''

''Why?'' Crichton was still laughing.

''Because one of these days someone will believe your silly yarns and make a complete joke of us in Sydney.''

''But you've told me yourself that Tom and Stranger grabbed a rope one day. Didn't he, Alex? I remember the day well. You were in here with him and Jim Hopkins.''

''I told you they were a bit frisky and Tom got the line caught under his fin when we were fast to a whale. That's nothing.''

"No, but all jokes aside, I'll tell you what actually did happen," Alex said. "We rarely ever use a gun on whales because the killers don't like the noise. Well, an opposition crowd here at one time used a gun on a whale at close range with the killers all around it, and George was so wild about it that he told them the killers wouldn't help them with the next whale. They bet him on it and the bet was taken. Next day two whales were sighted and we went after one while the opposition went after the other, but the killers stayed with our boat and our whale, which we killed. The other crowd lost their whale—couldn't get near it. You can believe that or not, but it happened, although it might have been only coincidence. I'll tell you what I do think, though. Our boats have always been painted green and these killers are so smart in many ways that it would be quite possible they know the green boats and stick to old friends. We treat them like old friends, captain, which is another thing to remember. Don't let any of your men hurt a killer, or we won't be responsible for what happens."

"I wouldn't have anything happen to them for the world," Young replied. "But just for fun, I'd like to bet you, Davidson, that the killers will help me."

"Very well," George said, grinning. "What do you suggest?"

"A five of beer and a bottle of whisky," Crichton, always with an eye to business, cut in.

"Right. Do you, Davidson?"

"Do me."

"Getting rather reckless with fives of beer these days, aren't you, George?"

"Charlie Harris. Good day." George introduced the newcomer who had interrupted. "Charlie is captain of the Eden cricket team," he explained. "We're playing them next week and I've bet him a five on the result of the game. There's great rivalry between the whalers and the town players, although these blokes have the edge on us because they get a lot more practice."

"This match is one of the big events of the year, captain," Harris said. "You'd almost think it was an England-Australia test-match."

"I hear this new fellow, Cook, is a pretty good bowler," Alex remarked.

Harris nodded. "Yes. He's played a bit in Sydney. Bowls a very fast ball. He got eight wickets for us against Pambula last week."

"Doesn't worry us," George said. "Well, we must be getting along to pick up our stores. See you again, captain."

"Best of luck. I'll be looking for you on the high seas."

''Not a bad sort of a bloke,'' Alex remarked when they were walking down Imlay Street.

''Not bad,'' George agreed. ''I don't think he knows much about whaling, though.''

The scratch crew. After George Davidson ceased regular whaling activities, there was still no shortage of willing hands ready to help George man a boat for a whale chase. This group went after a humpback that came into Twofold Bay in 1928, and comprised (from bow to stern) George Davidson (who had just lanced the whale), Eric Turnbull, Bill Warren, Jim Hopkins, Laurie Williams and Jim Davidson.

–Photo by A. G. Tooth

Chapter 19

"Well, what did you do?" Sarah asked when they arrived home. "Did you run him out of town?" George grinned at her and settled himself down in a chair by the fire. "No," he said. "He's not a bad sort of a bloke. He only wants a whale to take back to Sydney for some sideshow people. I made a peaceful deal with him."

"Thank goodness you're getting some sense at last. You risk your necks enough out there without fighting people."

The first whale made its appearance two days later. George had lanced it and the killers were dragging the carcass below before Young's boat arrived.

"Bad luck," George told him. "You've got to be quick off the mark in this game, captain."

"I can see that," Young replied. "Never mind. I'll be there next time."

He was there all right, but the whalers had to remind him when their lookout in Boyd's Tower saw two whales heading up the coast. Young, who had anchored the *Jenny Lind* about a mile off South Head, seemed to be taking no advantage of his favourable position. Even when the whalers were halfway out, there was still no sign of movement from the ship.

"What's the damned fool doing?" George muttered. "They must all be asleep."

"He's waiting for us to catch two and give him one," Penrith grunted, tugging at his oar. "Don't bother about him."

"No," George said. "We made a deal." He swung the boat across and kept ahoying the *Jenny Lind* until they were alongside and Young appeared on deck. "The killers have got them stuck up—two of them," George snapped impatiently. Young mumbled something and disappeared, but the whalers wasted no more time and they were streaking for Leatherjacket Bay while Young was stirring up his crew and getting the *Jenny Lind* on the move. Genrge was fast to one of the whales before Young had his boat in the water, but the line broke.

"Will I get fast to the other?" Young shouted as the two boats sped after the fleeing whales.

"No," George yelled back through the spray. "Leave it alone. We'll kill them both with one boat fast and the other loose. Whales won't leave one another when they're in trouble. See. They're swimming together."

But Young took no heed of the advice, and immediately when he had an opportunity, he harpooned the other whale.

"You blasted fool!" George roared, though it was doubtful whether those in the other boat even heard him. They were too busy trying to peak their oars as the boat was jerked forward and dragged madly through the choppy crests of the easterly roll. By this time they were just north of South Head, and George and his crew watched Young's speeding boat turn into the bay and head for Boydtown, followed by the *Jenny Lind*. Then they noticed that the killers had remained behind with them, and although George was annoyed at Young for having harpooned the other whale, he couldn't help laughing.

"Looks like you'll win your bet, boss," Arthur Ashby remarked.

"Well, you wouldn't imagine it, would you?" George replied. "So that's why they've been going so fast. No killers to slow the whales down." He laughed.

Tom, Hooky, Stranger, and most of the pack were swimming about in the vicinity. Apparently not even interested in the whales, they had stayed with George's boat. Alex, who had come along with the pick-up boat, was laughing too. "Won't Dave Crichton have a victory?" he crowed. "Look at old Tom. You'd think he was enjoying it."

"We'd better go with them," George suggested. "One of those things might tip them up. No, wait a minute. Head for the lighthouse, Alex."

They rowed steadily across towards the lighthouse, the killers frolicking about as they kept the two boats company, while farther in the bay Young and his crew sat white-faced, wondering when this mad thing that had taken charge of them was going to stop. It spun them round in Cattle Bay, cleared the point, and headed for the open sea again, the other whale swimming alongside, with yards of rope trailing from the harpoon in its back. Out from the lighthouse Davidson's two green boats were waiting, and so were the killers. George got fast to the lost quarry, finished it off, and then, assisted by his pack of sea hounds, helped Young to kill the other whale.

" 'Struth," Young said, wiping the dried saltspray from his face, "it's just as well they didn't want a dozen of these things instead of only one, but it was one they wanted and, thank heaven—and thank you, Davidson—it's one they've got. If they want any more, I'll recommend you for the contract. You can have it."

"I'd rather have a long glass of ale just now," Penrith muttered to Arthur Ashby.

"A glass of ale," Young repeated. "So you shall, too. Bring them all aboard the *Jenny Lind,* Davidson. We ought to be able to find a few bottles for an occasion like this."

George thanked him and when the whales had been anchored and buoyed, the three boatloads of men clambered up the steamer's side and filed into the main cabin. In a few minutes they were watching glasses being filled with bottled beer. Bobbo moved to grab his as soon as it was filled, but a quick look from Alex restrained him and he waited with the others. Then Young put down the towel with which he had been wiping his face and raised his glass.

"Well," he said, "here's to the whalers of Twofold Bay. As game a team as I've seen anywhere. And—" he paused with a merry glint in his eyes—"here's to your blasted trained killers. Good luck, men."

Bobbo and Penrith drank their beer at a gulp. They brought their eyes down again to see Alex looking at them reproachfully. "Well, well," he said softly. "You know, you should've made it last longer. You mightn't get another."

Penrith wiped his mouth with the back of his hand and grunted.

"Ship roll plenty. Might spill," was Bobbo's droll comment.

"You know, I didn't believe that publican when he reckoned the killers wouldn't work with anyone else," Young was saying. "They're certainly remarkable things—even get temperamental—though it's all the more amazing when you think that killers everywhere else in the world won't work with anyone at all. It's almost like black magic or something."

"Not quite," George said, laughing. "Although to be honest I didn't really expect them to desert you like that, especially when you were fast to a whale. But there's no knowing what they'll do sometimes. I've seen them do the most peculiar things."

"Have they always been here?" Young asked.

"Well, ever since I can remember. My father used the killers long before I was born, and his father before him, and they were helping whalers here back in Ben Boyd's day."

"The same ones?"

"I couldn't tell you that. All I know is that old Tom has been seen here every season for the last fifty years at least. What age they live to I don't know either, because Tom, for all his fifty years we can count back, seems to have plenty of life in him yet."

Young was ordering another drink for the company when one of his crew came in and handed him something.

"A telegram," he said. "Where did this come from?"

"Don't know, cap'n," the man answered. "A boat just brought it out."

"Well, we'll soon see."

The telegram was addressed to Captain C. E. Young, S.S. *Jenny Lind*, Eden, and read, "Don't bring whale Sydney any consideration."

"Don't bring whale?" Young's face went red and his mumble burst into a roar. "What the hell do they mean? What do they think I've been wasting my damned time for down here?"

"They don't give any reason?" George asked.

"Reason? No. All I know is that they don't want the damned thing after all the trouble I've been through to catch it. Wait until I see them."

"I'll make another deal with you if you like," George offered.

"What?"

"Well, seeing as your syndicate doesn't want the whale now, I'll buy it from you for a tun and a half of oil. You can sell that in Sydney and make a few quid for yourself."

Young scratched the back of his head for a minute, then the perplexed expression began to leave his face and he smiled. "Sure," he said. "Why not? I wouldn't know what to do with a stinking whale anyhow. It's a deal. I'll make arrangements tomorrow with that publican fellow. What's his name?"

"Crichton?"

"Yes, Crichton. I'll pay him for the five of beer and bottle of whisky he talked me into betting you. The experience was well worth it."

"When do you reckon you'll leave here?" George asked.

"Probably the day after tomorrow."

"When will you see Crichton?"

"Tomorrow afternoon. Why?"

"Well, if you bring your boys with you, I think we might drink it between us as a sort of farewell drink."

And so they did the following afternoon, although Young kept emphasizing that it was *au revoir* rather than farewell. When the time came for *au revoir* he was raving about the beauty of Twofold Bay and declaring that he would see more of it, free from the obligation of having to catch a whale.

"Do you ever go to Sydney?" he asked George.

"Sometimes," George replied. "Not unless I can help it."

"Well, look me up," Young invited, scrawling an address on a piece of paper. "If I'm not there, someone will know where I am."

George said he thought he might be in Sydney after the end of the whaling season, depending on how the season turned out, to buy a motor-launch which he could use, among other things, for towing whales.

"You might want someone to help you bring it back," Young suggested. "If you do, I'm your man."

During the following week the whalers devoted a portion of their thought to the cricket match against the Eden team, and when they rowed over to town on the Sunday morning they had talked themselves into a fair degree of confidence. Helped by a few rums apiece, they were even more confident after lunch, although their optimism was not shared generally by the large crowd of spectators that fringed the cricket ground opposite the School of Arts. A Bega bookmaker, in Eden for the weekend, was prepared to lay the odds on the game—threes the whalers, "take five to four" Eden—but there was little money for either side, most would-be backers believing the whalers had no chance, although they would not accept the short price for the other team.

"I'll give you fours about the whalers," the bookie appealed to Bill Holden, his eyes visualizing the pound note being twisted and twisted around uncertain fingers inside Holden's pocket.

"Fives," Holden suggested. "Five pound to one."

"Five quid to one?" The sporting gent drew himself up with mock dignity. "What the hell do you think I am—the flamin' benevolent society? It's an even-money shot, ain't it? Either team has as much chance as the other, yet I'm offerin' you fours about one of them."

"Yes, and five to four on about the other, indicating how much of an even-money shot you really think the game is," Holden retaliated. "Five pound to one."

"Nine quid to two make it."

"No. Five to one."

"All right, but it's extortion. That's what it is. And don't send any of your mates up either because the price is threes. Anything can happen in these so-called social matches, as I've seen too often."

George Davidson, having won the toss, decided to bat and instructed Charlie Adgery and Albert Thomas to "get the shin pads on." Jim Hopkins and Dave Crichton, who were to umpire, had donned white coats and were strolling out to fix the bails.

" 'Struth," someone remarked loudly from the edge of the field. "Jim Hopkins umpiring? He wouldn't know leg before from a leg of mutton."

"And Dave Crichton at the other end," another voice joined in above the laughter. "There's something crook about this."

"Wait until Reg Cook starts slinging 'em down," a youngster chirped. "Gee, he can bowl fast. The whalers won't even see the ball."

That was partly true of Cook's first two overs, but, fortunately, most of the balls were outside the off stump and Thomas, who weathered the brunt of it, left them well alone. They collected five between them from

Ross, a medium-pace bowler operating at the other end, and Adgery faced up to the third over from Cook.

The first ball came down at terrific pace, struck a rough spot on the rough wicket and whizzed past Adgery's right ear. The next ball hit the same spot and kicked up and Charlie, more for self-preservation than anything else, swung the bat over his head. He opened his eyes as he heard a snick and a roar from the crowd, and, turning round, saw a fieldsman chasing the ball to the fine-leg boundary. The next one he didn't see at all, but it went through for four byes, two more he managed to block out of his wicket, the sixth he poked at outside the off stump and snicked it almost through second slip's hands for four, and the seventh rolled off the edge of one of his pads, enabling a very relieved Charlie Adgery to scramble down the wicket for what he was determined would be only one leg-bye.

"Come on," Albert Thomas called to him. "There's two in it."

"Run, Charlie," Alex Greig shouted. "There's an easy two."

But Charlie felt much happier where he was, and there he intended to stay. He thought his judgment was vindicated when the last ball of Cook's over swung past the edge of Albert's bat and somersaulted the off stump. It was bad luck Albert going, he thought with a twinge of guilt. Albert was usually a good batsman. Still, one for eighteen wasn't bad with this demon bowling and he couldn't keep up that pace all day, surely.

Arthur Ashby came in and took a leisurely, but uneasy stand at the bowler's end and the game continued slowly until the whalers had thirty-five in the score book for the loss of one wicket. Then Ashby skied one from Ross and it came down into waiting wicket-keeping gloves. He was replaced by Sam Haddigaddi, who made a patient fifteen before Charlie ran him out trying to get away from Cook, who, to Charlie's surprise and discomfit, seemed to be bowling as fast as ever after six overs. Charlie Green came in, snicked a single from the first ball he received, and Adgery found himself again facing Cook.

"Hit him out of the ground, Charlie," a voice called from the eastern edge of the ground.

Cook shuffled his feet, raced up to the crease, over came his arm, down went his head, and Adgery lunged forward at where he thought the ball should be. Halfway through the stroke he heard the clatter of two stumps falling.

"Oh, not out," somebody yelled in cynical tones.

"Four for fifty-one," George Davidson remarked, as he got up from the box on which he had been sitting. "Could be better. Well, here goes."

"Step out to this bloke and hit him," Bill Holden advised. "Don't let him frighten you out like he did Charlie here."

"Who was frightened?" Adgery challenged.

"You were. You got two other men out trying to get away from him."

"He'd have you frightened," Charlie retorted.

"He's got me scared plenty, don't worry," Holden told the grinning circle. "I've got a quid on you mugs, although why I don't know. A man's not right in the head."

George shaped up with his bat, Cook ran up again and the ball raised a little cloud of dust as it thudded just short of a good length on the wicket. George played forward, missed, and a sigh of relief came from the rest of the whaling team as they saw the wicketkeeper take the ball behind. But their faces changed quickly when they saw George start to walk back towards them. Dave Crichton had shuffled over to the stumps and was replacing a bail.

"It bowled him," Ashby gasped. "I didn't think it went near the stumps."

"Just took the bail," Alex remarked.

"My Gawd," Holden moaned. "I don't like the chances of seeing my six quid."

Five for fifty-one. Dan Parsons made a stand with Charlie Green and they added another fifteen before Ross bowled Parsons. Six for sixty-six. Bullock went in with the intention of hitting everything for a series of sixes, but the only thing that went out of the ground after three mighty swipes, which would have achieved their purpose had they connected, was his leg stump. The whalers added only another seven before they were all out for seventy-three. Cook the terror had taken five wickets for twenty-five.

When the whalers took the field, the Bega bookie was quoting fours about them without attracting any business, but he quietened down slightly when Arthur Ashby bowled one of the Eden openers in his first over and had his partner caught behind in the following over. Two down for three was far from being a good start. Then when the first ball Dan Parsons bowled to Charlie Harris rapped his pads and Jim Hopkins raised a clearly defined index finger in response to a chorus of " 'Ow's that?" those who had been the most unkind to the whalers in their earlier comments turned their attention to the townsmen.

"How do you like your duck, Harris?" one raucous voice yelled.

"What does he think his bat's for?" called another.

Stan Connor and Fred Johnson turned the tide for a while and the score climbed to forty before Ashby caught Connor off his own bowling. Next man in faced the new over from Dan Parsons, played forward over the top of a ''wrong 'un'' and was out l.b.w. (leg before wicket)—Eden five for forty-one. The Bega bookie had dropped the whalers' price to twos and was not seeking business. Excitement was high as Cook strode out to the wicket, fully aware that the fate of the game might hinge on what he and Johnson could do to stop the disaster that had overtaken their side. Parsons bowled a slightly faster ball, pitched a trifle short, which Cook lofted high to long on and started to run while the murmuring crowd watched Bullock waiting under the descending ball. The big Swede grabbed at it somewhat like a baby groping for a rattle on a string and it dropped through his hands to the ground.

''Oh, get a bag,'' several onlookers roared above the laughter.

''Get a landing net.''

But Bullock ignored the barracking as he groped behind his feet for the ball. The batsmen had turned for their second run when he picked it up and tossed it smartly stump high to George Davidson behind the wicket. If there was one thing Bullock could do it was throw. George lifted the bails with Cook still a yard from home. Six for forty-three.

Holden was jubilant and so were the few others who had made a small wager on the whalers for the sake of the long odds. Only five more were added before Ashby caught and bowled Johnson's partner and then Johnson himself played back to one from Parsons and it thumped against his pads.

'' 'Ow's that?'' Parsons and George Davidson challenged.

''Out,'' Jim Hopkins nodded, raising his finger promptly.

The mob roared. Eight for forty-eight and Dan Parsons had got three of them leg before. The Eden barrackers turned their attention to Jim Hopkins.

''What's up with you Hopkins, you robber?''

''They must be going to give you a fair cut of the beer.''

''Get your eyes tested. It wasn't even on the wicket.''

Hopkins ignored the tirade and stood patiently surveying the scenery while he waited for the next batsman. But it could not last long and Eden's final wicket fell with the score only fifty-two.

Holden grinned at the bookmaker and rustled in his pocket. ''I'll take another quid,'' he said confidently.

''Not from me you won't,'' he was told.

Half an hour later Holden was thankful the bet had been refused. Cook had bowled fast and accurately and had taken seven wickets for fourteen. The whalers were all out for twenty-seven, leaving Eden only forty-nine to get for an outright win.

''You can have another five quid to one if you like,'' Holden was offered, but he just glared in reply.

Charlie Harris opened with Johnson. They took no risks, watching everything right up to the bat, and in three-quarters of an hour they were still there with thirty-five runs in the book. Then something as unpredictable as anything that ever happened in the unpredictable game of cricket intervened. A man came running down from Imlay Street yelling at the top of his voice, "Whale! Rusho!"

The players turned and stared, glanced back at George Davidson, and then began to run from the field, leaving the batsmen and the umpires standing. George flung the wicket-keeping gloves aside and struggled to unfasten the straps of his pads while the crowd cheered him on. Others were surrounding the bookmaker, arguing fiercely that all bets were off. In a few minutes everyone was trailing the whale crews down to their boats at the wharf.

Chapter 20

The whale that had upset the cricket match—a large humpback—was anchored and buoyed just after dark, and next morning a right whale caught trying to sneak past the heads joined the humpback on the seabed. Towards evening the south-easterly breeze blew stronger and by Tuesday morning it had freshened into a gale—one of those dirty, squally sou'easters that whistled up from somewhere in the Antarctic, brushed past Gabo, and pelted the coast with a relentless spite. To George and the others who watched all day for either of the whales to come to the surface it seemed that the weather was venting itself against them personally. Last season they had done well enough to clear the legacy of the previous bad year, and now, when they were starting off on the right foot with two whales in two days, this gale had come like a burglar at night to rob them; but if the carcasses came up, the whalers were prepared to battle the gale as they would have fought any common burglar. The boats were waiting on the beach in East Boyd Bay.

Dusk was beginning to shade in nightfall when George told Sarah they were going out. Not that there was any need for her to be told. The news only confirmed the horrible suspicion that had tormented her all day.

"I suppose you must," she said. "I'm terribly worried though. It's going to be a wicked night."

"Wicked?" He shrugged his shoulders and grinned. "I don't know. Might be a bit cold out there. But don't worry. We'll be right otherwise."

Sarah went into the bedroom and came out with a heavy woollen jacket. "Put this on," she said, looking up half reproachingly as she handed it to him. "I still think you're foolish and you'll never get me to believe that all the whales in the ocean are worth—to me, anyhow—spending the rest of my life a widow."

"That humper we killed on Sunday should've been up by this time," he explained by way of justification. "If it comes up during the night, we'll never know where it went. We've got to find the marker buoys before dark and stand by them."

"You couldn't tow it in tonight if it came up."

"We'd have to try if it broke loose from the moorings."

She heard the roar of the sea on the river bar and a slight shiver ran through her. "When will you be back?" she asked, half expecting the answer she got.

"That depends on the weather and the good Lord Himself."

"All right," she said half sullenly. "I should have known better than to ask."

"Why don't you go over to mother's place for a while?" George suggested.

"What? And leave the children?"

"Oh, yes, that's right. Well, send young Jack over to tell her. She can come and stay with you for the night. Where is he?"

Sarah walked to the door and the boy came running to her call. "Have you been over at the bunkhouse?" George asked sternly.

"No, dad. I was feeding the chooks. Are you going out in the boats?"

"Yes. Now listen. You run over to your grandmother's place and tell her I'm going out and she can come over and stay with your mother if she likes."

"All right."

"And wait a minute. Just once more. Keep away from the bunkhouse. It's no place for a boy."

The youngster stopped at the door. "When will you bring the whales home, dad?"

"Probably in the morning."

"Can I help chop off the blubber?"

"If you behave yourself and look after your mother and do anything she wants you to do to help her."

Sarah smiled after the departing figure of their eldest son. As full of life as a boy of fifteen could be, he was showing traces of an interest in the whaling business that was too keen for Sarah's liking.

"I suppose it won't be long before he'll be going with you," she remarked.

George, tugging on the jacket she had given him, did not reply.

"Have you got any provisions in the boats?" she asked.

"Of course, we have. We've had them ready all day. I told Alex to fit us out for a possible all-night session."

"Well, come on," she said, taking his arm. "I'll walk up the hill with you."

Sarah stood looking down towards the little beach feeling rather miserable after he had kissed her, told her to look after herself, and hurried off with his short quick strides to join the men waiting at the boats. She waved to him once when he turned round and then the trees hid him from view until he came out on the beach and jumped into one of the long green boats before it slid into the back-surge. In a few minutes the boats were throwing their bows high in the air as the oarsmen drove them over the tops of the big rollers sweeping into the bay. It would be dark soon. Instinctively Sarah drew her coat tighter about her shoulders, realizing suddenly that the wind's knife-edge was sharpening itself for the night. Across the bay near the lighthouse, the seas thundered against the cliffs, breaking asunder and sending their fragments up as if in a vain effort to carry the assault to the grassy, bushy heights. Sarah began to walk back to the house. She felt all alone.

Night was closing when the boats reached the marker buoys attached to the humper and took up their crazy vigil, one on either side tied to the lines, tossing about and lurching violently while the men at the steer oars tried to keep their craft head on to the seas.

"Thank God we'll have a bit of moon," Arthur Ashby remarked, glancing at the half-moon that had appeared through a break in the scudding dark clouds.

"If the sky breaks up a bit," said Harry Davidson. "It's pretty thick."

There was a vicious swish and spray flew all round them.

"As long as we keep head into these seas—that's all I'm worried about," Penrith muttered. "A comber like that last one would come right over the side."

"But if we had the moon we could see them coming," Ashby remarked. "It's not very nice sitting here in pitch dark not knowing what's racing at you. I reckon the sea's going to build up. There's no sign of the wind dropping."

"What odds?" George grunted. "It couldn't get much worse. I'm expecting to be thrown over the stern any minute. Look out—"

George clung grimly to the steer oar and the others tightened their grips on whatever they were clutching for support as the boat lifted high, nose first, almost stood on its tail, and then dropped like a stone down the back of the big wave.

"Again," George called, knowing that these outsize rollers often came in twos or threes.

"Better go home," Bullock suggested. "Bobbo will be getting sick."

"Who sick?" Bobbo scowled. "Plenty damn cold. Where's the rum, boss?"

George laughed it off.

Back at home Sarah was putting the children to bed, explaining to Effie, Roy, Sarah, and Jim in turn that daddy had gone out to bring home another whale and would see them in the morning. George's mother was bathing little Wallace by the fire. Outside the wind moaned through the trees, and down near the river mouth the sea kept up its constant roar. It didn't make sense to Jim.

"But why did daddy go tonight?" he asked his mother.

"Because he had to," she answered, hoping to avoid a string of further questions which, with the least encouragement, Jim could line up better than the average six-year-old. "Now you go to sleep, dear."

"But, Mummy, it's such a nasty old night. It's windy and the bay is very rough. Why didn't Daddy wait until tomorrow?"

"Well, you see, the whale might have got away if he had waited until the morning."

"But can't he catch a whale any time he wants to catch one? Roy said he could."

"Of course he can," Roy interjected.

"There you are, Mummy. Why did he have to go on a nasty night like this? I'm frightened."

"Dad isn't," Roy said with a cocky air, sitting up in bed. "He's not frightened of anything, Dad isn't. He's the best whaler in the world and—"

"Roy," his mother said firmly, "you lie down and go to sleep and keep quiet."

After Sarah had tucked Wallace into bed, she joined her mother-in-law at the fireside with her knitting and for more than an hour little broke the silence except the click of the knitting needles and the steady tick of the clock on the shelf. Jack was reclining on the floor reading. He too should have been in bed, although his mother did not seem to realize this until the clock struck nine; she glanced down at the boy on the floor and reminded him it was past his bedtime.

"Bring in some more wood for the fire before you go," she added.

"Are you going to stay up long, Mum?" he asked.

"Oh, I don't know. I might. Why?"

"Well, it's pretty cold. I'd better bring in a lot."

"You certainly did," she said when he staggered in with a huge armful and stacked it alongside the fireplace. "That's plenty. Now off to bed. You've been up long enough. Good night."

"Good night, Mum. Good night, Gran."

"That boy always seems to be reading something," Mrs Davidson remarked after Jack had gone inside. "Do you think he's getting lazy, Sarah?"

"Lazy? No. Jack is a very good boy. Nothing lazy about him."

"Well, I didn't mean lazy exactly. What I meant was dreamy perhaps. They say reading too much makes boys like that."

"In Jack's case I'd say he was thinking rather than dreaming," Sarah replied. "That shows itself in his attitude towards a lot of things and it's a good point in his character. For instance, he doesn't take for granted a fraction of what other youngsters do. He wants to know why and how about things and I've rarely seen him with a trashy book. What he does read he can learn something from and I'm glad. George and I believe he's got a good head on his shoulders that's worth a bit more education than he has now, and we're thinking seriously of sending him to night school."

The older woman smiled knowingly. "I suppose you're right," she said. "You don't want to see him spend his life in a whaleboat."

"What he might be allowed to spend," Sarah corrected. "He's got much of his father's reckless nature."

"I suppose so. Like all the other Davidsons before him. It's just as I've always said. If a man is born reckless, there's nothing you can do about it, and the sooner you resign yourself to that the better. Look at George now. You couldn't keep him ashore, even when he was nearly crippled that time. His father was the same, and from what they tell me young Jack is longing to get out in those boats already. You mark my words, Sarah. This whaling, it's got a strong appeal to a boy's imagination. I remember George—"

"Oh, rubbish!" Sarah tossed her knitting aside. She was worried terribly about George and those other men out in the boats, although she was trying hard to hide her concern. "They must be terribly cold out there," she remarked. Mrs Davidson watched Sarah staring into the fire, saw the look on her face, and decided to change the subject.

"I think I'll make a cup of tea," she said.

"Good idea," Sarah agreed. "I wish we could give some to those poor wretches—"

"Stop worrying. Where's the teapot?"

Half frozen and damp from spray, George and his men were still waiting out at sea, while the wind seemed to blow harder, the seas rolled up bigger and higher, and the darkness added misery and discomfort to the devilry of the weather. The sou'easter was supplying most of the devilry, cutting slantwise across the swell and setting up a vicious joggle, kicking up little combers and then flattening them in a spiteful swirl. Sometimes the planking of the boats shattered the tops of the waves and the wind blew spray over the grumbling, cursing men. George knew that if the whales did rise, towing them in would be a terrible job; but they had waited so long that he would not give in.

Back at the cottage fireside Sarah and her mother-in-law sat drinking their tea, Sarah sipping thoughtfully and the older woman chatting quietly. Effie made most of the conversation until the clock struck eleven, which drew her attention to the time. Then she yawned. "Good gracious," she said. "It's time I was in bed. You'd better get some sleep too."

"I'm all right," Sarah said. "I'll just sit here for a while longer."

The door closed and she was alone, listening to the crackling of the wood in the fireplace and the rustle of leaves against one of the tanks. It reminded Sarah that she must remind George to cut the tree back, otherwise that tank would be fouled by the leaves and they would lose a lot of the run-off from the roof next time it rained. She felt her head beginning to nod and changed position in the chair to wake herself, to keep herself awake. A shoe clattered on the floor of the back bedroom where Mrs Davidson was getting ready for bed. Sarah began to nod again and, through the haze that was deepening round the fireplace as her eyes blurred, her mind raced back to that day when she had come with George to tell his father and mother that they had decided to marry. She could see old John Davidson smiling as he wished them good luck, and then she was looking at the serious face of George's mother, listening to those words of advice she had almost resented then, but which had crept back into the ears of her mind on many occasions since.

"Keep quiet, John," Effie Davidson had cut short her husband's little joke about women not getting all the hardships of marriage. Pausing to glare at him, she had continued, "I was telling Sarah—and I should know after all the years I've been married to you—that her life with George might bring a lot of hardships and a lot of worry. You've seen some of the glamour of whaling, Sarah. You have yet to learn that for those who engage in it life is often very hard."

It was almost like that now. She was sure George never even realized the dangers and the hardships he faced, tossing them aside with a laugh if anyone tried to make him realize. He would always be the same and, she feared, so would his eldest son. Sarah's eyes felt heavier and heavier, the haze deepened, but the voice of Effie Davidson continued, "You'll sit home for hours many a dark night while your husband and the crazy fools who work with him are somewhere out at sea risking their necks for a whale. You'll hear the wind howling outside and the waves breaking on the beach and wonder if he is going to come back to you in one piece . . . perhaps wonder if he is going to come back at all. I know. I've done it. And you will too. . . . "

Of course, Sarah had sat and worried through many dark nights, although George didn't always know, because that was how she wanted things to be. It was bad enough for one of them to worry. She knew she should not, but she just couldn't help it—mainly, perhaps because she could never entirely subdue a terrible intuitive fear that some day the sea would break into the happiness of her life with her husband and family, snatch one or more of those she loved, and leave behind an irreparable breach. Sarah shuddered inwardly and then let her head droop and roll against the high back of the chair. It was easier and better to give up the fight against sleep than to fight that awful nagging fear.

She didn't hear the wind any more, but those out in the boats were aware only too well that it was getting worse, and by two o'clock in the morning George had to admit that it would be madness to stand by much longer with the seas rolling up like avalanching mountain ranges. They had shipped so many of the choppy ones during the last hour that they had to keep bailing and the men were nearly as cold and wet as the dripping seats, sides, and floorboards of the boats.

"I think it's got us beat, Alex," George yelled into the darkness.

"It had us beat from the start," Alex's voice came back. "What about going ashore until daylight?"

"Righto. Cast off and see if we can land near the inside of South Head."

Half an hour later they were standing round a big fire, sheltered by the hills from the worst of the wind, trying to get some of the dampness out of their clothes and some of the fire's warmth into their bones. Beyond the tops of the cliffs the wind whistled through the trees. Round South Head and across the bay under the lighthouse the breakers made one continuous roar. The men shivered with the cold, and the coast shuddered with the thump of the sea.

Sarah awoke with a start to find that the lamp had burnt itself out and the fire had died down to a dim redness. George was not back yet, obviously, or he would have found her there when he came in. What time was it? She sprang up, stirred the embers and tossed some wood on the new glow. Then she lit a taper and put it to another lamp on the mantlepiece. Ten to three in the morning! That fear surged through her again. She grabbed a coat and a hurricane lantern, dragged her arms through the sleeves of the coat, lit the lantern, and pulled open the door.

The wind slapped her face and hands, almost tore the door handle from her grasp and paled the glow from the lantern momentarily until its force settled down to a regular draught into the glass and the wick burnt steadily and brightly, shedding a small yellow circle about her as she walked briskly through the gate and up the incline towards the cliff top. About her she could hear the shrill fluttering of the leaves in the gum trees; above her, when she looked up instinctively for a few seconds, she saw black clouds scudding across a slate-coloured sky. Ahead was inky blackness until she reached the top of the rise and then she saw the fire in the distance. It could have been an aborigines' camp, but Sarah did not even think of that, probably because there had been no blackfellows camped nearby since last year. She moved nearer to the top of the rise, swinging the lantern.

Down under the lee of South Head they saw the tiny light back in the darkness of the bay and Alex remarked that it must be "the missus."

"What rot!" George said. "What would she be doing up at this hour?"

"You never can tell," Alf Gardiner said. "Women do the strangest things. She's probably woke up worried because we're not back and just wants to make sure it's us, although she should know blackfellows wouldn't be out on a night like this."

Bobbo grabbed a blazing stick from the fire. "I signal back with this, boss. Let missus know all right," he suggested.

"No," George said hurriedly. "Put it down. Light one of the lamps and wave that. She might think it's just a blackfellows' corroboree if you swing a lighted stick about."

Bobbo lit a lamp, moved a little distance away from the fire and swung it pendulum-fashion. The other light answered and then it was gone. Sarah, cold and tired, but happier than she had been a few minutes ago, turned and walked towards the house. The wind tugged her dark hair from under her coat collar and tossed it across her face, and in her ears was the roar of the sea. But she heard too the voice of Effie Davidson as the mother of her husband-to-be, "Many a night you'll stand up on the cliffs in the wind and the rain, staring out into the darkness, watching for a glimpse of a light or the sound of men's voices or the noise of oars, and if you don't keep a firm grip on yourself you can go nearly mad imagining all sorts of things. It's no use telling you not to worry, because you will. I can only hope that as the years go by you might become hardened, as I have, and then, when you've resigned yourself to the fact that your husband is a reckless maniac and all the worrying in the world won't do any good, your sons grow up and he takes them with him and you start all over again."

Daylight came and revealed to the dismayed and sleepy group of men the carcass of a whale adrift near North Head, but the weather was as bad as it had been when they came ashore; it would have been sheer madness to try to tow it back all that way into a howling gale. They could write off that one as a dead loss.

The whale caught on the Monday was still below, so the crews watched eagerly all day without rest for a sign of it rising until darkness began to close in again. Then George felt he would have to put it to the others and let them volunteer for another night-long watch, which would make two days and two nights without sleep, warmth, or proper food. But he had no need to ask. They undertook the job willingly. They waited until, as on the previous night, they were compelled towards morning to retreat before the fury of the weather, nearly exhausted from cold, hunger, and want of rest.

Again they built a fire and waited for daylight. When the dawn gave them their first revealing glimpse of the sea they saw the whale—like the first—adrift, going fast seawards. The picture did not encourage much enthusiasm. Although the wind seemed to have eased somewhat, it was still blowing very hard when the men piled into the boats, rowed like fanatics, and overtook the drifting carcass outside Middle Head. But it would have needed more than the strength of fanatics to tow it back against the wind and the sea, and they had to give up the struggle and rely on one last hope—more anchors.

Even while they attached new lines and dropped two more anchors, the wind was freshening. The anchors held for a time, then began to drag, and twelve tired, miserable, and helpless men watched the second portion of what represented hard-earned money being carried away.

Jack saw the boats coming home and told his mother, who hurried to get some food ready for the men. She ran to meet George as he came through the little orchard, kissed him, and curled an arm around his waist.

"They're both gone," he said in a tired voice.

Sarah held him tighter, as if she felt she had to help him towards the house. "No matter," she said, a faint smile showing on her face. "I missed you and I was worried."

Chapter 21

The loss of these two whales so near the end of the season was a bitter blow to George, particularly since he had been counting on the estimated profit to help buy the launch he wanted; it seemed that unless something in the nature of a miracle happened, he would have to wait at least another year. But it did happen more than a month later, when the killers, who for some unknown reason had stayed longer than usual, bailed up two very late whales near Leatherjacket Bay. That was as far as the whales got on their journey to the Antarctic. The following morning they were being floated over the Kiah bar on the high tide and by afternoon the first strips of blubber were going to the trypots.

These were both right whales, one fifty feet and the other sixty feet long, and as the blubber boiled in the pots and the baleen was stacked in the shed, George saw his launch materializing. Bone was bringing good prices, and right whales yielded plenty of bone in long strips. It seemed that fortune was with him. A week later he killed another right whale and two weeks after that one more had its last swim in the bay. George was jubilant. The oil and bone from these alone would pay for his launch. It was more than forty years since they had taken so many right whales in one season. And then, to cap everything, a humper cow and calf came into the bay, obligingly choosing a bright moonlit night.

With Christmas only a month away, George decided that no more of these late whales were likely to present themselves for slaughter and, besides, even if they did he was not very interested. He could go to Sydney, buy the boat he wanted, and bring it home before Christmas. Then, instead of having to turn to other occupations during the off season, he could continue to earn his living from the sea. Sarah did not need much convincing, although with so much money involved, George felt he had to explain everything to her in detail.

"It'll pay for itself in a few years," he told her. "Look at those two whales we lost in the bad weather; look at all the whales we've lost over the years. If we'd had something like this to tow them in, very few would have been lost. And the boat will be useful for other things in the off season too. I can take fishing parties out—there's good money in that—and I think I could get the Green Cape supply contract."

"You probably could," Sarah agreed. "I think you'd be very wise to buy something like that while you have some money. At least it would be an asset which, if need be, you could always realize on, but there is another matter needing some attention too—the education of the children."

"I know," George said. "I told you we'd get a governess as soon as we could afford it. The alternative is moving over to town and just using this place for the tryworks, although I don't want to do that if it can be avoided."

"We'll have to sooner or later because I think Jack should have decent schooling."

"He wants to go in the boats."

"Boats, fiddlesticks!" Sarah scowled. "He's too young. And, besides, the boy has to learn a thing or two more than mucking about with boats."

"We might send him to night school," George suggested.

"We might, too."

"It would still mean living in town. Anyhow I'll think about it. Now the question is, do I go to Sydney before or after Christmas? I can't make up my mind."

"Can't you?" Sarah grinned. "Well, listen to me, dear. The *Wakatipu* will be in on Monday and she'll leave for Sydney on Tuesday."

When the *Wakatipu* steamed out of Twofold Bay on Tuesday morning, George Davidson stood leaning against the starboard rail watching the waves break on the Kiah bar until the ship turned and headed up the coast and he found himself staring across the open sea. Less than a fortnight later, he was steering a big green launch into the Kiah River, waving to Sarah, Jack, and Roy, who had gone down to the tryworks to meet him.

"*Excelsior*, she's called," George told them proudly when he came ashore after mooring the launch in the river. "Just the very thing I wanted. She'll carry a lot of people and do better than ten knots."

"Will you chase whales in her?" Roy asked.

"Don't be silly," Jack said with a superior air. "You don't chase whales in a launch. What sort of an engine has she got, dad?"

"A Jersey City Standard and she—"

"George," Sarah interrupted, "you haven't introduced your friend."

George came back to earth and turned his attention from the launch to the man with him. "I'm sorry," he said. "Sarah, this is Captain Young. You remember he was down here before with the *Jenny Lind*."

"Oh, yes, captain," she said, smiling. "I'm very glad to meet you. I heard about you when you were here before."

Young laughed. "No doubt," he said. "Anyhow, I'm not after whales this time. I liked this place so much that when your husband mentioned he might be coming to Sydney to buy a launch, I told him I'd help him bring it down. And here I am, glad of the excuse to see Eden again."

"Captain Young is going to stay a few days with us before he goes back to Sydney," George explained.

"We'll be very pleased to have you, captain," Sarah said warmly. "There's no need to tell you the place is yours as long as you like to stay. But I suppose the first thing you want is something to eat. Come on up to the house, both of you."

After dinner they sat on the veranda in the cool of the evening. Young, romancing about the glories of nature and their generous expression in Twofold Bay, had ample inspiration in the red and gold-flaked clouds streaking the sky round Mount Imlay in contrast to the sombre shading of the hills. In the grass nearby a cricket trilled intermittently, and down in the river fish were flopping about.

"There's no doubt you certainly picked a lovely place for a home," Young remarked. "I've never seen anything like it, although I suppose you've lived here for so many years now that you just take it all for granted."

"I've never taken anything for granted in my life, captain," Sarah said with a slight smile. "Not even my husband,"

The conversation veered to domestic matters, and George asked if any of the crews had been about.

"Haven't seen any of them since you left," Sarah told him. "No, that's not right. Alex was here the other day. Most of the others seem to have gone back to cutting wattle bark."

"Alex got any news?"

"No. Said his boy Bill had been sick. That was all."

"Where's Arthur?"

"Arthur Ashby?"

"Yes."

"Over in town . . . oh, wait a minute. Alex did say something about Bobbo getting into some trouble and fighting with a half-caste fellow over a half-caste woman."

"Was her name Lucy?" George asked curiously.

"Oh, I don't remember. I didn't take that much notice. Why?"

"Nothing in particular. If it's the one I think it is, Bobbo should have more sense. I told him a long while ago he'd land in trouble there."

"Is Bobbo that big islander you had in the boats with you?" Young asked.

"Yes, that's him."

"He should be quite capable of looking after himself. I wouldn't like to be the other party in an argument with him."

"Neither would I," George agreed, "but that's the danger to Bobbo himself if he gets fighting with these darkies. He'll strike one of them who knows he's got no chance except to hit Bobbo over the skull, or knife him or something like that, particularly when they get mad with that rotten firewater they drink down at the Cattle Bay camp. Bobbo used to drink a lot once, and he was a wild man, though I thought he'd quietened down in recent years. Still, I suppose, I can't be worried."

George took Young over to catch the *Eden* back to Sydney at the end of the week, and when the ship pulled out from the wharf, he wandered into town to buy a few supplies. It was then that he heard about Bobbo and went to the police station.

"Well, it looks as if he's been done in, George, but we have no proof," Constable Jackson told him. "All we know is that some articles we believe to be his were found on the rocks at the bottom of the cliffs near Aslam's Beach and Bobbo is missing. Have a look at these things and see if you can identify them as his."

George went with the constable into a back room and saw two fishing lines and a tomahawk. "Looks like his tomahawk," he said. "The fishing lines I couldn't swear to. He always used to carry that tomahawk, or one just like it, in his belt. But are you sure he's dead? Couldn't he have gone walkabout and cleared out somewhere for a few days?" George knew it was a vain hope and the policeman's answer did not support optimism.

"Not very likely. We've good reason to suspect, as I mentioned before, that he was done in, although the evidence is too circumstantial to pin anything on the person we suspect."

"Who?"

"A half-caste bloke named Harry Wilson who's been hanging round town for a while. We know he had a set on Bobbo because only last week they had a fight over the woman, Lucy. Anyhow the facts as we know them are these. Bobbo was camping near the surf beach with Lucy. Wilson had also been paying a good deal of attention to Lucy and apparently had a fair run until the week before last, when Bobbo shifted across to town from your place. Then, it appears, Lucy changed her favours and moved into Bobbo's camp and Wilson, becoming jealous, challenged Bobbo. The two men fought and Bobbo got the better of the fight, sending Wilson away to lick his wounds. A few days later Bobbo left his camp carrying his tomahawk and two fishing lines, telling Lucy he was going to catch a couple of fish from the rocks at the end of Aslam's Beach."

"And that was the last anyone saw of Bobbo?" George asked.

"Well, apart from a person or persons unknown. When he didn't come back, Lucy went looking for him, found the lines and tomahawk on the rocks, no sign of Bobbo, and came up here half hysterical. No trace of Bobbo has been found. The theory seems to be that Wilson sneaked up behind Bobbo, hit him with the tomahawk, and pushed him into the sea."

"That's the way it looks," George agreed. "What has Wilson got to say about it?"

"Nothing. Says he knows nothing and will say nothing. He claims he was at Cattle Bay camp all day and has two witnesses apart from his wife who say they saw him there, although his wife is the only one who can say she saw him there all day. He could have been away for a couple of hours and his wife is too scared to let on."

"I'd like to get my hands on Wilson," George muttered fiercely.

"You've got no proof," Jackson cautioned him.

"That's what makes the law so silly," George exploded. "You know in your own heart a man's done a thing, yet you must have proof before—"

"Is it so silly?" Jackson remarked quietly. "I don't know. Perhaps it's a good thing, because with all the inevitable faults any law system must have, British justice is still the best. Under our system, George, a man is innocent until he has been proved guilty. In some other countries it is the other way round. I've known cases where a man looked to be as guilty as hell on circumstantial evidence, yet wasn't. I agree Wilson's part in this looks pretty black, but I'd hate to make a mistake."

George picked up the tomahawk and looked at it closely. "Was there any blood on it?" he asked.

"No. We looked for that, though of course it could have been washed off in the sea and then dried to prevent rust stains. There's no rust on the blade either."

"He could have hit Bobbo with the butt end."

"Possibly. But you're still overlooking one of the most important things. There's no body. We haven't even any proof that Bobbo is dead, and it's necessary to prove that a man has been murdered before you can charge anyone with murdering him. Bobbo has just vanished without a trace. If he was murdered and pushed into the sea, we should have found his body by this time."

"Not necessarily," George said. "There's been very little sea running for the last week. Besides, he could've been taken by a shark like some of the big ones I've seen about here at times. They'd make a pretty good meal off a man."

"Well, whatever happened, the facts as we know them at the moment are not good enough to charge Wilson, but if he gets in my way he'd better look out,'' George replied. ''In any case, if I don't give him what he deserves, he'll get it in some other way, you mark my words.''

George did not go looking for Wilson, but he could not resist wandering down past the convent to the edge of the cliffs, above a narrow track that provided a precarious pathway through overhanging scrub to the beach and the rocks about a hundred and fifty feet below. From where he stood, the big red rocks looked so small and the foamy pattern left by the back-surge from the sea appeared like tiny white lace. That was the only sign of movement he could see—the perpetual movement of the waves. The only sound came from a flock of sea gulls, screeching as they wheeled and dived over the rocks.

George stood sadly pensive for a while, then turned and walked back up the street, trying to think of what he had to buy before he went home. Sarah wanted a new mop, two buckets, a cake tin, and there was also flour, sugar, and some meat. He had the list somewhere when he left. Rice was one other thing he could remember. Good Lord, he could never cart all this down to the wharf. The new launch was a good idea certainly, but with the old whaleboats he always had to bring somebody else and they could carry parcels. He should have brought Arthur.

George eventually struggled down to the wharf, laden like the proverbial packhorse. Fortunately he had seen few people about the streets and had spoken to even fewer. For this he was grateful, because he had no desire to be drawn into discussions about poor Bobbo's disappearance or death.

Sarah's eyes flashed when he told her, but only for a minute, and then they were sad. ''Poor Bobbo,'' she said feelingly. ''I couldn't imagine anyone wanting to harm him. He was such a likeable fellow—so full of fun, always laughing.''

''Yes, when you saw him,'' George agreed, ''but don't forget Bobbo was a pretty wild man sometimes, particularly when he'd been drinking, and he gave this Wilson bloke a fair sort of a belting. Besides that, he let himself in for trouble by hanging round with that woman. I warned him ages ago. Strange thing that. I seemed to get a sort of premonition.''

''Yes,'' she remarked, ''you're always getting premonitions.''

''I did about this.''

''Couldn't he have just gone bush for a while?''

''I'd like to think that, but I can't.''

''Well, call Arthur and I'll make a cup of tea.''

Sarah tried to turn the conversation away from the subject of Bobbo while they drank their tea and succeeded when she asked George how the launch was going. Then she had another idea.

"You know," she said, "I've been thinking about the possibilities of that boat in the off season. How many people will it carry?"

George looked at her curiously. "Quite a lot," he answered. "Why?"

"I've been thinking," she said.

"Yes?"

"You've got a lease of pretty well all the land between here and South Head. Why not make a picnic ground at East Boyd around Brierly's old cottage? There's a nice beach in front of the house and another around the side. Christmas and New Year holidays—"

"Are only a couple of weeks off," George interrupted.

"Well, what of it? You and Arthur could put up a few tables and seats in a few days. Now you listen to me. I'm talking sense. That area would make a wonderful picnic ground for people living in town who never see this side of the bay because there's no way for them to get across, but if you ran your launch on holidays and other days when people want to picnic, it should pay rather well. You could charge them so much for the return trip and make it include a small amount for using the ground and facilities."

The two men looked at each other and George's grin turned into a broad smile. "I think she's got something, Arthur," he said.

"Sounds good," Ashby agreed.

"Right. Let's go and look the place over."

Sarah watched them walk up the hill and then turned to face a new worry—Jack and Jim coming through the orchard, Jim crying bitterly.

"What's the matter with you?" she asked, noticing black stains on Jim's shirt. He continued to cry, and said nothing.

"I've got some fish, mum," Jack said, holding out two black bream and a small flathead.

"Yes, I can see that," Sarah said grimly, "but what's the matter with Jim?"

"There's nothing the matter. He came down when I was fishing near the tryworks and he's just kicking up a fuss because I brought him home."

"He didn't," Jim said. "He hit me with an octopus and it put ink all over me and they're nasty things."

"He was throwing rocks into the water to frighten the fish away," Jack countered.

Sarah began to see daylight. Jack had been fishing, Jim had wandered along and been told to go about his business, Jack being too occupied with fishing to be bothered with his brother. Then, she gathered from the evidence of both sides, when Jim refused to leave, Jack had tried to frighten him with a small octopus he had caught. Jim had apparently become annoyed and thrown stones into the water, whereupon Jack hit him with the octopus.

"You can both go inside," she said sternly. "We'll see what your father has to say about this later. Jim, it was very naughty of you to throw stones in the water when your brother was fishing, but that was no excuse for him to hit you with—of all things—an octopus. Good gracious! Just look at your shirt. That black stuff won't come off either."

Sarah was setting the table for dinner when George walked in. She said the clock had stopped and asked him the time.

"I don't know," he replied, looking at the watch he had extracted from his vest pocket. "This thing has stopped too."

"Well, why don't you wind it up?" she suggested.

"That's just the trouble," he told her. "I'm trying to wind it now, but it seems to be stuck."

He opened the back of the watch case.

"Good Lord," Sarah said. "It's rusted. How did that happen?"

George pretended to look mystified, but she could see the pretence.

"Come on," she insisted. "How did the watch get that rust inside?"

"Probably from the spray on the way down from Sydney with the launch."

"The spray wouldn't get inside the watch case." She looked at him fixedly and he could see it was no use.

"All right," he confessed. "I fell in."

"Where?"

"At Jervis Bay. We called in there for the night and I threw the anchor over and myself with it." He laughed. "Poor Young. He thought I was gone. When I pulled myself up the rope and climbed aboard he was on his knees praying."

"A pity you didn't join him," Sarah remarked. "If you only knew how often I pray for you."

"Yes, dear."

"Oh, and there's another thing for you to attend to. Those two boys are inside—Jack and Jim. They've been playing up. Jack hit Jim with an octopus."

"An octopus?"

"Yes. Go and speak to them—and pretty sternly too."

He went.

"I don't know," Sarah mumbled. "If women went on like men do . . . "

Chapter 22

Christmas came and went quietly, apart from the terrific noise the younger children made with a few tin drums and bugles that George, lacking foresight, had included among their presents. New Year's Day, for which he had arranged the first trip to East Boyd, was one of those perfect summer days, and many Eden folk patronized the picnic launch.

Young and old, the visitors had a happy day, exploring the grounds round the historic old cottage, eating the mulberries from the trees on the edge of the slope down to the water and picnicking in shady spots. For the older folk who knew its history, there was a romantic atmosphere about the old cottage. It had been called Merton after Merton Hall in Scotland, where Benjamin Boyd had lived before he came to Australia. But now, when the cottage was going to ruin, the curious visitors evidently thought there was no harm in hastening its destruction by souveniring whatever they could and scribbling their names all over the walls. Some of the older men recalled stories of how the old cottage was supposed to be haunted. A ghostly figure used to enter the building at night and walk to the fireplace, they said. There was also the ghost of an aboriginal woman who had been killed outside the cottage with a spade.

The young couples found more solid romance in the small rock caves near the water's edge and other youthful spirits tried their prowess at climbing a big Norfolk pine that towered above the cottage. As an added attraction, George had engaged the Dark Town Leaf Band, a group of aborigines, who played the latest tunes on their gum leaves. Everyone was happy, particularly Sarah, whose idea had turned out so well.

By the end of the month, George had the Green Cape contract, and this, with his fishing excursions and picnic trips, kept him busy. Arthur Ashby usually went with George on the fortnightly run to Green Cape and sometimes young Jack formed a very proud third member of the crew. Ike Warren, who had the Eden-Mallacoota trade run, was not worried seriously enough to admit the possibility of competition, but, he told folk about town, he was going to Sydney to look round because he thought it was time he ordered a new boat.

''Huh,'' Sarah commented when George mentioned it. ''Really, you know, men are ten times worse than women. Just because you get a new launch he wants one. Talk about women and their clothes!''

''I can tell you, our launch has caused a bit of talk,'' George taunted her.

''No doubt,'' she replied. ''Still, I suppose it's a good thing they've got something like that to talk about over in town, instead of gossiping scandal about people.''

''And don't you like me to bring back the gossip when I go over,'' he remarked triumphantly. ''Wouldn't you be disappointed if I came home with nothing to tell you?''

''No. Not a bit.''

''We'll see. I'll tell you nothing next time.''

But he did tell her something. John Hopkins had died in Sydney. George found out when he landed at the wharf and asked why the lighthouse flag was flying at half-mast. He called on Jim Hopkins to offer his sympathy and then wandered across towards the post office, where he could see Alex Greig, Dave Crichton, and a few others gossiping in a footpath discussion group.

''I've just been to see Jim,'' he told them. ''Bad luck about poor old John. I didn't think he was that bad.''

''Well, Jim reckons he never got over that nasty operation he had some time ago,'' Dave said.

''What really started him cracking up was young Henry getting drowned at the wharf,'' Alex remarked. ''He's never been the same since.''

''Jim tells me he sort of took a stroke three weeks ago and became paralysed,'' George said. ''It's a terrible thing for a man to have to drag on and suffer that way. Give me a quick death like drowning any day.''

''They reckon drowning is a quick way, but I don't know whether even that's very pleasant,'' Dave Hines, an Eden carpenter, commented. ''Anyhow, poor John isn't suffering any more.''

''We'll miss seeing him about,'' said Alex.

''Everyone in Eden will miss him,'' said George. ''They'll miss his cheerful 'Good day, boy' and the warm way he used to shake hands. I think John Hopkins riding along Imlay Street is one of the first things I remember as a kid.''

''He could ride a horse, too,'' Dave Crichton said. ''I remember years ago when the Duke of Edinburgh came to Australia. That was in the days before there was any telegraph in Eden and the harbourmaster had to send a message to Sydney when the Duke's ship passed here. Well, they got John Hopkins to ride with the news to the Mountain Inn at the foot of the Tantawanglo Mountain, where a telegraph battery had been specially fitted up, and he rode the forty-five miles in two and a half hours, which is pretty good going through that country.''

''They've found no trace of Bobbo?'' George asked suddenly.

''No, and they're not likely to,'' Alex replied. ''Looks as if he's gone.''

''Is that darkie still about town?''

''Who? Wilson?''

''Yes.''

''Oh, he's still hanging about. Someone gave him a decent sort of a belting the other night and it was too good a doing for his missus to have handed out.''

''Who do you reckon it was?'' George grinned, knowingly.

Alex dug his hands in his pockets and looked out across the bay. ''Well it could've been one of our darkies, but then again it might not have been and I wouldn't like to say for sure,'' he answered with an equally knowing grin. George changed the subject.

''How's that lad of yours, Alex?''

''Young Bill? Oh, he's right. Fit as anything again. Wants to come whaling with us.''

''Good idea. We might need him next season. He's old enough, isn't he?''

''Almost. He's sixteen.''

''Good. See you later. I must collect the mail and a few other things and get back home.''

''Look in at the pub on the way down,'' Crichton called after him.

''No thanks,'' came back. ''I've seen the light—been saved.''

''For how long?'' Crichton retorted. ''You know,'' he said to the others, ''if I thought George was serious I'd give the pub away.''

''Give it to me,'' Alex suggested amid the laughter.

Summer burnt itself out and after the first of the winter gales, the killers announced their return by cruising into the bay, but as the days turned into weeks and no whales came, George felt a growing impatience. Perhaps old Tom and his pack felt like that too, particularly when they attacked a big team of porpoises one cold mid-July morning, ripped some of them to pieces, and feasted off the remains—a thing the killers rarely did. George and Arthur Ashby, watching from the headland, had seen the porpoises chasing a large school of salmon for about two hours in the outer bay, driving them from South Head towards Aslam's Beach and back again and gulping their victims as fast as they could catch them. The porpoises had a merry time until the killers appeared. Then, while the salmon scuttled seawards, Tom and his boys rounded up the panicking porpoises, herded them into East Boyd Bay, and set upon them with fierce energy.

''They must be hungry,'' Arthur remarked.

''So will we be if these whales don't hurry up and put in an appearance,'' George commented dryly.

''Well, they chase the porpoises out of the bay often enough, but they don't kill and eat them as a rule.''

''There you see an illustration of the survival of the fittest,'' George told him. ''In the sea everything lives on something else, and when its regular food isn't available, a substitute has to be found. The whales haven't shown up yet. I don't think I've seen even a grampus this season.''

''Anyhow they've had a feed and some excitement.''

''Yes,'' George agreed, smiling somewhat cynically. ''We're not getting any excitement though.''

Arthur shrugged his shoulders. He was feeling rather glum too, although he was never the type to worry. ''Aw, you're too impatient, boss,'' he said in a half-bored tone. ''You wait and see. Something'll turn up and we'll get more excitement than we want.''

Arthur's prediction, ironically enough, was right, and there was a bitter irony about the form it took. Another three weeks had passed without even one whale appearing and, while they had been watching and waiting, their stores had dwindled to the stage where they needed replenishing. George could have sent one of the men over to town, but, having some private business that would have to be transacted sooner or later, decided to leave the crews on watch and go over himself in the *Excelsior*.

Arriving in Eden about 10.30 in the morning, George walked up the hill from the wharf and strode briskly along Imlay Street, whistling quietly to himself, and nodding to the few people he passed. It was a lovely sunny morning—one of those days when all who had time to spare were relaxing on verandas and doorsteps in the sun's warmth. In the middle of the road near the Great Southern Hotel, a cow reclined on her haunches, chewing her cud; another stood nearby, chewing leaves from one of the small trees in the street. George passed the Great Southern and continued on towards the far end of the town until somebody hailed him outside the new Hotel Australasia. He turned at the sound of the voice and recognized Harry Wilson, the supposed slayer of Bobbo.

''What do you want?'' he asked curtly.

''Buy us drink, boss,'' Wilson said beggingly, getting straight to the point.

''What?'' George saw at a glance that Wilson was the worse for drink already and he was dirty and bedraggled. ''Buy you drink? Not on your life, you mongrel. Not if you were dying of thirst.''

''But, boss,'' Wilson pleaded. ''I've got money. Look, here it is.''

He dragged about four shillings in small change from his pocket and held it out in his hand. "Take it and buy me whisky. They won't give it to me."

George knew well enough that publicans were prohibited by law from selling intoxicating liquor to aborigines, and this was certainly one case in which he would not help to circumvent the law. He looked the pathetic figure up and down scornfully and then pushed him away.

"Get it the same way as you got what you've soaked yourself with already this morning," he suggested and walked on. Wilson glared after him, spat viciously on the footpath, but curbed the abuse on the tip of his tongue, probably aware that police inquiries about any more trouble in which he might involve himself could have unpleasant results.

It was late in the afternoon before George finished his business and he was thinking about making a move towards home when Constable Walz came running round the corner near the Great Southern Hotel.

"Can you give us a hand down here?" he called to George. "I think a darkie might have gone over the cliff."

"Who is it?" George asked as he trotted alongside the policeman.

"That Wilson fellow." Walz was panting. "I was chasing him and he disappeared on the edge near the convent. He might be hiding in the bushes, but I don't want to take any risks with him because he's pretty full."

They slowed to a walk when they reached the cliff track and a man called to them from the rocks below. George saw it was Dave Hines.

"Any trace of him?" Walz shouted.

"Yes," Hines called back. "He's here."

"Stick to him then."

"There's no need for that. He's dead."

George and the policeman stopped and looked down. Then they saw, farther in, near the base of the cliff, a man's spread-eagled body.

"Good God!" George exclaimed. "I should think he would be dead. It's about a hundred and fifty feet down there. Ooh, what a mess!"

Walz's face had turned pale. "Drunks' luck didn't hold in this case," he remarked. "Come on, let's go and get him up."

About thirty feet from the cliff-top they noticed a piece of shirt caught on a twig. Farther down the bush was broken and flattened near the edge of the track.

"That's where he rolled over," George said. They paused to look and George's gaze fixed on the rocks below—the same rocks where Bobbo must have met his death. It seemed even more than a coincidence. Perhaps it was really an ironical turn of fate and Wilson had got what he deserved, although George's former revulsion of the man turned to pity when he saw the battered remains and the smashed head from which the brains were protruding. In silence the three men picked up the body and ascended.

As was only natural, rumours began to spread. A few people who had no particular liking for the police contended that Constable Walz had pushed Wilson over. The coppers had done it, they said, because they couldn't pin Bobbo's murder on Wilson. Others said the police might have done it, but in any case it was probably just as well.

The little courthouse was packed a week later when District Coroner Martin opened the inquest, and although everyone knew just about all there was to know of the case, they listened eagerly as each witness pieced the story together.

Wilson's widow told how she and her husband had been camped at Cattle Bay and how he had come to the camp on the fateful afternoon.

"He was drunk and had a bottle of whisky with him," she said. "He tried to hit me, but I ran away."

Elsie Hopkins, a half-caste woman living at the Cattle Bay camp, also told of Wilson's behaviour on that afternoon. "I was with Maria Wilson when 'er 'usband came in," she said. "I'd reckon 'e was drunk all right, and fightin' mad. He pulled me down on the ground and kicked me in the face and I 'adn't done a thing to 'im. Made me nose bleed too, 'e did. Then 'e started chasin' Maria."

"What did he do to her?' asked Constable Jackson, who was assisting the coroner.

"Nothin'."

"Nothing?"

"No, because 'e couldn't catch 'er."

The public gallery laughed. So did Mr Martin, who suggested that Mrs Wilson must have been able to run fast.

"I don't blame 'er," Elsie retorted. "So would I with that mad devil after me."

"Thank you, Mrs Hopkins," said Constable Jackson when the laughter had died away. "Step down and sign the depositions. Call Dr Howle."

Wilson, according to Dr Howle, had two compound fractures of the skull. Either of the fractures, he believed, would have been sufficient to cause death. The wounds on the body, in his opinion, were caused by a fall from a considerable height.

George Davidson told what he knew of the incident from the time he had met Wilson outside the Hotel Australasia.

"Have you any idea how this man got the whisky which his wife and Mrs Hopkins say he had in his possession?" Mr Martin asked.

"None at all," George replied. "I told him straight I wouldn't get him any."

"Yes. Somebody did, obviously. Mr Davidson, this track down the cliff face you mention. It would appear to be a very dangerous track."

"Well, yes and no. It would be safe in ordinary circumstances, but definitely not for a man under the influence of drink."

Patrick Joseph Collins, a contractor, told of a visit Wilson had made to his camp on the afternoon of his death.

"He was very drunk and very quarrelsome," Collins said. "He had with him a bottle in a calico bag and made such a nuisance of himself that I hunted him from the camp."

"Did he show any signs of violence?" Constable Jackson asked.

"Yes. He picked up a stone and threw it at me, then took off his coat and vest and wanted to fight me."

"What did you do then?"

"I left to complain of his conduct to Constable Walz."

Dave Hines entered the witness box.

"What is your full name?" Constable Jackson asked after he had been sworn in.

"David Hines."

"You are a carpenter by occupation, living at Bass Street, Eden?"

"That is right."

"Bass Street is the street running along near the convent and the edge of the cliffs, is it not?"

"Yes."

"Now Mr Hines, do you remember August the tenth?"

"Yes. That was last Friday."

"Would you tell His Worship the coroner how you come to remember that particular day?"

"Yes, Your Worship," Hines said. "I was working at my house that afternoon. Some time between four and five o'clock—I don't remember the exact time—I heard footsteps like as if someone was running, and then I saw a darkie tearing for his life down Bass Street with Constable Walz after him. He ran past my house towards the convent, close to the cliffs, and I lost sight of him in the scrub about seventy yards away."

"Did you see anything before he disappeared in the scrub?" Constable Jackson asked, glancing at the statement Hines had made at the police station earlier in the week.

"Oh, yes. Wilson was running very fast, about twenty-five yards ahead of the constable. Crossing a clear space, the darkie fell over a small embankment, but got up again. The constable gained on him and was only about twenty yards behind when I lost sight of them. About a minute later the constable came back and said the darkie had disappeared. He said he thought—"

"Excuse me, Mr Hines," the coroner interrupted. "You can't tell us what the constable thought. He told you something, did he?''

''Yes, Your Worship. He told me something and I went with him down the track, and while the constable searched the bushes, I went along the beach and saw the body on the rocks.''

''Did you form any opinion as to the probable cause of his death?'' Mr Martin asked.

''Well,'' Hines replied, ''he fell about a hundred and fifty feet to the rocks. That should be enough to kill any man.''

''Mr Hines,'' Constable Jackson asked, ''there's just one other question. You didn't see Constable Walz catch Wilson, did you?''

Hines shook his head. ''No,'' he answered. ''At the speed Wilson was going, I don't think the constable could've caught him.''

Constable Walz took the Bible in his right hand and added ''So help me God'' to the declaration that he would ''tell the truth, the whole truth and nothing but the truth in this inquest touching upon the death of Harry Wilson.'' He released the Bible, clasped his hands loosely behind his back, and stood looking at an angle towards the ceiling.

''Peter George Walz, constable of police stationed at Eden,'' his voice droned. ''About 2.00 P.M. on the 10th instant, Your Worship, as a result of something I was told, I saw Mr Patrick Collins, who said Wilson was at his camp causing a disturbance. He asked me to see about it. I went with him and saw Wilson in Imlay Street, but he ran away towards Cattle Bay. Later Wilson's gin came to the lock-up and said she and Elsie Hopkins were afraid to go to the camp as Wilson had beaten them. I went looking for Wilson and found him in Imlay Street, but he saw me when I was some distance away and ran round into Bass Street. I took a short cut across the cricket paddock to Bass Street and came out in the street about thirty yards from Wilson. I called out, 'Wilson, I want you.' He started to run, with me after him. Near the convent he ran along a track among some tea tree on top of the cliffs for about sixty yards.''

''How far behind him were you?'' Constable Jackson asked.

''About twenty yards was the closest I ever got to him,'' Walz answered. ''Suddenly he turned off the track, and when I reached the spot I looked over the cliffs and saw the bushes moving about halfway down. I came to the conclusion that he had fallen down there and went back for Mr Hines and then Mr Davidson.''

Constable Walz told of finding Wilson's body and bringing it back up the cliffs and that concluded the evidence. Mr Martin wrote on some paper for a few minutes, then sat up, adjusted his spectacles, and looked at the back of the courtroom.

''I find,'' he said, ''that the deceased, Harry Wilson, died from the effects of injuries accidentally received by falling over the cliffs near

Bass Street, Eden, on Friday, August the tenth, 1906. I find also—'' and he looked all around the room—''that no blame is attached to Constable Walz, who was simply doing his duty when the accident occurred and could not avoid what happened. The whole thing is very regrettable, but there is no doubt that Wilson contributed to his misfortune by getting himself into a bad state of intoxication.'' Mr Martin folded his papers and leant slightly forward across the desk. ''There is one other aspect of this case which I feel calls for some comment,'' he continued. ''That is the fact that this unfortunate aborigine was able to get so much to drink. As far as I know, the law says that publicans shall not serve intoxicating liquor to aborigines, but apparently some publicans don't care whether they break the law or not and will serve even the Devil himself to add another shilling to their tills. This law was designed because of the tendency of native people to become violent under the influence of liquor and the wisdom of its enactment has, unfortunately, been demonstrated at this inquest. I cannot reprimand too strongly the publican or publicans in this town who supply aborigines with strong drink, causing them to be a nuisance to the residents of the town and district and resulting, as in this case, in a man's death.''

Chapter 23

Another fortnight passed before the first whale of the season made a belated appearance just as George and his crew were going out for the day's patrol. The welcome sight of the killers thrashing the water near South Head and the sound of the whale blowing when it surfaced helped the rowers to shed their early-morning drowsiness. They shoved the long green boat smartly through the smooth waters of the bay, as yet unruffled by any breeze. The killers, apparently as impatient as the whalemen after waiting so long for action, seemed to be in their best form. Attacking the whale furiously, they forced it relentlessly into the inner bay towards the approaching boat, which met them between the lookout and East Boyd. Alex Greig and his crew had only crossed the bar in the pick-up boat when Arthur Ashby's harpoon thumped into the whale; it sheered off towards South Head, Tom and his killer pack snapping at it like hungry hounds, frolicking round the boat.

That was what caused unexpected trouble. Tom, more exuberant than the others, pounced on the whale line, grabbed it in his strong teeth and dragged it out of the boat.

"You rotten swine!" George screamed. "I'll take the skin off your back."

Albert Law, his back to George, was grinning, but the others failed to see quite so much humour in a situation that meant more hard work to recapture the whale.

"Blast him!" Ashby mumbled. "That was a fair-sized humpback that one, boss."

"Well," George growled, "don't sit there gaping. Get after him."

Five oars jabbed at the water and the boat shot ahead again.

"I'll be damned," George remarked suddenly. "Tom is still hanging onto the line."

The rowers glanced over their shoulders. The whale had surfaced about three hundred yards away towing a struggling killer, who, it seemed, knew he had done wrong and was trying to make amends by braking the whale's progress as much as he could. George couldn't help being amused. His anger melted and he laughed.

Alex Greig and the crew of the other boat were laughing too. "You'd never believe it.'' Alex chuckled. ''Just fancy. One whale towing another.''

''Put some salt on his tail, boss,'' Alf Gardiner yelled.

But ''boss'' and his crew didn't even hear. The oarsmen were pulling like fury, hoping Tom would help them get fast to the whale again by holding that line long enough. And he did hold tight until they caught up and Arthur Ashby put another harpoon into the humper's back. Then Tom dropped the line and spurred his team into such renewed energy that it was not long before George Davidson was standing in the bows of his boat lancing the whale. Tom swam round the boats, rolling on his side and looking at the whalemen with mischievous eyes as if to say, ''What a good boy am I?'' before he dived down to join his companions.

''You'd swear that old wretch was human,'' Alex remarked.

''Satanic,'' George corrected. ''Talk about the Devil in human form. Well, anyhow, that's a start for the season, and not before its time.''

''Shouldn't we celebrate, boss?'' Bullock suggested.

''Why not?'' George agreed. ''I'm prepared to buy a drink. Get those marker buoys fixed and let's go into town.''

Dave Crichton greeted them with a broad smile. ''So you've got one at last, eh?''

''Yes,'' George told him. ''The first of the many that are going to make a record this season.''

''Good luck to you. What are you going to have?''

''A pot of ale for me.''

''Me too,'' said Alex.

''Give me a double-header rum,'' said Alf Gardiner. ''Too cold for beer this morning.''

''You wouldn't have been cold if you'd been rowing with us,'' Arthur Ashby gibed.

''We rowed enough, especially when you were so damned sleepy as to let Tom drag the line from you,'' Alf retorted.

''Tom been playing up again?'' Dave asked, reaching for the rum bottle.

''Yeah,'' Alex said. ''After they got fast he took it into his head to play games with the line and dragged it right out of the boat, but he held on and let the whale drag him about until Arthur harpooned it again.''

Crichton was so amazed that he poured the rum over the top of a full glass while he looked incredulously at Alex for a brief instant.

''Pour it into mine if you're going to toss it all over the counter,'' Albert Law drawled.

Dave came back to earth with a start, stoppered the bottle and began wiping the counter. ''You're having a man on.'' He grinned.

''No fear,'' George said. ''That's right. I'd hardly believe it myself—even of Tom—if I hadn't seen it.''

''Well!'' Dave gasped. ''That bloke who was down here with the little steamer and bet you about the killers that time—Captain Young, wasn't it—he'd laugh at this.''

''We didn't laugh at first,'' George remarked. ''I thought we were going to lose the whale.''

One of the bar doors swung back to admit Jim Hopkins and Ike Warren.

''Good day,'' Jim said. ''Where did you leave the carcass? I'm short of a few roasts for the weekend orders.''

''A couple of miles off South Head,'' George told him. ''You can help us tow it in when it comes up if you like.''

''No thanks, I'd rather have a pot. Give us one, Dave.''

''What about the *Excelsior*?'' Dave asked. ''Why don't you use her to tow it home?''

''She's out of action until we get the magneto fixed. There's something wrong with the wiring. Nothing much. Probably a simple job if you know how those things work, but I don't.''

''I'm getting a new boat,'' Ike Warren announced.

''Don't tell us,'' Albert Law said ironically. ''You're getting as bad as old Cappy Russell used to be.''

''Well,'' Ike replied, ''you'll see for yourself next week when she arrives here.''

''I remember you saying some time ago you were thinking of getting a new boat for the Mallacoota run,'' George said. ''What's she like?''

''Should be pretty good. Dunn built her at Berry's Bay in Sydney. She's 11 tons, 38 feet by 11 feet 6 beam, with a 4-foot–deep hold and a 12-horsepower Standard oil engine. He's given her an overhanging bow and counter, which'll make her look like a yacht, and she'll sail like one too because she's got a 30-foot mast and a centreboard.''

'' 'Struth,'' Alf Gardiner exclaimed. ''He rattles it off like a flamin' parrot. Ike, you talk like a boatbuilder's catalogue. Shut up and buy us a grog to celebrate, seeing as how George says plenty more whales are coming and we mightn't see you next week when the new craft arrives.''

''I'll do that too,'' Ike said, digging in his right-hand trouser pocket. ''Give us another round, Dave.''

They tossed off the drinks and then Ike, a cunning glint in his eye, suggested that Alf might buy one to celebrate the first whale of the season. ''You know,'' he remarked, ''this is such an important national event that the Prime Minister himself should hear about it.''

''Why not?'' George cut in quickly while Alf glared at himself in the back mirror and dragged out a handful of small change. "It's a good idea. I'll send him a wire. Get me a pencil and some paper, Dave."

"Get us the drinks first," Jim Hopkins added, fearing that George might be in earnest.

George was. "Come on, Dave, I'm serious," he said. Crichton looked at him and brought a pencil and writing pad from under the counter. George wrote, mumbling to himself: "Mr Deakin, Prime Minister, Parliament House, Melbourne. First whale of the season captured this frosty morn. Eden whalers drink to the success of the industries of the Australian Commonwealth and give three lusty cheers for the Prime Minister for sticking to Dalgety as the capital. No place in Australia to beat it."

"Except Eden," Jim Hopkins grunted. "Why don't they make this the Federal capital and be done with it? Then they'd have the capital and its port all in one."

"That's what they don't want," Dave Crichton explained. "They reckon a national capital on the coast like this would be a sitting shot for warships to sail in and bombard if a war started, and so the capital has to be inland."

"It's damned silly," Alex said thoughtfully. "Some day they'll invent such fiendish weapons for war that it'll make no difference whether a place is on the coast or hundreds of miles inland."

"It'll make no difference in any case," Dave added. "You see, Dalgety won't be the capital and Eden won't be the port, and you all know why—because Sydney will see it isn't."

"Well, I'm going to send the wire anyhow," George said, draining his glass. "It'll give them a reminder. Come on, you crowd. We've got work to do." The bar swung back with a slam behind the last of the departing whalemen.

Jim Hopkins blinked at the publican. "Give us another drink," Jim requested. "I've got a bit of work to do, too."

The telegram went to the Prime Minister and next day one came back addressed to George Davidson. He opened it and read to the boys, "Congratulate you upon your successful catch and thank you for your congratulations. Alfred Deakin."

"There you are," George said. "I knew he was a sport."

Some notice must have been taken of it in Melbourne because later in the day George received another telegram from Eden's Federal member, the Postmaster-General (Mr Austin Chapman). It said, "Congratulations. You are a whale. We will hold as fast to Dalgety as you have to the first catch of the season."

Although the whale had been killed about nine o'clock on Friday morning, the carcass did not resurface until after noon on Sunday. A strong westerly wind was then blowing so hard that attempts to tow the dead whale to the tryworks had to be abandoned and it was feared that this would be lost like the first two captured in the previous season. Late in the afternoon what they feared did happen.

The dead whale broke adrift from its moorings. The wind was still blowing strongly and a nasty sea was running, but the men put out in the boats and caught the drifting mass about six miles out from the coast. They then turned to the formidable task of towing it six miles in the teeth of the wind, which, they hoped would go down with the sun. The sun went down, but the wind did not, and after struggling gamely for five hours, the rowers had made scarcely any headway at all. They stuck to their hopeless task until George, seeing that the men were quite exhausted, decided to put down more anchors and leave the whale to its fate while they went back inside the headland to camp for the night. Dawn was only just tinting the horizon before they were in the boats again, but the wind had blown itself out during the night, and as the sun peeped over the edge of the sea they found the whale still safely moored. It was midday when the group of weary men hauled the boats ashore, thanked the Lord's name in vain that they were home, and staggered off to get some rest.

But if they thought they were to have a good night's sleep, they were mistaken. About ten o'clock the killers brought another whale into the bay. Even George grumbled as he struggled into his clothes, but what he thought was nothing to what his crew said when he started to prod them out of their beds in the bunkhouse. They turned out, cursing, blaspheming, and rubbing their eyes.

"Can't a man get any rest?" Albert Law complained.

"There's no rest for the wicked," George chided him. "Come on. Look sharp."

"I was dreaming of a good sort, too," Alf Gardiner moaned. "She was beautiful. She—"

"Oh, shut up," Bullock snapped.

"Leave him alone." Albert Law yawned. "It's probably the nearest he'll ever get to a good sort of a sheila."

"Is that so?" Alf retorted.

"Come on," George repeated. "You can resume your dreams later."

By the time the boats cleared the bar, the sounds of the tussle between whale and killers were growing fainter and before long it was obvious that the whale was running from the killers too fast for the boats. The men stuck at it until they had rounded North Head, when for some strange reason the killers gave up the chase.

"That must have been a finback," George said, peering into the darkness and listening.

"I'd say he was, judging by the way he went," Alf agreed.

"Well," George remarked, "it's no use hanging about now. We might as well go home."

"Good idea," Albert said. "Alf can look up that good sort again. That is, if she'll recognize him after he's left her to chase a whale."

"Shut down on the mag and start rowing." Arthur Ashby yawned. "I'm tired."

"All right," George said. "Let's get moving. We'd better get some sleep in case business starts looking up."

"We'd get some sleep if you told those damned killers to knock off at a respectable hour," Alf said, stifling another yawn.

George swung the steer oar and the boat slewed round towards home. "I'll speak to Tom about it in the morning," he promised. "Although, seeing how they went on strike tonight, the killers seem to have formed a union."

Alf's hopes were short lived. At seven o'clock on Sunday night he was torn away from the fireside to join the chase after a humper the killers had rounded up in East Boyd Bay. The moon had risen, and although the night was cloudy, they could see the whale distinctly by the phosphorescent trail streaking from its body. Darting constantly across the trail and ahead of its path, the killers flashed through the blackness of the water like comets.

Ashby managed to get a harpoon in, but for some time they could not use the lance because the whale, lashing the water into silvery foam in its mad panic to escape, forced them to keep at a safe distance. When eventually George was able to lance the whale, it rose flukes first and began to back through the water. It kept up this peculiar movement for more than a quarter of a mile, then turned suddenly, nearly upsetting the boat, and backed away in another direction for about the same distance, which made lancing a very difficult procedure. It could only be done effectively from behind because of the position of the whale's large ribs.

The killers had been working splendidly, harassing the whale and preventing it from making any great headway, and when finally George sent the lance in and the whale began to kick in its death-throes, the killers roused themselves into a frenzy, making desperately savage efforts to force open the whale's mouth and tear out the tongue. The dying whale lashed the water frantically, then, using its last remaining energy, lifted its head twenty feet into the air with three killers—Tom, Stranger and Humpy—still hanging to its lips.

"Look out," George yelled. "Back, quick."

The men, who had been watching, needed no command. As the boat moved backwards, the great bulk toppled and fell, hitting the water with a shuddering smash. The men were drenched with spray, the boat rocked violently in the surge, and then all was quiet. But only for a minute. Tom, Stranger, and Humpy returned with reinforcements and the whalemen, working feverishly, had hardly fixed the anchors and buoys before the dead whale was being dragged down into the dark depths.

Two days later they caught a black whale, making three in a fortnight, and the trypots boiled overtime producing the oil that meant so much to the small community. Young Jack, just sixteen, took his turn with a boat spade, and with Jim Hopkins slicing the blubber like mutton chops, the work went along merrily, even when a visitor provided a diversion. He was one of the many who came to Eden in the whaling season seeking to cure rheumatism by using a whale as a sweatbox. The visitor introduced himself as George Arnold, of Darlinghurst, Sydney.

"A friend of mine says he was told about this cure by another bloke what swears by it, and I'm so crippled I'm willing to try anything, so help me Lord, Mr Davidson," he said.

George looked at the man's red chubby face and grinned. "Well, Mr Arnold," he said, "you're certainly welcome to try the treatment, but, mind you, we can't give you any guarantee. It seems to work in most cases."

"How does it work?" Arnold asked.

"That's more than I can tell you because even doctors don't know. All we know is that the whale's body keeps a certain heat long after death—a sort of fermentation heat—and this must be what does the trick. Doctors have been quite baffled by some of the cures."

"They'd be baffled if I was cured. They reckon they can do nothing for me."

"Well, we'll see. Those men carving the blubber off with the boat spades will dig a nice hole in the carcass for you. We'll put you in the hole and you've got to stay there as long as you can stand the heat and the smell. That's probably the worst part of it, the smell, and it's only fair to warn you that the after-effects might not be so nice because you'll stink to high heaven for a week or so. Even a dog won't go near you, let alone your best friend."

Arnold sniffed the breeze from the direction of the tryworks and screwed up his face. "H'm," he remarked, spitting on the ground. "It does smell pretty crook."

"You'll smell nearly as bad. What do you say? It's your own responsibility."

Arnold sniffed again, then set his jaw determinedly. "All right," he said. "I'm game. I'll try anything."

The men dug a hole in the black whale's body, stripped Arnold of his clothes, and lowered him in to his neck.

" 'Struth it's rotten," he moaned, unable to see the humour the laughing whalers saw in his plight.

"Ah, you'll get used to it," Albert Law consoled him. "If it's no better in a few hours, we'll bring you a bottle of eau-de-Cologne."

"A few hours!" Arnold repeated, a pathetic look on his face.

"If you get hungry, we'll feed you a couple of nice juicy pork chops," Alf Gardiner offered, innocently tossing a hunk of blubber with a boat spade.

"Pork chops!" Arnold gulped and said no more. He was too busy holding his nose, and when he was lifted out some time later his nostrils were still twitching violently.

"I reckon a man deserves to be cured after going through that," Alex remarked after they had seen Arnold off in the boat that was taking him back to Eden.

"I hope it fixes him," George said. "The poor devil looks as if he hasn't got much money and it'll save him a few quid in doctors' bills."

Chapter 24

Time turned slowly but surely and the years moved on, although to many Eden folk who watched the progress of time through their newspapers, it seemed that the world was heading towards a muddle, if not something worse. In the winter of 1908, while George Davidson and his crews were scouring the ocean off Twofold Bay for whales, Eden people read of the Young Turk revolution, then Austria's annexation of Bosnia and Herzegovina. Not that it mattered much then. It all seemed so far away.

"Bosnia and what?" Jim Hopkins grunted at a customer in his butcher shop. "Ah, them mad Latins is always trying to kill each other off."

In Eden it still didn't matter much and it still seemed so far away, and, besides, George Davidson had caught a whale he claimed must be a world record—a blue whale, sometimes called sulphur bottom, ninety-eight feet long, and with her she had a fifty-foot calf. That was much more exciting than political shuttlecock on the other side of the world. Calculating on a rough estimate of a ton for each foot of length, George estimated that she weighed about ninety-eight tons. Fortunately the killers drove her inshore and she stranded beyond reach of the angry killer pack, much to the relief of the boat crews because, instead of struggling afloat again, a stranded whale will only drag itself farther ashore.

George himself would have chased the whale, even if it had not gone ashore. That was why they called him Fearless long before young Roy Hordern dubbed him with the name. Roy, the son of Sydney retail store director, Alf Hordern, craved more excitement than the Pitt Street emporium of Hordern Brothers offered. Probably in the hope that a bout of whaling might cure Roy's lust for adventure, his father wrote to George Davidson asking whether the boy could spend a fortnight with the whaling crews. But Roy stayed five weeks, most of it in the boats with the men, and helped them kill five whales.

One of these whales caused plenty of trouble. In the first place it upset a cricket match between the whalers and Kiah when it chose to come up the coast just before the game was due to start. George, as captain of the whalers, was about to toss with the Kiah captain for choice of innings when someone dashed down from the lookout yelling, "Whale."

That finished the cricket before it even started, but the whale nearly finished some of the cricketers by coming up suddenly under the nose of the boat after it had been harpooned. The boat was beginning to lift from the water when George, quick as a flash sprang onto the whale's back, shoved the boat off and scrambled back over the gunwale as the boat slid into the water again. Roy Hordern grinned when Sarah asked him later if he had been frightened.

"Well I was, mum," he admitted. "But when I saw old Fearless jump on that whale's back and shove the boat off, I reckoned the Devil was protecting us."

The beginning of 1911 brought more talk of war in Europe, with Germany and France snarling at each other and the Balkan States getting ready to tear each other to pieces. But of more immediate importance to Eden was the passing of the two Acts that ceded to the Commonwealth nine hundred square miles of land near Queanbeyan for acquisition as the Australian Capital Territory. The Dalgety site had gone by the board and with it had gone Eden's chances of development as a port. Eden was probably the least excited place in Australia a couple of years later when Lady Denman gave the name Canberra to the city being built for the national capital.

But before many more months had passed, events on the other side of the world suddenly began to throw their shadows even into Eden's isolation from international power politics. Suddenly the news burst that Britain and Germany were at war, and, with Britain, Australia too. Some said it would not last long, but to most it was apparent that this was something more serious than the Boer War, which had taken men from Australia only fifteen years before. The Army was calling again for men to enlist and recruiting officers were canvassing the rifle clubs—quite a profitable source with something like ten thousand members in New South Wales alone. Jack and Roy Davidson, who worked in the whaleboats with their father, both belonged to the district rifle club and both decided to enlist. Neither George nor Sarah really wanted the two boys to join up and Sarah breathed a secret sigh of relief when Jack was rejected because he wore glasses. But Roy went, eager in his youthful enthusiasm, and they would not stand in his way.

It left George a man short for the boats. Jim and Wallace were not old enough, many of the town's young men were going to the war, and of all the occupations women were filling in this state of emergency, whaling was definitely out of the question. The girls—Effie, Sarah, Elsie, and Carrie—stayed at home with their mother.

Then Jack was taken for duty at Green Cape Lighthouse and George was two men short, but he carried on with darkies and half-castes from

Bermagui. Jim was just beginning to give a hand in the boats when he enlisted, too. He had waited until he turned eighteen, being careful not to give any hint to his mother for fear of upsetting her, knowing how she worried over Roy and knowing too that her worries were not helped by the grim news and heavy casualty lists from France and Belgium. Roy did not say much in his letters, although the newspaper accounts indicated that things were not going too well after two years of war. The German attack at Verdun had been causing fearful losses for months.

Jim had hardly left when the great battle of the Somme opened. This was the Allies' reply to the Germans' advance at Verdun, and as the casualties mounted in almost incredible numbers, an appalled world gasped helplessly. Sarah Davidson was only one of the thousands of women who spent sleepless nights. She had received no word from Roy in months and began to dread what ultimately did come—a telegram stating that he was missing. George tried to comfort her, saying that with millions of men involved, hundreds could be lost for weeks and thousands were taken prisoners, although he did not dwell on the subject, keeping his fears to himself.

Occasionally he talked to their neighbour, John Logan, a wealthy man who had built a luxurious big home at East Boyd. George had helped Logan to build it. They made the bricks on the flat area near by, heavy timber was cut on the ground, and George brought across the bay in the *Excelsior* the tiles and other materials shipped from Sydney. Logan had a fine auxiliary yacht, *White Heather,* in which he frequently followed whale chases.

George was thoroughly bitter when a telegram conveyed to them the news he had dreaded, that Roy had been killed in battle at Pozières. Sarah took it badly, as was to be expected, even though the months of waiting and knowing he was missing had partially prepared her for the worst. Then, when she knew he was gone and her hopes had been in vain, it seemed difficult to face up to the stark reality. Poor Roy. It was almost only yesterday when he was a bright and cheery little boy playing about the rocks near the tryworks. Now he was gone. For many evenings Sarah watched the sun go down alongside Mount Imlay and the lovely changing tints of the clouds brought her no joy. She saw only the blackness of night rushing to strangle the sun's last efforts to emphasize the world's brightness, just as men were blindly doing in a crazy war of destruction that had taken one of her sons and could claim another.

But Jim came home again, grown suddenly to manhood, slightly more serious than the youth who had gone away. He didn't talk much about the war, except sometimes when he was with his father. It was something he wanted to forget, if it could be forgotten. He merely hoped, like many others, that what they had been through might be worthwhile, even if it only convinced what was left of the world of the wickedness of mass murder, no matter how much nations justified it under a cloak of patriotism.

The end of the war released Jack Davidson from Green Cape Lighthouse and he returned to whaling with Jim and his father, although he was actually to be resident overseer of the new State pine plantation at East Boyd, the fringe of which came almost into George Davidson's backyard. Jack brought with him his wife, Anne, and two young children—Roy, just three, and Marion, not quite one. George was glad to have the two older boys back because, apart from the pleasure of having the family together again, it gave him a boat crew. Another acquisition was Norman Severs, who had married George's daughter, Elsie. In place of a second boat, Alex Greig was to follow with the launch as a pick-up boat. They needed him sooner than they expected, for the first whale they chased smashed their boat.

"A humper with a calf," George said thoughtfully when they sighted her.

"Which could mean trouble," Jack added.

"Well, they're always liable to be a bit cranky," George remarked. "We'll watch her."

They did, but she swung back and went right through under the boat, breaking the keel in three places with her hump. In two seconds the men were in the water, splashing about where the whale had gone down with the killers. Jim Davidson and Norman Severs swam across to Greig's launch, while George swam about collecting the oars and other gear. Jack sat in the damaged boat, which was floating in waterlogged fashion.

"What about the whale?" George moaned when they were all picked up.

"Damn the whale!" Jim exploded.

"But we could pick her up again. She's got an iron in her already."

"Swim after her if you want her," Norman Severs retorted, wringing the water from the tail of his shirt.

Alex Greig twisted a line from the whaleboat around a bollard and kicked the launch into forward gear. "Looks like the only thing we'll be towing home is the boat, George," he said dryly.

Sarah received the news laconically, and although the only concern she showed was her anxiety to get them into dry clothes, she was fighting inwardly that terrible fear which the incident had revived—the dread that sooner or later the sea would take one of them for good. And because of this, she did not think to tell George, until he asked if there was any mail, that she had received a letter from his sister.

"Margaret?" he asked.

"Yes."

"What does she say?"

"Rene has been sick lately, but he seems to be getting over whatever it was. Margaret's all right. The main thing is that young Cedric and a friend want to come down here for a fortnight's holiday. They've heard so much about the whaling and reckon it'd be more fun than staying in Sydney."

"Well, let them come. Write and tell her tonight."

"You write to Margaret yourself. It's about time you wrote your sister a letter. If it wasn't for the letters I send her, she'd never know whether we were dead or alive."

But Sarah wrote and a few weeks later the two youths arrived. She and George hardly knew their nephew, now a strong youth of eighteen instead of the little fellow who had come from Wolumla with his mother to visit them some years ago before Rene and Margaret had gone to live at Penrith, near Sydney. Cedric Bragg introduced his friend, George Craig.

"George would like to go with you on a whale chase," Cedric told his uncle.

"Would he?" George laughed. "What about you?"

Cedric grinned. "Well, I'd like to go, but mum issued strict orders against it."

"Yes, and I'll see that they're obeyed," Sarah cut in. "I told your mother I'd be responsible for both of you while you're here and whaling is one thing you're not going to do. You can do anything else you like. Your mother knows what it's all about. She saw enough of it in her younger days."

"Ah, they'd be all right," George argued.

"Perhaps. But they're not going."

That was final. Cedric and George saw a whale chase from the cliffs with Cedric's cousins—Wallace, young Sarah, Effie, and Carrie—explaining the finer points of what was going on. They saw the whale at close quarters when it was brought in to the tryworks.

"They're too big for me," Cedric remarked.

"Me too," George Craig agreed. "The best I ever caught was a yellowtail from the wharf at Pyrmont."

"Plenty of fish here," Wallace told them. "I get any amount of black bream and flathead just out there where the *Excelsior* is moored. Try it after lunch when the tide starts running in. I'll come with you if the old man doesn't want me to help with deblubbering, though I suppose

Looking south across Aslam's Beach in Calle Calle Bay to where the town of Eden straddles a high peninsula dividing the two folds of Twofold Bay. Mount Imlay rises in the background.

The man-eater shark which nearly got Cedric Bragg and George Craig, who were unwise enough to think about swimming in the Kiah River while a whale was being chopped up at the tryworks, seen in the background at the far right. This monster was 17 feet 8 inches long and 12 feet around the girth. Standing behind the shark are (from left): Arthur Atkins, Harry Davidson, Jack Davidson, Cedric Bragg, George Davidson, George Craig, Bill Greig, Alex Greig, and Charlie Davidson. In front of them are two of George Davidson's children.

—Photo by W. T. Hall, Eden. By courtesy of the Eden Killer Whale Museum.

he probably will, we're so shorthanded now.''

After lunch Wallace found himself handling a boat spade instead of a fishing line, casting occasional envious glances at the two sitting in the stern of the big green launch and thinking that on a warm afternoon like this, fishing would be much more pleasant and comfortable than slicing blubber from a whale. Evidently Cedric and his friend had not been falsely modest about their fishing ability, or perhaps the fish were not biting fast enough, or perhaps the warm sun gave them the idea that swimming would be a better pastime. Anyhow, that is what they did. Wallace looked round when he heard the splashes and yelled to them to get back in the launch, but they took no notice if they heard and swam round the launch in a wide circle before climbing aboard again.

''They're mad,'' Arthur Ashby gasped. ''I wouldn't swim there for a tenner, or even ten tenners.''

Wallace shuddered, thinking of the sharks he had seen chasing schools of mullet about the flats inside the river mouth and the big fellows he had seen prowling along the shore, attracted by the smell of the whales and the waste from the tryworks. Sometimes sharks would try to tear pieces from whales lying near the skids.

''Keep out of the water, Cedric,'' he shouted. ''Don't dive in there.''

Cedric, poised on the back of the launch for another dive, waved back. ''Come on in,'' he replied. ''It's good.''

Cedric was preparing his balance, stretching his arms forward, when George Davidson came out of the tryworks, and in the same instant that his keen eyes saw the youth poised to dive they saw something else—the fin of a huge shark rippling the smooth water, heading towards the launch.

''Stop,'' George screamed. ''Stay there.''

There was no mistaking the urgency of this request. Cedric settled back onto his heels again, relaxed his limbs and looked towards the shore.

''There's a shark,'' Ashby shouted.

Cedric looked to where they were pointing, but George Craig had seen it already and grabbed Cedric's arm. Gaping, they looked over the side of the launch and watched the shark swim slowly by within a few feet of where they would have dived, its great tail moving gracefully just a little from side to side. They could see its piglike eyes and its gills moving concertina-fashion.

'' 'Struth,'' Cedric gasped. George Craig just gulped. Then they saw the men on the shore tumbling into the whaleboat and while they were trying to guess what was going to happen, Arthur Ashby stood up in the bows and hurled a harpoon. A dull splash was followed by a cascade of spray as the line tautened and the shark lashed the shallow water to foam, dragging the boat round and round in circles. It seemed ages before the half-drowned shark was hauled close enough to the shore to be attacked with boat spades and Cedric and George Craig rowed across in the dinghy to see the end of what could have been for them a tragic drama. Sarah and the girls, who had heard the commotion from the house, were standing on the rocks near the tryworks. Effie ran to the house for a camera and eleven men stood on the bleeding carcass while photographs were taken. Then George Davidson and Alex Greig measured their catch—17 feet 8 inches long and 12 feet round the girth.

"And it could have got us," Cedric said quietly.

Alex prised the jaws open with a stout tree branch and showed the rows of terrible teeth.

"You can thank Heaven it didn't," George Davidson said. "I've seen them maul a whale."

Chapter 25

The years after the armistice brought many things to support Effie Davidson's contention that the world was going mad. It seemed she was right about half of the world at least. Russia had gone Communist, to avert the same fate Italy had gone Fascist, and nobody quite knew what would happen to Germany, although by 1926, much to the surprise of those who read about it, Germany had weathered her economic disaster and had regained—even surpassed—her prewar standard of living. Perhaps it was not surprising that some Australians became slightly cynical about the progress being made in their own country.

In Eden, progress still seemed to be pegged by some invisible hand, as John Logan put it. He contended that the neglected South Coast of New South Wales and portion of north-eastern Victoria should be made into a new State with Eden as the capital and port of trade, or, alternatively, he thought Eden would be better attached to Victoria, which might do something to develop the port instead of keeping it back, as New South Wales had done for so long. But this was only one injustice in a world full of injustice and trouble and everything seemed to bring more trouble, even the first whale George Davidson tried to capture that winter.

George had just gone for'ard to lance the whale when it swung its tail across the nose of the boat and George went out head first, almost on top of the kicking whale. There was white water all round him and the rope had curled about his arms so that he was unable to swim. Fortunately the whale broke loose. Jack pulled his father into the half-swamped boat and they sat there laughing at him while they waited for Alex to come with the launch and tow them home.

"Well, look at old Fearless," Alex roared when he arrived.

"It's nothing to laugh about," George retorted. "It could've been very serious—for me."

Losing the whale was a bad start for the season, particularly as George was without most of his old crews now and had to rely on casual help to man the boats when the few whales that seemed to be about that year came along. It was not like the old days when they had the boats waiting inside South Head. More than once, by the time he had collected a crew from town, the whale was safely away. To make things worse, the killers seemed to be thinning out too. For some years back, familiar old fins had been missing when the pack returned each season, still led by old Tom, with Humpy, Hooky, the Kinscher, Charlie, and young Ben as his lieutenants. Humpy and Hooky were showing signs of age, though strangely enough Tom seemed to retain perpetual youth.

Alex Greig, convinced that the game was not what it used to be, spent more of his time fishing with his son Bill in their launch. Yet he was ever ready to forget fishing for whaling at a moment's notice, as he did one afternoon when a humper came up and blew almost alongside the launch. Quick as a flash, Alex had the kellick in and was heading towards East Boyd, yelling "Rusho" long before George Davidson appeared on the cliffs behind his house. Alex didn't stop the launch. He cut across to Eden wharf, knowing that George and a couple of the boys would have the boat out in the bay by the time he returned with some men to make up a crew. But getting his own boys was George's problem. Jack, now resident overseer of the State pine plantation, was away somewhere in the bush, and he had only Jim and Wallace. Alex came back with the Eden police chief, Sergeant Dumont, and the only two recruits he could find—Jack and Bill Warren.

"You'd better take young Bill with you," Alex suggested, and the younger Greig, needing no second invitation, went.

They got fast to the whale at Leatherjacket Bay, where the killers had it cornered, but the boat had hardly begun to move in tow when the line slackened and the tow became a drift—only for a minute or two though. Then the boat rocked violently and its startled occupants could feel themselves being lifted right out of the water, which was swirling like a whirlpool. The whale had doubled back and surfaced right under the boat. Alex Greig and Sergeant Dumont, watching from the launch, saw the boat roll on its side and two of the oars fall out and slide across the whale's barnacled back into the water. They could hear George roaring from the stern, where he clung grimly to the useless steer oar, telling his men to keep their heads and hold tight.

It was the best advice he could have given them. The danger would come when the whale dived again, as Alex knew only too well from the many times he had been within swinging distance of one of those great tails. But this was different, he realized with an inward shudder. His boy was in that boat, still swaying in its stranded position on the whale's back, being carried along pickaback fashion. Alex watched, hardly breathing, until the whale's tail lifted slightly, tossing a sheet of spray skywards which curved sharply as it lost its strength to the nor'easter and blew in a shower across the helpless whalers, sending a few hovering sea gulls screaming to higher altitudes. It was an extraordinary sight, even for a man like Alex Greig, who might have been so blasé about the extraordinary things whaling produced for those who engaged in it.

Now, as an onlooker, the main feeling Alex had in those racing minutes was one of helplessness. Inevitably, it seemed, the boat must be smashed to pieces and men, possibly badly injured, would be in the water. All he could do was to get the launch there quickly to pick them up. But after the whale had carried the boat for about sixty yards it submerged quietly and the boat floated back on an even keel. A few seconds more and it was speeding away again in tow of the whale.

Dumont spoke for the first time since the sight of the boat being lifted from the water had drained the ruddy tinge from his face. "Good Lord!" he said. "That man must have a charmed life."

Alex, relaxed once more, spat over the side and scratched the back of his head under his hat rim. "I'm pretty sure of it," he agreed. "I've seen some strange things happen in this game, but that just about beats the lot."

Half an hour later George was lancing the whale near South Head.

Sarah laughed with them when they told her how Fearless had at last achieved one of his life's ambitions—to have a ride on a whale's back—although she was under no illusions as to how seriously the incident could have ended.

"I wish Jack had been with us," George said. "He would've enjoyed it."

"It's a good thing he wasn't with you," Sarah said meaningly. "Jack has a wife and three kiddies to think of."

"Ah, he's going to seed in that forestry job," George retorted. "Besides, we don't see much of him now."

"You'll see him on Sunday evening. He's going over to Eden to play cricket. He's taking Anne and the children with him and they're coming back here to dinner. Elsie and Norm Severs are coming over in the afternoon and they're staying for dinner too."

Jack and Anne called in early on Sunday morning on the way down to the boatshed to ask if they could bring back anything from town, but Sarah could not think of anything she wanted. Jim and Wallace had gone over for the weekend and would bring stores home with them on Monday morning.

"Just bring yourselves home safely in time for dinner," she said as she walked through the orchard with them. Jack was carrying little three-year-old Patricia. Marion, aged eight—they usually called her Tommy—walked alongside holding her mother's hand, and Roy, ten, was bringing up the rear, swishing at the long grass with a stick. Sarah stopped at the beginning of the path leading down to the water.

"Well, have a nice day," she said, smiling at little Patricia, "and, Roy, you look after your mother going down the path. Take her hand. Go on now. I'll wave you good-bye from here."

They waved back to Sarah from the small double-ended boat as Jack pulled out into the river. Then she turned back towards the house, reflecting that it was a good day for cricket. The sun was shining pleasantly from a cloudless sky and hardly a breeze ruffled the water in the bay. Along Whale Spit beach, the smooth rollers of a light ground swell thumped as they met the sand and disintegrated into foam suds. Up in the hills among the pine trees, which Jack now regarded almost as his own children, a bellbird chimed out a morning song. Sarah stopped to pick some flowers for the house.

Elsie and Norman arrived about four o'clock, just as Sarah was making afternoon tea, and they sat gossiping for nearly an hour before Sarah realized she had better attend to the dinner. George was saying something about the possibility of a storm blowing up. The weather, he thought, was too good to last.

"The wind has gone right off, but that ocean swell is building," Norman said. "There was a fair roll when we came across."

"What was the bar like?" George asked.

"A bit nasty. It'd be worse now with this big out-tide."

George got up and tapped the barometer. "Doesn't show any change," he grunted, reaching to the shelf for his pipe. "Oh, well, I'd better go and feed the chooks."

Elsie went into the kitchen with her mother and Carrie and kitchen things occupied their attention until suddenly they heard George outside, calling in what sounded like a frantic voice for Norman. They rushed out to see George, white faced, and gasping as if from running.

"Quick," he snapped. "Help me get the boat out. Jack's capsized near the bar. You come too, Elsie."

Elsie dropped the apron she had been holding and ran with them, leaving her mother standing horror-stricken at the door. "Capsized near the bar . . . Jack's boat," Sarah's partially stunned mind repeated, and that terrible fear she had known in the past engulfed her, immobilizing her, until she regained her senses and ran towards the cliffs behind the house, hearing as she ran Anne calling for help. George and Norman raced madly down the path to the tryworks with Elsie not far behind and shoved one of the whaleboats from the skids, all three jumping aboard as it floated off. George and Norman grabbed an oar each, Elsie took the heavy steer oar and as skilfully as if she were a seasoned whaler instead of a slightly built young woman guided the boat, pulled frantically by her father and her husband, through the heavy surge to her brother's capsized dinghy. There was no time for talk. Elsie kept the whaleboat headed into the seas while George and Norman dragged Anne and Tommy aboard just as Anne, with the little girl clinging around her neck, lost consciousness. Another minute and she would have slid from the desperate hold she had retained on the dinghy's keel.

Two still white figures lay on the whaleboat's floorboards, but of Jack, Roy, and little Patricia, there was neither sign nor sound. All the three conscious occupants of the whaleboat could hear was the crash of the greenbacked rollers tumbling over themselves in the shallows and the lap of the water against the boat's planks. A big comber broke close to the nose of the boat. The following wave, fortunately, rolled through, and with Elsie struggling at the steer oar, the boat seemed to stand almost on its stern for a second or two before gravity brought it down to hit the water again with a terrific thump.

George's voice trembled when he spoke to express his fears that Jack and the other two children were gone. ''Back away,'' he said brokenly. ''We'd better get Anne and little Tommy ashore anyhow.''

They were met on the landing by Sarah, who had run down from the cliffs as soon as she saw the boat turn back, and young Sarah and Carrie, who had followed their mother.

''Good God,'' she sobbed. ''Where's Jack? Where is he, George?''

''I'm afraid he's gone,'' he replied falteringly, as if reluctant to tell her the worst.

''And Roy and Patricia?''

''Them too,'' Norman said when George didn't answer.

Elsie had broken down now that the strain was over. The two younger girls were sobbing bitterly.

''Take Anne and the little one,'' George said. ''We're going back.''

Sarah and Carrie tended them on the grass near the tryworks while young Sarah ran to the house for blankets and towels, but they still had not moved when the others came back with the boat after another vain search of the area. It was not until they had been carried to the house that Anne and then Tommy showed faint signs of life, rewarding the anxious watchers with the only consolation they could expect out of the whole tragedy. But they were not out of danger and George knew he would have to take the launch across to Eden to bring the doctor. Sarah knew too, and, although the thought terrified her on top of what had happened already, she would not try to stop him.

Next morning every boat in Eden was being used in a search for the bodies, and by lunchtime dozens of horses were tied up in the paddocks behind the house while their owners, who had ridden from all round the district, helped in the search of the foreshores. Dr Marion Fox returned to Eden, satisfied that the two patients would recover with ordinary care, though she warned Sarah that the shock to Anne's nervous system would have its effects for some time to come.

News of the tragedy had stunned Eden more than anything in years, and the fact that a Davidson should have been the victim seemed almost incredible. Jack Davidson, as a member of the whaling crew for more than fifteen years, should have been thoroughly familiar with the peculiarities of the Kiah River bar. It appeared ironic that he had met his death at a place which to him must have been like his own front gate.

"I can't understand it," George told Sergeant Dumont and John Logan.

"He was a good swimmer, wasn't he?" Dumont asked.

"Well, he could swim, but I wouldn't say he was really good. He never had to swim all the times we were smashed up by whales, because there was always a boat handy to pick us up."

"Looks as if he might have got into trouble trying to save the two children," Logan suggested.

"Probably," George replied. "Anyhow we won't know until we hear Anne's story of what happened, and she wasn't in a condition this morning to tell us. All I know is that I heard her calling out and saw them in the water near the upturned boat when I ran out onto the point. By the time we got there with the whaleboat, Anne and Tommy were the only ones we could see. Another minute and we'd have lost them too."

The search was abandoned at nightfall without any of the three bodies having been sighted, but several of the searchers took blankets and slept in the bunkhouse so that they would be on the spot to start again early next morning. Anne recovered sufficiently after dinner to tell of her horrible experience, and although the grief-stricken little circle thought perhaps she should have been kept quiet, nobody stopped her because it was on her mind and she might as well talk about it. Besides, they wanted to know.

"I started to worry when we were halfway home," she told them in a hoarse, trembling voice. "I knew by the way the sea was running it'd be nasty on the bar, but Jack said it was nothing—only a bit of a swell from a disturbance out at sea. He said it was as calm as a mill-pond compared with what he'd seen his father go out in after whales sometimes, and he laughed when I said that with a big out-tide like it was those rollers would have no bottom in them near the bar. Poor Jack. He only wanted to stop me from worrying." Anne began to cry softly. "We were just at the edge of the channel when it happened," she continued. "A big wave seemed to come from nowhere and race up behind the boat. Jack did the only thing he could have done and tried to ride it through, but it was too strong and swung the boat broadside on, then turned us right over.''

George saw now what had happened. A whaleboat with a good stout steer oar might have ridden that wave, but a dinghy, guided by one man and the oars with which he was rowing, was at its mercy.

''I remember grabbing Tommy's hand as we turned over,'' Anne told them. ''Another wave must have broken over the top of us because I could see nothing for what seemed like hours—only hear a terrible bubbling. When I saw daylight again I heard Jack calling to me to hold onto the boat, which I did, and he got Roy and Patricia and held them there too. It was then that I began to call out for help.''

''Jack was swimming near the boat when I ran up onto the point,'' George said.

''He was trying to save the children,'' Anne explained. ''The seas kept breaking right over the boat and they swept the two kiddies away from Jack. I didn't see either of them again. Jack dived for them a couple of times and then . . . then he made what was like a despairing cry. I'll hear it as long as I live . . . I . . . I can't . . . '' Sarah held her hand, unable to control her own emotions, while Anne sobbed violently. It was no use continuing the ordeal. George ushered the others outside, leaving Sarah and his daughter-in-law alone.

Apparently Jack had become exhausted while trying to save the children in the heavy seas, or Roy might have drowned himself and his father by hanging on too tightly in terror. They would never know exactly.

Chapter 26

The following afternoon, Roy Goward recovered the little girl's body with grappling irons from shallow water halfway out to the bar. It had been found by Arthur Galli, who had come down from Bega to help with the search. Early on Wednesday morning, George, who was in one of the whaleboats with Alex Greig, Roy Goward and Jack Warren, saw little Roy's legs protruding from the sandy bottom near the mouth of the river, but was too upset to do more than point out the discovery and Alex and Roy Goward picked up the body.

Later that afternoon silent groups stood outside closed shops in Imlay Street and watched two little white coffins draped with flowers being driven to the cemetery near the ocean beach behind the town. Women wept openly and even the hardiest of men shielded their emotions behind the hats they held in their hands. By the sea that had claimed their innocent young lives, the two children were laid to rest, while the parish priest, Father Carey, pronounced the last sad rites. George could not help noticing the sea as they turned to leave the cemetery. It had been so quiet that he had been completely oblivious of it before. Hardly a roll disturbing its surface, it lapped the edge of the yellow beach, and farther out, where the sunlight emphasized the sea's bright blue, it seemed to smile like a treacherous woman. This was the sea George had loved so much. He turned away bitterly. He hated it.

As if to add mockery to its cruelty, the sea remained calm all that week. Never a roll came up and scarcely a breeze added its mischief. And while they searched for Jack, combing the area again and again, old Tom was always there, swimming back and forth near where the dinghy had capsized. His presence brought the only tinge of comfort to George's grief, confirming more than ever the tenderness he had always felt for the old killer. George thought of the time Tom had swum alongside him when he went overboard and had to wait for the whaleboat to come back, and now, as faithful as any dog could be, he was there again in time of need. It seemed almost as if Tom was trying to guide them, as he had done on countless occasions in whale chases, but although they searched every inch of that vicinity, they could find no trace of the body.

On Thursday morning, the Coroner, Arthur Nicholson, came across the bay and opened an inquest in the front room of the Davidson home. After Sergeant Dumont had given formal evidence of the recovery of the children's bodies and Dr Marion Fox had certified the cause of death, the inquiry was adjourned because Anne Davidson, the principal witness, was still in a serious condition from shock and exposure.

While the inquest was going on, Tom left his patrol outside the bar and cut across to Cattle Bay, where the other killers had penned a humpback whale and her calf they had shepherded into the bay early in the morning. Tom, apparently not satisfied with the way things were going, decided to take a hand himself, and when Logan's launch came along towing one of the whaleboats—manned by a scratch crew—Tom went mad with delight and worked with a frenzied ferocity. But the whales broke out of Cattle Bay and, as they fled round the shore towards Snug Cove, onlookers on the cliffs could see Tom through the clear, smooth water deliberately getting underneath the large whale and turning it right over to expose it to better attack from the other killers and the men in the boat. Although it must have been getting weaker, the whale kept warding off its tormentors, even when wounded by a bomb from a whale-gun, and fought its way out to the Blowhole. The battle continued round the bay until well into the afternoon when, just as the attackers seemed to have it won, part of the boat's gunwale broke away from the strain of the steer oar. The whale and her calf were held up by the killers near Quarantine Bay for hours afterwards, but, though badly injured, they managed to escape to sea during the night.

For once George Davidson didn't care. Five days had gone without any sign of Jack's body, despite a thorough combing and recombing of the area where it must have been. Nobody said so, but the only explanation they could think of was that sharks, which made the river mouth a favourite hunting-ground, were responsible. They might as well have said what was in their minds because George had the same horrible fears. Friday passed and by Saturday afternoon the searchers had given up hope. Dusk was closing in when George decided it would be no use keeping these men any longer on what seemed to be a futile quest and told them so.

"I don't mind," Alex said. "Bill and I and the launch are at your service as long as you think there's a hope."

"That goes for me too," Alby Greer added. "Give it another day."

"Please yourselves," George replied. "If he was there, we should have found him by now." He looked up at the sky, where low floaters were sliding north-west. "Anyhow, you'd better get home before dark. I don't like the look of that sky."

Alex sniffed the air. "Could get a sou'easter, and, of course, if we do that finishes the search, but if the weather is all right tomorrow we'll be over."

The two launches headed out of the river and George turned to walk wearily up to the house. He walked so slowly that he was only at the top of the pathway when he heard the engine of one launch slow down and heard Alby Greer calling to Alex Greig. Glancing back, he saw Greer bending over the side of his launch, peering into the water near the bar. Then Greig brought his launch alongside and they all looked.

George's heart beat faster as he saw two of the figures—Bill Greig and Archer Davidson—straighten up and jump into the dinghy Alex had been towing behind his launch. Then, when the grappling irons went overboard, he forgot his tiredness and ran back to the tryworks.

"How did you find him?" he asked when they brought Jack's body ashore.

"Only by accident," Alby told him. "Alex and the others thought they saw something white on the bottom as they crossed the bar. I was a bit ahead of them and I left the tiller to go to adjust the jib. I don't know what it was, but something made me look over the side and I saw him clearly on the bottom. That was when I called the others over."

"You wouldn't believe it," Alex said. "We've been over that spot dozens of times."

"You know," George remarked thoughtfully, "I reckon old Tom knew and was trying to tell us."

John Logan came to see George later in the evening to offer his launch for the first stage of the funeral from the Kiah to Eden wharf and to ask if there was anything else he could do.

"Is there anything you or Mrs Davidson would like?" he asked.

George thought for a moment. "Well," he said quietly, "there's one thing I would like. I'd like the Reverend Forbes to bury Jack. He married Sarah and me and he christened Jack."

"Good, I'll get him for you."

"He's not in Eden, you know."

"Doesn't matter where he is. What denomination is he and where can he be found?"

"Well, he's a Presbyterian minister and as far as I know he's retired and living at Wyndham. That's a few miles out in the country."

"He can probably be contacted by telephone. Anyhow I'll have him here for you even if I have to go to Wyndham and bring him."

Logan was as good as his word. On Sunday morning he was back with the news that Mr Forbes would be waiting at Eden wharf ready to go with the funeral that afternon.

Fortunately the gale had not eventuated and Logan's launch with

Jack and his grief-stricken relatives aboard chugged from the river into a calm bay. Outside the bar a long fin broke the water behind the launch—a long fin with a knob on its tip. It was old Tom. There, it seemed, to pay his last respects, he swam behind the launch right across the bay and when the launch tied up at the wharf, Tom turned about and headed for the open sea. That was the last time he was seen in Twofold Bay until the following winter. George, when he thought of the incident weeks afterwards, was convinced that Tom had only waited for Jack's funeral before setting off on his summer trip to the Antarctic.

Very few people in Eden did not attend the funeral and many others came from Bega, Pambula, Towamba, Kiah, Burragate, Merimbula, and all around the district. First to meet the Davidsons on the crowded wharf was the Reverend Forbes, now a grey-haired old man. He shook hands with each member of the family and in an unobtrusive, but comforting manner conveyed his personal sympathy. It was the largest funeral Eden had ever seen. More than forty cars followed the hearse, and behind the cars a long procession of people walked through the silent streets to the cemetery, where the two children had been buried only a few days earlier. There, beside the beach and the sea Jack Davidson had loved so much, the whalers who acted as pallbearers rested the coffin, while the old minister opened his book and heads were bowed—some in prayer, all in sad mourning.

"The Lord giveth, and the Lord taketh away. . . . He who is born of man hath but a short time to live." Mr Forbes closed his book. "Let us pray. Almighty God . . . " Around the feet of the mourners, the breeze rustled the long grass and stray leaves came floating down from the gum trees to join decaying comrades on the graves and the pathways between. Other Davidsons were buried there too. A. W. Davidson, died July 8, 1897, 92 years, the inscription on one tombstone announced. Near by were others: Jean Davidson, died June 27, 1892, 87 years; Alexander Davidson, died August 13, 1907, 69 years. Another marked the last resting-place of "Captain William J. Gregg, out of Port Jackson, who departed this life at sea in latitude 25.56° longitude 153.14°, August 25, 1851, 28 years," his wife, Mary Ellen (née Davidson), who had died at Kiah on June 12, 1852, aged 22, and the infant daughter, Elsie Jane, 5 months. Mr Forbes concluded the prayer, and raising his head looked round at the silent groups.

"When death comes as tragically as it came to Jack Davidson and his two dear young children, there is not much that can be said to give any real comfort to those on whom the terrible burden of sorrow falls," he said in a soft voice. "Those who bear the burden are those left behind—in this case Jack's wife and daughter, and, of course, his father and mother, brothers and sisters. I knew Jack's father and mother many years ago, when they came to me in Eden and asked me to marry them, and looking back over those years it is a great comfort to me as a minister to know that the performance of that marriage ceremony was one of the happiest tasks—if you could call it a task—that came within my work in the church. George and Sarah Davidson have as fine a family as you could find anywhere, and the traditions and inspirations of family life have been passed on from their children to a new generation of young Davidsons. A minister of the church finds much happiness in his work. He finds much sadness too." Mr Forbes paused for a moment and only the rustle of the grass and the soft surge of the sea broke the stillness.

"But if marrying George and Sarah Davidson is one of my happiest memories, the burial of their eldest son, Jack, is one of the saddest ceremonies I have ever had to perform. Here was a man, loved by his family and with the respect and sincere friendship of everyone in the community in which he lived, and he was taken without warning—without any earthly reason why. 'I shall come like a thief in the night,' God said, and it is true. At a time like this, we see clearly the terrible meaning of those words. 'Like a thief in the night. . . . ' " There was underlying bitterness in the old minister's voice as he continued, "No thief could have struck more swiftly—could have robbed a woman and an innocent child of more. But we can only accept what has happened as God's will, strange though His purpose may appear to us sometimes.

"It has been said that greater love hath no man than that he lay down his life for a friend. Those are very true words too. Jack Davidson gave his life in vain trying to save his son and baby daughter. The safety of his wife and children was his only concern from the moment this terrible tragedy struck. Had he chosen to save himself he would still be alive, but for Jack Davidson that would have been no life. He was not that kind of a man. And so, in the ghastly depths of sorrow, his parting has brought to those who remain, there is one corner where a light burns brightly and proudly. Jack Davidson was a man. That is the one consolation I can offer to those he has left behind. Thy will be done."

Mr Forbes stood back and the pallbearers lowered the coffin.

Chapter 27

For three seasons after Jack's death, George whaled with casual crews—whoever he could get to man a boat. That in itself was bad enough, inexperienced men being often more hindrance than help, but the market for bone and oil was no good and prices were so low that George was losing money on the number of whales he was catching. His main worry, though, was that the killers either seemed to be dying off or had forsaken Twofold Bay, and without them whaling, as had been carried on from the bay for more than eighty years, would be impossible. The pack dwindled to Tom, Humpy, and a few small killers. Then Humpy disappeared. Alex and Bill Greig saw him for the last time when they were fishing near South Head one day and they knew Humpy would never come back for another whaling season. He was like a feeble old man taking a tired farewell of the scenes of a long lifetime of frolics.

Next winter Tom came back alone and nosed about the place—a lost soul. He would mope for days in the old haunt at Leatherjacket Bay, apparently no longer interested in how many whales were passing along the coast. Sometimes he would go down to the Kiah mouth and flop about as he had done in his more active days when summoning out the whaleboats. Then suddenly, though it seemed hard to believe, Tom was dead.

The winter sea looked terribly lonely that day when they towed Tom's body across the Kiah bar and dragged it up the skids at Davidson's tryworks to carry out John Logan's proposal to clean down the skeleton. Logan measured the carcass—for the interest and benefit of posterity, so he said. From nose to flukes Tom measured 22 feet, the width of the flukes from tip to tip was 5 feet and following the semicircular sweep around it was 8 feet 7 inches. His dorsal fin was 5 feet 8 inches and the side fins each 4 feet 6 inches by 2 feet 6 inches across.

What had actually caused Tom's death remained supposition. The most likely theory was that he had died of starvation. He looked very poor compared with the healthy frisky Tom of previous years, and when George cut him open there was not a particle of food inside, although he had been active enough to catch a grampus only a week earlier.

''I don't know,'' George remarked. ''It's got me beat. He could have fed himself if he wanted to.''

''Perhaps he just lost interest in life,'' Logan said thoughtfully. ''You know human beings can get like that when they reach old age. What probably happened to Tom was that he became lonely without his old mates and fretted at his loneliness. Then, losing interest in life, he couldn't be bothered looking for food.''

When Tom's skeleton had been cleaned of its flesh, Wallace helped his father and Logan to wire the bones together, and they took the skeleton over to town to a building behind some shops in Imlay Street. By charging a shilling admission to anyone who wanted to see Tom, Logan raised seventy pounds and gave the money to the Imlay Shire Council, who agreed to build a small museum in lower Imlay Street as a home for Tom and other relics of Eden whaling. Visitors to Eden contributed most of the money, their curiosity aroused no doubt by the fantastic stories written about Tom in some Sydney newspapers. One of these, in the Sydney *Daily Pictorial,* caused both amazement and resentment when the *Eden Magnet* reprinted it. Under the headings ''Killer History—A Sydney Version'' the *Magnet* said, ''From the *Daily Pictorial* of September 18 we extract the following, which comes as an anticlimax to what has already been written about the history of the famous pack of Twofold Bay killer whales and the wonderful part they have taken in whaling at Twofold Bay as allies of the local whalers. Thus the *Pictorial* version:

> EDEN, Wednesday—An historic character was found dead this morning floating in Twofold Bay. Examination proved him to be old Tom, last of a famous pack of killer whales which frequented this part of the coast.
>
> For many years he and his mates were sworn enemies of the whalers and fought many fierce battles with the men in the boats. The killers would lurk off the bay for their foes, the humpback whales, and stage royal battles as their prey came northward. They seemed to know that the whalers were out to interfere with their pastime and would savagely attack the boats.
>
> Gradually they faded from the scene, the last being Old Tom, who, covered with scars, apparently died of old age.

With Tom's passing, George Davidson knew that his whaling days were over too. Jack was dead, pick-up crews—even if he could get them—were almost useless to him and it would have been impossible to pay the rising cost of wages and keep for permanent crews. Cutting up blubber was dirty work. Men would not work for less than a pound a day and the price of oil had dropped so much that it was difficult to sell at all.

The season after Tom's death not a killer appeared, and the few odd whales sighted were far out at sea. George sold his two whaleboats for five pounds each—one to Lloyd Franks, an Eden fisherman, and the other to Reg Perry, who wanted to make it into a launch. Parting with the boats nearly broke George's heart. He had paid twenty-seven pounds each for them when he bought them from Archie Boyd. He could not even give away the tryworks plant, for which he had paid Boyd a hundred pounds.

Perhaps this thing called the depression had something to do with it. Nobody seemed to have any money for anything, and as the months passed and thousands all over the country joined dole queues, the face of the nation reflected depression. To George and Sarah, it did not mean as much as it did to most people, because apart from meat and a few groceries they had to buy very little. They had their comfortable little home, a cow to provide milk, cream and butter, there were always vegetables in the garden and fruit in the orchard, or, by way of a change, fish in the bay.

The depression was showing signs of lifting when Alex Greig took ill and died suddenly. Alex was eighty-six. His death came as quite a shock to George Davidson, probably because he had never thought of him dying. Alex was one of the first people George remembered in his boyhood days. It seemed inconceivable he was dead. First Jack, then Tom, and now Alex.

It was only natural that Alex's funeral should take George's mind back over the past and the people who had faded into those years. His father, Peter Lia, Bobbo, Cappy Russell—they were all gone now. His children—the tots who had played round the tryworks and in the orchard—had children of their own, and Arthur Ashby was almost a stranger nowadays, since he had gone to a forestry job at Orbost. That left only Sarah with him at the old home and, of course, his mother, who was nearly a hundred. They were growing old.

Advancing years did not worry George as much as what the years brought with them now, particularly when he thought of his grandchildren and the young men and women who were growing up in Eden. Although it seemed that the depression had been weathered, new clouds were on the horizon overseas, where the armaments race was on again, led by the Germany that so many had given their lives to curb some twenty years previously. Then it had been the Kaiser; now it was someone named Hitler, and his intention, clearly enough, was to finish what the Kaiser had left undone. In the spring of 1939, when the wattle was daubing the Kiah hills with golden bloom, the storm broke, showering a shocked world with the first drops of the new rain of death which was to follow. Thousands were slaughtered as Hitler's bombers pulverized Poland, and in a matter of months Hitler was master of Europe. For the second time in their lives, George and Sarah saw Eden's young men being marched to a war from which many would never return.

But the whole district forgot the war—bad and all as it was—to wish George's mother many happy returns on her hundredth birthday. From seven o'clock in the morning until late at night, the old lady shook hands and chatted with a steady stream of visitors to Elsie's house, where George and Sarah had taken her. They wanted her to be in town ready for the party they had arranged for the following Wednesday night in her honour. It was Sarah's idea. She contended that anyone who lived to be a hundred was entitled to a good party. The guest of honour thought so too. She was looking forward to that party as much as any of the younger folk—even Carrie's husband, Eric Turnbull, who was making the biggest cake ever ordered from his bakery.

Sarah sent invitations to all the friends and relatives she could think of and then advertised a general invitation in the *Magnet* to friends and relatives she could not think of. That did it. Nearly everyone in the district accepted the invitation. Nor did heavy rain during the day discourage scores of others who came from Pambula, Bega, Wyndham, and even as far as Cooma. George and Sarah had catered for two hundred and fifty guests, but the crowd that greeted them when they arrived at the School of Arts Hall escorting Effie Davidson looked more like four hundred and fifty. The Kiah and Nullica folk were there in force and so, it seemed, were the whole South Coast and Monaro districts.

"Good God!" George gasped. "Where did they all come from? I've never seen some of these people in my life."

"Neither have I, but never mind," Sarah whispered, smiling response to the cheers that greeted them from the doorway.

Inside the hall Eric Turnbull's beautiful two-decker cake with its hundred candles was a conspicuous landmark among the masses of food that covered the tables. When most of the food had disappeared, Mr Duffy, headmaster of the Eden school, who was acting as chairman of proceedings, rose and called for attention in his best classroom manner to convey to Mrs Davidson the congratulations of the whole South Coast on reaching the venerable and grand old age of a hundred years.

"This function," he said, "has been arranged by the George Davidson family in honour of this unique occasion, and all of us must feel very honoured to be present. However, as there are many other speakers, I will confine myself to a small tribute to this grand old lady whose main pleasure in life has been helping others in distress. There is no need to emphasize the esteem in which she and other members of her family are held. I hope she will be spared for many years to come and will be as active physically as she is mentally, which is saying a lot. In these days of perverted sense of effort, it is gratifying to see a woman who has attained the best in life by helping others. On behalf of the Davidson family, I ask everyone present to partake of their hospitality."

When the time came to light the candles on the cake, the hall lights were dimmed. One by one the candles came to life in the spreading circle of light they cast, until eventually Eric Turnbull blew out the taper and stood back to survey proudly the masterpiece he had created. George and Archer blew out the candles for their mother, but she performed the cutting ceremony after the hall lights had been switched on again.

Community singing of "Auld Lang Syne" brought the formal part of the evening to a close and the floor was cleared for dancing. Then George and Sarah, thinking the old lady must be tired, suggested that she should call it a night and let them take her home. But she would not hear of such a thing.

"I'd know if I was tired, and I'm not tired, which means I'm not going yet," she said politely, but firmly. "I want to stay awhile and watch the young folk dancing. I'll probably never see them again."

They gave in. When Effie Davidson said anything she meant it. She sat there, chatting with old-timers and smiling at the young people on the dance floor until the party ended at 1.00 A.M.

Not long afterwards Effie Davidson went to stay with her son, Charlie, at Newnes Junction and there, two years later, she died. The grand old lady, who had lived a hundred and two years and four months, was buried in Lithgow cemetery. Eden mourned her passing almost as if she had died there. Certainly her remains were resting in the cold, mist-shrouded Lithgow valley, but her spirit, everyone felt, would always smile over the blue waters of Twofold Bay and the wooded hills behind the golden sand at the mouth of the Kiah River.

Chapter 28

A lazy roll lapped the rocks at the foot of Point Brierly. From where they stood on the cliffs, George Davidson and Arthur Ashby could see clearly the sand bottom, the patches of seaweed swaying slowly to and fro in the slight surge, could hear the gentle gurgle of the water as it slid back over the edges of the red rocks which showed themselves a few feet from the shore. Far out to sea, near the end of the shimmering path sprawled by the bright sunlight, a smudge of smoke indicated the progress of a big ship making its way down towards Gabo Island. Across the bay the sun glinted on the new iron roof of a cottage being built in the sleepy township. Over the three miles of water separating them from the town, the two men on Point Brierly could hear faintly every now and again the rattle of winches from Eden wharf, where the coastal freighter *Cobargo* was unloading merchandise for the town and a New Zealand steamer was taking on railway sleepers. They could hear, too, the brittle purr of diesel engines from the trawler *Harvey Star,* lying at the other side of the wharf, and the high-pitched whine of circular saws tearing through logs at the sawmill behind the wharf.

It was one of those days when only a perpetual grouch could have found fault with the weather, which made it all the harder to realize that in this same ocean not far north of Australia men were being killed in thousands in one of the most terrible wars ever known. This was the month of February, 1945. A few weeks earlier, General MacArthur had fulfilled his promise to return to the Philippines and American troops had occupied Manila. Now American forces had landed on Iwo Jima and Super-Fortresses were bombing Tokyo, but the end of the war and the devastation it had brought to the Pacific was not yet in sight. In the Solomon Islands and the Australian territory of New Guinea, thousands of fanatical Japanese still held out, determined to fight to a finish. The atomic bomb was a surprise in store. It was certainly far from the thoughts of the old whaler and his former boat-steerer, who had come up from Orbost for a few days on one of his occasional visits.

"They tell me these shipyards are going to be a big thing for the town," Arthur was saying.

"While the war lasts," George grunted. "You see. When the war finishes, they'll drop it like a hot spud. The same thing happened last war and it'll happen again.''

''But they could build trawlers and other small ships for the coast. There should be a good market for them here when the fishing starts again properly.''

''They want them now. Most of the trawlers were taken from here for supply ships in New Guinea and the islands. It's a pity. With meat-rationing on and the big steam trawlers doing mine-sweeping, those working seine trawlers are earning big money, though it's the same story—a few opportunists and racketeers getting most of it.''

''How?''

''Well, one of those trawlers over there is owned by some bookmaker who's never been to sea in his life. He sits on his backside ashore, making a fortune by black marketing the fish these men catch.''

''They're out before daylight, I suppose.''

''And finish all hours at night. Of course they are. Another one of those ships is owned by a builder, another by a publican, and two or three belong to Sydney fish agents—anyone except the fishermen who do the work and catch the fish.''

Arthur grinned. ''Why didn't we think of some lurk like that when we were whaling?''

George withdrew one hand from his trouser pockets and idly snapped a small twig from a nearby bush. ''Yes,'' he said wistfully. ''Why didn't we? Well what about a walk round near Logan's before dinner?''

Arthur settled himself on the grass. ''Break it down, boss,'' he said. ''You've got too much energy altogether for a man your age. Sit down and take it easy. I came up here for a rest and to see you and the missus.''

''Anyone would think I was getting old,'' George said, throwing the twig away and leaning against a tree. ''I'm only eighty-one and the old lady was a hundred and two before she died, but the way the kids go on. . . . Young Sarah is always at the missus and me to go and live in town.''

Arthur could understand why the children thought their parents were getting too old to live by themselves on that side of the bay, dreading the possibility of either one being taken ill suddenly, three miles across the bay inside a river bar, which in bad weather could be impassable and which had already claimed the lives of three Davidsons. Certainly they had a telephone now, but the only other means of contact in bad weather was a thirty-mile trip through Kiah over bad roads, for the most part only rough bush-track. But he could understand, too, why George and Sarah wouldn't leave. They had spent most of their days on the whaling station and they wanted to spend the rest of them there.

"You don't want money to live here," Sarah would tell visitors. "That's the trouble with city people nowadays—too many fancy things. All they think about is money."

George looked down at the strong stocky frame reclining on the ground. "You're getting lazy, Arthur," he said. "Don't they give you enough work to do at Orbost? Or did you really come up for a rest?"

"Rest is right, boss. We've been felling big stuff for the last fortnight, and I'm not a young man now."

"I thought gangers just stood by and gave orders."

"Maybe they did once; not these days. You know we've hardly any men left. Most of the young blokes are at the war and old coves like you and me have to do the work. It's pretty tough sometimes. I'd rather be back whaling again."

George laughed. "I'd start again too if you'd come with me and if we could get some of the killers back."

"Ever see any now?" Arthur asked pensively.

"Not a one. It seems as if they knew what it was all about when Tom died and I put the boats away for good. That's about fifteen years ago. There hasn't been a killer sighted here since—only an odd whale occasionally. Two humpers came in the other week and the missus nearly had a fit because she thought I was going out after them in the dinghy with the gun. I suppose she's right though, Arthur. Our whaling days are over."

Arthur grunted and turned over to rest on his other elbow and look out towards the heads, as he had done in the days when they had sat there for hours scanning the sea for those telltale spouts that would send them racing down the hill past the house to the boats. George, looking towards the house, saw Sarah walk up the yard and begin to feed the chickens. Then the telephone rang and she hurried inside. He was wondering who the caller could be when Ashby mumbled something and jumped to his feet.

"What's wrong?" George asked casually.

"Look, boss," Ashby directed, pointing over the bay. "Killers. Coming across from the lighthouse."

"Well, I'll be damned." George stood upright, his keen eyes following the direction indicated. "Looks like three of them."

Turning and rolling porpoise-fashion, the killers approached within about two hundred yards of Point Brierly and then veered towards Boydtown. Sometimes they would disappear for a few minutes and reappear spouting like whales, but with that distinctive noise similar to a horse snorting which the two watchers knew so well.

"There must be whales about," Arthur remarked excitedly. "Remember how Tom and Jackson and Hooky used to come in and floptail to let us know they had a whale bailed up outside?''

''Perhaps,'' George replied. ''But these aren't the old gang. We never saw these killers before, Arthur—unless that one with the straight fin is young Ben. He could still be alive and he's probably brought the others in to show them the old hunting grounds.''

They turned at the sound of footsteps and greeted a tall, fair, middle-aged man who had approached unnoticed. It was Jim Davidson. Jim, the overseer at East Boyd plantation, always called in for lunch when his work brought him over to that edge of the pine forests.

''Hullo, Arthur,'' Jim said, holding out his hand. ''They can't keep you away from the place, eh? Like a murderer returning to the scene of his crime. I suppose you and the old man have been talking about your fish stories again.''

''No fish stories, Jim,'' said Ashby. ''We've been watching those killers. You haven't seen any in here since the boss turned in whaling.''

Jim took in the killers at a quick glance. They were about a mile up the bay now, just off the nasty reefs near the Boydtown end of Whale Spit Beach. ''That's strange,'' he remarked. ''Mum said something about a man ringing to ask if we'd start whaling again. I didn't take much notice, though. She was busy getting the dinner. Told me to come up and get you two.''

''She must have known I was feeling hungry,'' said George. ''Anyhow, we'd better go down.'' He took a last look at the killers, still sporting and frolicking in the bay, and the three men began to walk towards the house.

Sarah emerged from the kitchen as they entered the long dining room. ''About time you came down to dinner,'' she said reprovingly. ''I sent Jim to hurry you up and he stays there too. What on earth have you been doing?''

George hung his hat on a peg and seated himself at the end of the table. Fully twelve feet long, this table, a relic of a ship wrecked near Gabo Island, provided a safe barrier when he kept Sarah waiting at mealtimes. He had brought it home and installed it in the dining room in the days when a twelve-foot table was necessary to seat the whaling crews. Nowadays it gave the room an atmosphere of loneliness, but they still ate there.

Jim broke the brief silence. ''Dad and Arthur were watching some killers,'' he said. ''There's three of them in the bay.''

''Killers?'' Sarah put down the teapot she was about to take into the kitchen. ''You're not joking, are you? I know George and Arthur see nothing else but whales and killers when they get together.''

''No, mum,'' Jim assured her, ''I saw them myself. They've gone over near Boydtown.''

''Strange,'' she remarked. ''They haven't been in here in all the years since you stopped whaling and they should pick on today to come back. The manpower office in Bega rang a while ago to say the Government wanted to start whaling as an industry in co-operation with some firm. A man is coming here tomorrow to talk to you about it.''

George looked across at Arthur, who had paused with a lump of roast beef halfway to his mouth, and then at Sarah. ''Start whaling again?'' he repeated. ''What do they want me to do?''

''Oh, the man on the phone asked if you or anyone else here could work with them.''

''Did he?''

''Yes, but don't worry yourself. Don't get all excited. I told him quite definitely that you couldn't because you're much too old. He asked about the boys and I said it was unlikely they would take it on without you. In any case, Wallace can't get out of the Army to go whaling, even if he is interested these days, and I don't think Jim would leave his job in the forestry.''

''You're right, Mum. Not for a thousand whales.''

''I'd like to,'' Arthur remarked. ''Common sense tells me, though, it's a game for younger men.''

''I don't know,'' George said thoughtfully. ''I'd start again if Arthur and a few more good men would come with me.''

''You wouldn't,'' Sarah retorted firmly. ''The trouble with you is you're too restless altogether. If it hadn't been for me keeping you in check I don't know where this family would have finished up. Come on now. Forget about your blessed old whales and start eating that dinner before it gets cold.''

They ate in silence for a while, but it couldn't last long. Arthur, too, was obviously restless. Suddenly he looked across at Sarah, complete innocence on his face.

''I wish you could've seen those killers, missus,'' he said. ''They'll probably still be in the bay after dinner.''

The expression on Arthur's face was too much for Sarah and she had to laugh. Perhaps it reminded her of the innocent little face she had seen more than fifty years ago when Arthur, then a ragged little half-caste boy, had stood near the tryworks, clinging to old Lucy's hand. She didn't say much more, but Arthur, who had regarded her as a mother all those years, knew what she thought. And who could blame her for thinking that after fifty years and more as the wife of a whaler she was entitled to some relaxation in her old age? The Government could start whaling again. George Davidson wouldn't.

She made this quite clear next day to a man who introduced himself as Mr Jones and explained that he had been sent to interview George Davidson on behalf of the Commerce Department and a firm that proposed to co-operate with the Government in establishing an Australian whaling industry based on Twofold Bay. The three sat round a table in the living-room. Jones talked almost incessantly, his eyes roving from George to Sarah Davidson, to the whaling pictures on the walls, the complete scale model of a whaleboat on top of the radio cabinet, the harpoon, lance, and strips of whalebone in the corner near the fireplace, and occasionally to Arthur Ashby, sunning himself on the doorstep.

"But I can't see where you'll get the men here," Sarah told him during a lull in the conversation. "Most of them weren't young men when George stopped whaling thirteen years ago, and there are no young fellows about now with any experience. Besides, since the killers left, the whales don't come in here like they used to—apart from an odd one every so often."

"I killed one a couple of years ago," George reminded her.

"You mean you turned on an act for the crowd over in town," she gibed. "What would you think, Mr Jones, of a man nearly eighty years of age who goes out by himself in a dinghy and attacks a whale with a lance?"

"I'd think he was pretty game."

"Oh, that doesn't matter. He never had a fear in him all his life. It's just the foolhardiness of it. Anyhow, with the crowd on the cliffs cheering him on, he lanced the whale, just out from the lighthouse, and how he wasn't smashed to pieces, I don't know."

"My eyesight must still be pretty good," George said, a pleased glint showing in his eyes. "Three days later the tide brought its carcass back into the bay and it stranded on a reef just near the tryworks."

"You see," Sarah continued, "he's got too much energy. The other week a humper came in and I had a hard job to stop him taking that gun out and having a shot at it from a dinghy."

Jones looked curiously at the brass gun—a cross between a sawn-off shotgun and a small cannon—which George produced proudly from another corner of the room. It occurred to him that the recoil from this fearsome weapon might have been enough to throw the old man overboard and capsize the dinghy, but he could easily believe the story. Although not a big man, and despite a slightly stooped appearance, George Davidson for all his eighty-one years seemed stronger and far more active than most younger men.

"I think you have the wrong idea, Mrs Davidson," he said when he had finished examining the gun. "We don't want your husband to go whaling again in small boats. This would be an industry on a large scale and what we want is men who know something about it to help at the base here and to advise others. The Commonwealth Government is concerned at the opportunities this country is missing, particularly in the Antarctic, where tens of thousands of whales are killed every year by foreigners in waters which are an Australian protectorate. Do you know that in 1938 Japanese, Norwegians, and others killed forty-four thousand whales in the Antarctic summer season and most of them were only between six and eight years old? They produced something like three and a quarter million barrels of oil, according to the figures we have.''

George looked at him incredulously. ''Nearly fifty thousand whales in a year,'' he gasped. ''Good Lord, it's a wonder there's any more left.''

''Well, if they continue to be slaughtered at that rate, it leaves a big problem for the future. That's why international regulations were being tightened up before the war.''

''What do you propose to do with the whales you bring in here?'' George asked.

''Well,'' Jones explained, ''it's a highly scientific business today. The oil has very valuable uses in munitions production alone. When you were whaling, you probably discarded everything except the oil and bone. Today there are so many valuable by-products. For instance, we estimate we can produce each year about 4,000 tons of dehydrated whale meat, another 1,000 tons of meat meal, and 1,000 tons of organic fertilizers, or, if we like to use all the meat for making meal, it would yield about 5,000 tons. Whale-bone, too, still has many uses.''

''They mean to use this bay as depot and bring the whales in here, do they?'' George asked.

''Yes. Why?''

''Only that I think whaling must be done differently if it's to pay nowadays. The Japs and Norwegians have the right idea. Instead of spending thousands of pounds on shore plants, they follow the whales north and south with factory ships and treat them as they catch them. I'd suggest building a proper factory ship with small chasers. Then you could start in the Antarctic season and follow the whales north up the coast when they migrate in the winter. There are still plenty of whales, but they don't come into the bays now without the killers to hunt them in.''

''I've heard a lot about these killers,'' Jones said. ''Some of the stories are almost fantastic.''

''No doubt you've heard some tall stories, but they did some fantastic things,'' George told him. ''Anyhow, the killers won't interest you people.''

''No,'' Jones agreed. ''Not commercially.'' He looked at the clock above the fireplace as it began to strike four. ''H'm, I'd better be getting back to town. That fellow Reynolds who brought me over in his launch will be thinking I'm staying here for the night.'' He stood up and reached for his hat. ''Well, thank you very much for the information. You too, Mrs Davidson. You and your husband have been very helpful.''

''There's not much we can do for you, but George will always be pleased to help in any way he can, provided he doesn't go chasing whales himself,'' she said with a smile.

George and Arthur walked down to the water's edge with Jones, who, like other visitors, had succumbed already to the beauty of the place. He was also very interested in the old tryworks. It was obvious to him that it had not been used for many years, although the rough shelter of wood and galvanized iron was in fair condition. He couldn't help drawing a mental comparison between this relic of a primitive industry and what the new whaling station would be like with up-to-date equipment and facilities. Here, over what had once been a rough slipway of tree trunks, men had strained and sweated round a simple wooden capstan, hauling up chunks of blubber to be minced for the trypots, which were still there, covered with spiders' webs and coatings of rust and dust.

''Well, you certainly earned whatever you got out of the game,'' Jones remarked. ''It seems to me that catching the whale and killing him was the least part of the work.''

Jones walked to Reynolds' launch and stepped aboard. ''Well, I hope to see you again before long, Mr Davidson,'' he said as he leaned over to shake hands with the old fellow. ''You too, Ashby. There'll be work for you if you're interested.''

Arthur, who had been leaning against a post of the old tryworks, came out of a daydream. ''Who, me?'' he said with a grin. ''No, mister. Thanks all the same. I'll stick to the forestry job.''

George and Arthur watched the launch turn and head for the river mouth. Then they began to walk slowly up the hill towards the house.

''They won't make it pay like he's talking about,'' George remarked.

''Don't know, boss''—Arthur removed his hat and scratched the back of his head—''they've got some ideas, though, and where we used to catch 'em one at a time they might catch dozens.''

''Maybe,'' George commented.

Out in Twofold Bay, Jones sat in the stern of the launch looking back at the Kiah inlet and the old whaling station. Over to his right he could see a white building standing all by itself, just a hairline of green grass separating it from the golden sands of the beach, which in turn served as a buffer for the slight easterly swell. It was the Seahorse Inn—all that remained of Ben Boyd's dream city. Boyd certainly had the right idea, he thought. Wonder what his Boydtown would have looked like today? He was still thinking of what might have been when Reynolds eased down the motor and the launch glided slowly past the trawlers loading their fish into lorries on the wharf. Flocks of sea gulls whirled and screamed round masts and rigging, waiting for the right moment to dive on the offal thrown away by a group of men in a launch who were cleaning barracouta. It reminded Mr Jones of Grimsby, or one of the other English fishing ports.

"A lot of these skippers are old North Sea fishermen," Reynolds told him when he remarked on the fact. "There's Bill Smith, Jocky Lowe, Jack Campbell, and several others.They learnt the game the hard way, working all round the clock for a few miserable shillings a week in the old country. They're doing much better out here, though the set-up is still wrong when people who've never been to sea in their lives can exploit the fishing industry. The fishing industry should be reserved for fishermen."

That was what the trawlermen themselves thought too, when they had time. Eden, Jones found, was concerned with only one thing—fish. It was the main topic of conversation on the wharf, in the streets, and in the town's two hotels. Later in the crowded bar of Barney Welsh's Hotel Eden, he sipped a glass of beer and listened to the hum and chatter of voices. It was no different to the noise in any hotel bar between five and six in the evening, but somehow it was a change after city and suburban pubs.

A big fellow wearing rubber sea boots, which reached almost up to the bottom of his navy-blue sweater, came through the door and pushed his way to the counter. "Two please, Kitty," he said to the barmaid, who was struggling with four glasses and a jug of beer, mumbling something about having only one pair of hands.

"How did you go today, Jack?" he shouted to a young fellow leaning over the far end of the counter.

"About thirty baskets," came the reply after a hand had wiped a blob of beer from under the speaker's nostrils. "Struck a good few off Merimbula, otherwise, only patches."

Two men behind Jones were engaged in a quite amicable argument about the respective merits of certain marine engines.

"I wouldn't have one of them engines in my ship as a gift," one declared emphatically. "Although that thing they put in last year isn't much better. No guts in 'em. Wouldn't pull the hat off your head, let alone drive a ship her size and work the gear."

"Hey, Jocky, where's your glass?" shouted a tall fellow, hanging over the edge of the counter with one hand and stretching his other arm back into the crowd.

"Wait a minute. I haven't finished this one yet. Not gonna waste good beer." That was probably Jock Lowe, if the touch of Scotch accent meant anything.

"Hurry up. It's going off in a minute. Stop ear-bashing him and drink it if you want another one."

"I'll get another one."

"If you could only catch fish half as well as you can talk—"

"Oh, go and jump in the bay. I was fishing before you were born."

Jones smiled to himself, emptied his glass, and quit the bar for the dining room and some food.

"Who's the little bloke in the blue suit, Barney?" Bill Smith asked casually.

"What?" Barney Welsh looked up from the jug he was filling.

"That fellow who just walked out," Jock said. "We saw him come back from over the bay this evening."

"Oh, he's some Government official," Barney told them. "The Government is going to start whaling here again and he came down to see George Davidson. He's going away in the morning."

"Whaling!" Bill and Jock looked at each other. Then Jock's laugh drowned the rest of the bar commotion.

"Doesn't want a couple of good men, does he? I'm sick of catching flathead, Barney. Bill and I are just the boys to show 'em how to catch whales."

"Oh, shut up, Jocky," somebody else chipped in. "I'll show him how you ran for your life when that whale came up near you off Gabo and you thought it was a Jap submarine."

"Whale be damned!" Jock yelled. "It was a submarine all right, and a big one too. Anyhow, I'd like to see you stop and shake hands with those cows. You know what they did to the poor devils on the Mimbi. . . . Blew 'em out of the water."

"Here, that's enough," Barney Welsh interrupted. "Jocky, I wish you'd keep quiet. You make enough noise for a dozen men. It's six o'clock. Look at the time. I'll have to kick the team of you out if you don't stop the row."

Mrs Welsh, standing near the door into the parlour, shook a finger reprovingly. "You're a terrible man, Jock," she said. "Why don't you behave yourself like Bill Smith. He has his drink quietly."

Jock looked at her with wide, innocent eyes. "Who, me? I wasn't making any noise, Mrs Welsh."

She smiled. She was one of those naturally placid women who believed life was worth smiling through. Jones would go away tomorrow, but long before he was on the road, these men would be out at sea after the fish that were beginning to bring wealth to the little town. Tomorrow evening they would be back, drinking a hard-earned beer after the day's work. Good fellows, all of them. She would miss them if they were not there.

Over the bay, George Davidson sat on the veranda of his home watching the huge bulk of Mount Imlay merging into the shades of evening. Down in the Kiah inlet, he could hear the occasional flop of a fish; somewhere in the pine forests behind the house a kookaburra laughed briefly and then it was quiet again, except for the swish of the rollers on the beach. For George Davidson it was evening. He knew he would never see dawn again standing against the thigh-board of a whaleboat.

The last reflections of the setting sun drowned themselves in the sea of evening mist flooding over the top of Mount Imlay. George reached for a tobacco pouch, filled his pipe, struck a match, and settled back in the old armchair amid clouds of smoke. So they were going to start whaling again. Yes, he thought, they would probably build a modern factory and big chaser ships to catch the whales and no doubt they would catch plenty, but it would not be like the whaling he knew. George puffed harder at the pipe for a few seconds, then relaxed, his eyes half closed. And as he dozed the years rolled back and people and things came to life again through the haze—his father, Peter Lia, Cappy Russell, Bobbo, Alex Greig, old Tom. It would never be the same.

Sarah found him there and took his hand. "Come on, Fearless," she said tenderly. "It's time you got some real sleep."

George Davidson, aged in his eighties, holding the whale gun. This picture was probably taken circa 1950.

GLOSSARY

Bloke	A colourful Australian colloquial term for a man.
Quid	Common name for the Australian pound note - before the introduction of decimal currency.
Tun	A measure used for whale oil.
Gin (black gin)	Common name for Australian native aboriginal woman at this time.
Darkie	Slang term for aboriginal man, often used in these times.
Skite	A boaster or big-mouth, one who brags.
Corroboree	Gathering of Australian native aboriginals for tribal song and dance.
Kellick	Anchor for a small boat.
'struth	A common expression or exclamation, often used in these times to precede a sentence - abbreviation of "God's truth".

About the Author

Tom Mead was a journalist, Editor and Chief of Staff with a career spanning more than 50 years on major city and country newspapers including the Sydney Daily Telegraph and Sunday Telegraph, and was an author for almost as many years. Tom discovered the story for his first novel *Man Is Never Free* while working in the Canberra Press Gallery. Published in 1946, *Man Is Never Free* was an authentic account of the saga of the Tolpuddle Martyrs, English farm workers unjustly convicted of conspiracy and sentenced to transportation to Australia for 7 years.

Tom unearthed the story for this second novel *Killers of Eden,* while on a visit to the NSW coastal town in the same year, but his work commitments as a journalist meant that it was 15 years before this book was first published.

Three years after the publication of *Killers of Eden,* Tom entered State Parliament and served for 11 years as the Member for Hurstville, an electorate in Sydney NSW. Yet the pressure of a political career did not blunt Tom's love for writing or indeed, of the sea. Tom's third book *The Seven Mile Ships,* the story of the Manly Ferries of Sydney Harbour, was conceived while Tom was a member of Parliament, yet it took another 13 years before it was first published in 1988. *The Fatal Lights,* the story of the wreck of the clipper ship Dunbar in 1857 beneath the Macquarie Lighthouse on Sydney's South Head soon followed, and then *Breaking the News,* the story that includes the events surrounding Tom's own career in newspapers and politics during some of the most turbulent years in Australia's recent history.

Later in his life, Tom lived at Manly. From his desk overlooking Sydney Harbour, Tom watched the Manly Ferries pass every day outside his window, and looked across to South Head where the top of the Macquarie Lighthouse could be seen above the place where the Dunbar was wrecked.

Also by Tom Mead

The Seven Mile Ships - *The Manly Ferries of Sydney Harbour.* The colourful history of arguably the world's most famous line of ferry steamers, and the people and events surrounding them. Large format / illustrated / colour 190 pages.

Empire of Straw - *The rise and fall of dashing colonial tycoon Benjamin Boyd.* The enthralling true story of Ben Boyd, Australia's first commercial empire builder and 'corporate cowboy'. Benjamin Boyd plundered the funds of the Royal Bank to finance his enterprises, which ultimately failed with disastrous results. Illustrated / colour / 288 pages.

Breaking The News - *Journalism and politics from World War 11 to the Cold War.* The people and events that shaped Australia in the latter half of last century, seen through the author's eyes. Illustrated / 280 pages.

Man Is Never Free - *The Tolpuddle Martyrs.* The true and fascinating history of one of the most outrageous injustices ever committed, a conspiracy that rocked England's legal system and parliament. Illustrated / 248 pages.

The Fatal Lights - *The Dunbar and the Ly-ee-Moon.* The story of the mystery surrounding the loss of two fine ships, both wrecked directly beneath lighthouses. Illustrated / 128 pages.

All titles available from bookstores.
If out of stock please order from:
Tower Books - Phone: 61 2 9975 5566
Address general inquiries to the publisher:
Dolphin Books
18 Herbert Street Oatley NSW 2223
Phone: 61 2 9570 1972
Fax: 61 2 9570 7270